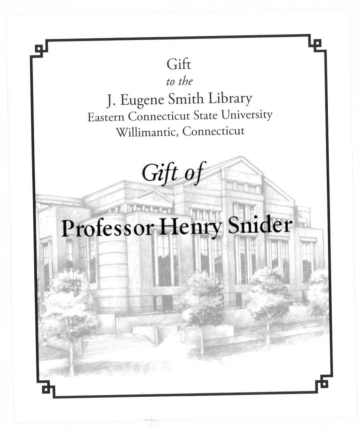

Geometry of Sandstone Bodies

Published with the aid of a fund established by the New York Committee
for the mid-year meeting of the Association, November 1926.

GEOMETRY OF SANDSTONE
BODIES

A Symposium, most papers of
which were presented before the
Association at its Forty-Fifth annual
meeting, Atlantic City, New Jersey,
April 25–28, 1960.

Edited by JAMES A. PETERSON and JOHN C. OSMOND

Published by The American Association of Petroleum Geologists
Tulsa, Oklahoma, U.S.A., 1961

LIBRARY OF CONGRESS CARD CATALOGUE NO. 61–17026

Published, September 1961

Reprinted by offset, April, 1967

Composed, Printed, and Bound by The Collegiate Press
GEORGE BANTA COMPANY, Inc.
Menasha, Wisconsin

CONTENTS

INTRODUCTION

JAMES A. PETERSON[1] AND JOHN C. OSMOND[2]

Farmington, New Mexico, and Salt Lake City, Utah

This volume contains the eight papers presented as a symposium of the Research Committee of The American Association of Petroleum Geologists at the 1960 annual meeting in Atlantic City, New Jersey. One paper presented in the General Session at that meeting, one reprinted paper, and three other solicited papers are also included.

The choice of "Geometry of Sandstone Bodies" as a timely and pertinent subject for the 1960 symposium was made after an extensive canvass of Research Committee members and about fifty other geologists vitally interested in research in petroleum geology. From a group of about 15 proposed subjects, this one was selected as first choice by almost all those canvassed. Partly because of this high level of interest, the decision was made to attempt publication of the symposium as a special volume of The American Association of Petroleum Geologists. The word *geometry* in the title probably had several different meanings among the selectors, and for this reason an attempt was made to define the term adequately in order to establish uniformity of communication among symposium participants.

The dictionary definition of the word "geometry" is *the science of magnitudes in space*. In applying the term to the symposium theme, some modification and interpretation of its formal meaning were needed, and the following definition was therefore proposed for use in this volume—

Geometry of Sandstone Bodies—*Spatial relationships of sandstone deposits within the sedimentary framework.*

As used in this book, the subject is more than just a three-dimensional study in which thickness is added to areal distribution. It can be considered as applied to two extremes in size—one is the primary sedimentary unit such as a single bed, elongate, and with lenticular cross section in the scale of a few feet; and the other is the composite unit made up of several primary units and generally referred to as a formation or larger stratigraphic unit. In dealing with primary and composite units, the discussions include the following aspects of the geometry—*shape, size, trend*, and *internal characteristics*, and their *physical* and *genetic* relationship to adjacent sediments.

Solicitation of papers for the symposium was made with a four-fold purpose in mind (1) *Completeness*, including examples of as many types of sandstone bodies as possible, (2) *Timeliness*, avoiding a rehash of old ideas and including as many relatively new authors and new ideas as possible, (3) *Conciseness*, stressing short, but complete, easily understood, and well-illustrated papers, and (4) *Usability*, especially with respect to subsurface predictability of sandstone-body shapes, and porosity, petroleum economics, and practical application to problems of the operational subsurface geologist. A deliberate attempt was made to avoid highly theoretical works requiring specialized training for applicability. Obviously, this volume has not completely attained these ideals, and despite extensive inquiry it is probable that some desirable works have not been included. However, because of the difficulties associated with the planning and preparation of a symposium publication, the necessity eventually arises to achieve a balance between availability, publication deadline, and size of volume. In view of these inherent restrictions, the ideal symposium volume probably will never be published.

The group of papers included presents a reasonably broad range of coverage from at least five viewpoints (1) *Geologic distribution*, ranging in age from Mississippian to Recent, (2) *Geographic distribution*, including the Gulf Coast, Mid-Continent, North Central States, Pacific Coast, Rocky Mountains, Bahamas, and other more gen-

[1] Shell Oil Company.
[2] Consulting Geologist.

1

eral papers, (3) *Sandstone types*, including eolian, fluvial, marine, deep water, and shallow water, (4) *Methods of study*, including theoretical, experimental, and statistical, as well as surface and subsurface studies, using data from well samples and cores, mechanical logs, thin sections, size analysis, and mineral determination, (5) *Author affiliation*, comprising four oil company geologists, two consultants, four university professors, and three federal or state survey geologists.

The larger number of papers from the Rocky Mountain region is the result of several factors—sandstones are important deposits in this region and much work has been done on them; examples of numerous types of sandstones are present; most of the sands are well exposed, thus facilitating conclusive studies and interpretation; and much of the work is relatively new and has not been published previously.

Decision to include a paper on the lime-sand bodies resulted from the interest in their probable depositional and geometric similarities with the quartz-sand bodies.

Several conclusions become apparent from the symposium group of papers. An obvious one is that additional well-documented studies of both modern and ancient sand bodies are needed before genetic comparisons can be adequately made. The scarcity of examples in the literature is emphasized by repeated references to the same sources.

A further need is for a satisfactory and universal classification of genetic sand-body types and criteria for their recognition, particularly in the subsurface where the problem is most critical, but also from the standpoint of outcrop criteria.

Another interesting point is that many sands are referred to under the gross term "deltaic." This is probably for two reasons (1) deltas contain some sands similar to fluvial deposits and some similar to shore and near-shore deposits, (2) modern deltaic deposits have been described extensively in the literature and provide some of the few bases for comparison. However, it may be that in general usage most depression-filling shale and sand deposits are considered to be deltaic. It appears to be difficult to distinguish any other than deltaic deposition where the shore consists of coalescing deltas.

Acknowledgments are made with thanks to Lloyd C. Pray and John Imbrie who contributed editorial comment and advice on several of the papers. Recognition is also due to Clarence O. Durham and Joseph F. Rominger who served for varying lengths of time on the Symposium Committee during its approximately three years of tenure. Many other individuals, including Research Committee members and others too numerous to mention by name, were frequently solicited for suggestions and advice during the planning and execution of the project.

PROBLEMS AND PRINCIPLES OF SANDSTONE-BODY CLASSIFICATION[1]

GORDON RITTENHOUSE[2]

Houston, Texas

ABSTRACT

The geometry of sandstone bodies involves their shape, size, and orientation. The original geometry is subject to later modification by erosion, faulting, folding, tilting, compaction of underlying sediment, and internal compaction.

Although orientation or "trend" has been, and will continue to be, used successfully in some cases without knowledge of the origin of the sandstone bodies, greater predictability should be possible if the origin can be determined—provided that the distributional patterns of sediments of various origins are known. Insofar as geometry is concerned, three major problems are (1) to reconstruct the geometry correctly, (2) to know what it implies regarding origin, and (3) to know the distributional pattern of sediment of that origin in an analogous depositional situation.

For reconstruction of sandstone-body geometry, total sand thicknesses or sand/shale ratios for thick sedimentary sequences are of limited value. Isopach maps of individual sand bodies define their size and orientation but only partially define their shape; cross sections "hung" on a closely related underlying or overlying bed whose original attitude relative to the sandstone body is known or can be reasonably assumed are required to define shape. Possible modification of original shape by compaction or other processes must also be considered.

The plan dimensions of present-day deltas, barrier bars, and other sedimentary types are rather well known, but three-dimensional data are scarce. Too commonly, three-dimensional data from ancient sediments are misleading, because the origin has been incorrectly determined.

Internal features such as cross-bedding, flow markings, grain orientation, and bed or grain-size sequences and the relationship of a sandstone body to beds above, below, and laterally, are important for interpreting origin, particularly where control is too sparse to define the geometry.

INTRODUCTION

It seems appropriate at the beginning of this symposium to define what we mean by the geometry of a sandstone body and to outline briefly why we, as petroleum geologists, should be interested in this geometry. Knowledge of what we mean by geometry and an understanding of the ultimate application of this knowledge are fundamental to consideration of the problems and principles of classification of sandstone bodies.

Shape, size, and orientation of a sandstone body define its geometry. Shape involves more than relative maximum length, width, and thickness—a prism and a lens may have these dimensions in common, but they are quite different in shape. All dimensions—the whole form—are involved in shape. Because sandstone bodies of the same shape or form may differ in size, this is also a factor. There is, of course, some lower limit of

size, not clearly defined but probably in the order of feet or tens of feet in width, below which the term "sandstone body" would not be applied. The third factor, orientation or trend, is also important, particularly if a sandstone body is elongate. If you do not agree, ask the operator who offset a north-south-trending shoestring sand to the east or west.

Why are we, as petroleum geologists, interested in defining the shape, size, and orientation of sandstone bodies? Basically, we wish to increase our ability to predict where rocks of sufficient porosity and permeability to hold commercial accumulations of oil and gas may occur in places where the hydrocarbons may be trapped. This increased ability to predict should be helpful in locating new prospects, finding extensions to existing fields, evaluating competitors' discoveries, developing our own discoveries completely with a minimum of dry holes, obtaining better reserve estimates, and aiding in secondary-recovery operations. Stated another way, this increased ability to predict should enable us to find and recover more oil and gas at lower cost.

As pointed out repeatedly by others, the ge-

[1] Read before the Association at Atlantic City, New Jersey, April 25, 1960. Manuscript received, April 26, 1960.

[2] Consultant, geology, Shell Development Company (a Division of Shell Oil Company), Exploration and Production Research Division.—(Publication No. 231.)

ometry of sandstone bodies is only one of several types of information that should be used to obtain maximum effectiveness in the search for, and development of, accumulations of oil and gas. Very recently, Busch (1959) has stressed the importance of relating the geometry of sandstone bodies to the erosional, depositional, and structural history of the rock units of which they form a part. Critical information can also be obtained from internal features such as cross-bedding, flow markings, grain orientation, and bed or grain-size sequences, particularly where control is too sparse to define the geometry. These features are commonly difficult or impossible to obtain from the vast number of wells already drilled, and the need for obtaining them in wells currently being drilled may not be appreciated. In contrast, electrical or other types of logs are obtained as a matter of course and have been run in most holes drilled in the past two decades; these can be used to obtain the geometry of sandstone bodies. For these reasons, emphasis in the following discussion is placed on geometry. It should be clearly understood, however, that by this emphasis I do not depreciate the importance of other factors.

I should like first to discuss the need for relating geometry to the origin of sandstone bodies and to follow this with consideration of problems involved in reconstruction of geometry in the subsurface. Finally, I should like to outline briefly some ideas on classification of sandstone bodies.

GEOMETRY AND ORIGIN OF SANDSTONE BODIES

Because prediction is our primary interest in investigating the geometry of sandstone bodies, it seems pertinent to inquire how prediction and geometry are related. Let us consider the relatively simple case, shown in Figure 1-*A*, of a shoestring sand trending normal to the regional dip. From the geometry alone, we can assume with reasonable confidence that the trend will continue. Also, from the geometry alone, there would be no reason for not assuming that the extension will be indefinite. Anyone might make these predictions, but we, as geologists, would reject the assumption of infinite length. This is a case in which geometry alone is helpful in prediction but does not provide the entire answer—namely, how far does the trend extend?

Now let us add to Figure 1-*A* another well—a dry hole having no sand—which gives the situa-

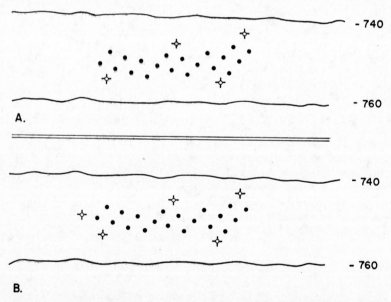

FIG. 1-*A*.—Diagrammatic plan view of producing wells and dry holes in and adjacent to a shoestring sand that trends normal to the regional dip. *B*—Same, with additional dry hole at left end of trend.

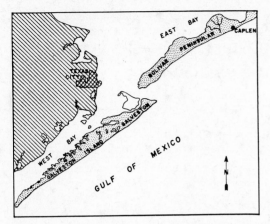

FIG. 2.—The Galveston Island-Bolivar Peninsula segment of the Texas shoreline showing offset of barrier bars (modified from LeBlanc and Hodgson, 1959, Fig. 12).

tion shown in Figure 1-B. After study assures us that faulting is not responsible, we are faced with the problem of what to do next. Do we drill more holes, and if so, where? Geometry alone does not provide an answer, either for geologists or for non-geologists. Both have lost their basis for prediction if geometry alone is considered.

The point I wish to make is certainly not a new one; it was presented by Rich (1923, p. 109), who stated

If the origin of the sand body can be determined, the task is simplified, for sand bodies originating under different sets of conditions have quite different "habits." A coastal sand bar, for instance, will differ widely in section and pattern from a deposit made in the bed of a winding stream.

The first question, therefore, which is presented for solution when a shoestring is to be traced is: "What is its origin?" That question leads to consideration of various possible ways in which long, narrow sand bodies may be formed and preserved, and of the distinguishing features of deposits of each type.

Rich also pointed out some years ago (personal communication) that not only may barrier bars occur in a series, separated by tidal channels that could later be filled with clay, but also the ends of the bars may be offset, as shown in Figure 2. If the shoestring sand of Figure 1-B is a barrier bar, we now have the basis for the prediction shown by Figure 3—namely, that there may be another bar of about the same size to the south or west, depending on its history, the direction of the long-shore current, and the relative positions of land and sea. If the shoestring sand in Figure 1-B is not a barrier bar, other implications as to the existence of an extension and the position and size of the extension may be possible. Thus, if geometry can be related to origin, our ability to predict is greatly increased—provided that the "habits" of sands of different origin are known.

Although I have used an example of a shoestring sand that forms a stratigraphic trap to illustrate the relationship between geometry and origin, the principles involved are of widespread application in the search for, and recovery of, hydrocarbons from both stratigraphic and combined structural-stratigraphic accumulations. As our knowledge of sandstone bodies increases, we are finding that more and more blanket sands are discontinuous, and the influence of nonuniform sand distribution in many "structural" fields is becoming apparent.

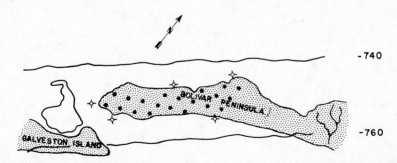

FIG. 3.—Possible relationship of shoestring of Figure 1-A, if it is a barrier bar. Another bar might lie to the south (as shown) or to the west, depending on the history of the bars, the direction of longshore currents, and the relative position of land and sea.

It should be clearly recognized that determining origin from geometry has limitations; some are inherent, and some are due to our present lack of knowledge. A major inherent limitation of geometry, of course, is its three-dimensional aspect; therefore, a considerable amount of control is necessary before the geometry can be defined sufficiently to be helpful. Other limitations are the small size of some sandstone bodies relative to the spacing of control points; the complexities that result from gradual transgression, regression, and other primary factors; and the modification of the geometry by later erosion, faulting, folding, tilting, compaction of associated sediments, and internal compaction.

Concerning knowledge and the limitations resulting from lack of it, the plan dimensions of present-day deltas, barrier bars, and other sedimentary types are rather well known but are not well summarized in the literature. Three-dimensional data are scarce. Although fairly recent work by Fisk (1944, 1954), LeBlanc (1959), Bernard (1959), and their associates, as well as by others, is beginning to rectify this, much remains to be done, particularly in understanding the principles that control the variations of bars, beaches, and other genetic types from locality to locality. Too commonly, three-dimensional data from ancient sediments are misleading, because the origin has been incorrectly determined. Reexamination of these data is needed.

Insofar as geometry is concerned, three major problems are (1) to reconstruct the geometry correctly, (2) to know what it implies concerning origin, and (3) to know the distribution pattern of sediment of that origin in an analogous depositional situation.

RECONSTRUCTION OF GEOMETRY OF SANDSTONE BODIES

In the following paragraphs, an attempt will be made to point out very briefly that correct reconstruction of the geometry of sandstone bodies may be influenced by the type of data available, their abundance, the ability to correlate, the methods used to represent data on maps or cross sections, and the apparent or real effects of depositional topography and compaction. Although these factors have been discussed by others, the understanding of them is so fundamental that this repetition is warranted.

Types of subsurface data from which the geometry of sandstone bodies can be reconstructed include the following.

a. Rock materials, either cuttings or cores, that are brought to the surface.
b. Drilling rates.
c. Measurements by various types of logging devices that are lowered into the hole to measure resistivity, self-potential, or other properties of the rock.
d. The behavior of gases and fluids when holes are drilled or during their subsequent history.

Knowledge regarding the depth—actually, the position in space—from which the data are obtained is assumed. Outcrop data may or may not be available to supplement those from the subsurface.

Outcrops, cuttings, and cores provide a direct means of delineating the boundaries of a sandstone body. Other data are measurements of rock properties which, through experience or comparison with rock materials, are interpreted in terms of lithology, porosity, permeability, or some combination of these. Thus, they are considered indirect means. A detailed discussion of each of these types of data will not be presented here, but information is available in publications by LeRoy (1950), Bass (1941), and others. The geometry obtained will be dependent upon the quality and quantity of the basic data and the validity of their interpretation in terms of the actual lithology.

In reconstruction of the geometry of individual sandstone bodies, one of the first problems—and in some situations one of the most difficult—is to establish the equivalency or nonequivalency of sandstones at the available control points, or, expressed more commonly, to correlate from well to well. In establishing the major correlation framework, both laterally and vertically, paleontology has been, and will continue to be, invaluable. Within this major framework, however, the second- or third-order subdivision which may be necessary to determine the geometry of individual sandstone bodies is generally based on lithology.

In those places where distinctive lithologies occur in close vertical sequence and are persistent laterally relative to the control, as in much of the Mid-Continent area, correlation is generally easy unless the rocks have been strongly folded or faulted. As the vertical lithologic sequence becomes less distinctive and the control becomes more widely spaced relative to the lateral persistence of the beds, correlation becomes more difficult and questionable. In such places, folding or faulting, particularly contemporaneous or growth faulting, may result in problems of correlation that are, or at least seem to be, insurmountable. Correlation has been, and remains to be, a major obstacle in determination of the geometry of individual sandstone bodies in the thick Tertiary sand-shale sequences of the Gulf Coast and California, and in the Cretaceous and Tertiary of some parts of the Rocky Mountains.

After correlation has been established between available control points, various methods can be used to represent the geometry of individual sandstone bodies. Probably the most common are isopach maps and cross sections. These are commonly used alone, but they should be used in combination. For the isopach or thickness map, the first question is, "thickness of what?" Of sand? Sand and coarse silt? Sand and gravel? Sand, gravel, and coarse silt? All porous and permeable rock? Or just porous and permeable rock that contains hydrocarbons, that is, net pay? The answer depends partly on how the isopach map will be used and partly on the types of data available. In some cases of field development or for estimating reserves, one of the types of porosity and permeability maps may be desirable. For understanding the origin of the sandstone body, however, it seems desirable to use the thickness of genetically related rocks of sufficiently coarse texture to have originally held hydrocarbons. If thicknesses are obtained from electric logs, the maps actually represent the thickness of rocks having relatively high resistivity and a self-potential equal to or exceeding a selected absolute or relative value. The map represents sand only to the extent that the relationship of resistivity and self-potential to sand is actually correct.

Let us now consider what the isopach map of an

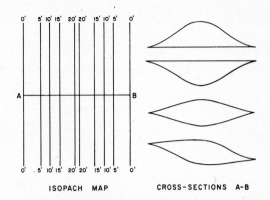

FIG. 4.—Idealized isopach map of part of an elongate sandstone body, and four of many possible cross sections that meet the requirements of this map.

individual sand body means in terms of origin. Figure 4 is an idealized isopach map of part of a sandstone body. This map gives width, length, and thickness, but, except for some information about the symmetry in the third dimension, does not define the shape of the sand body. Each of the four cross sections—flat bottom and rounded top, flat top and rounded bottom, symmetrical lens, and distorted lens—meets the requirements of the isopach map. These are merely four of many possible cross sections that might be drawn. Which is correct? The isopach map does not tell us. Cross sections are required to provide the third dimension. Conversely, cross sections alone are also inadequate.

In constructing cross sections, we are faced with the problem of selecting a datum and determining how that datum was originally related to the sandstone body. Commonly, we assume that the datum or marker bed was horizontal or had a negligible depositional slope, and that by assuming this we can reconstruct the shape of an underlying or overlying sandstone body. Is this true? To explore this, we might consider what would happen if the water level along the Gulf Coast rose rapidly 50 feet or more and conditions became suitable for deposition of a widespread limestone or clay marker bed. Figure 5-A shows a cross section of Galveston Island (modified after LeBlanc and Hodgson, 1959), to which I have added a hypothetical marker bed that would conform to the topography. In Figure 5-B, in

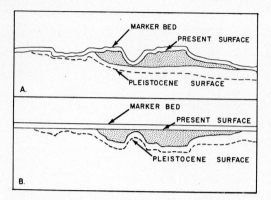

FIG. 5-*A*.—Cross section of Galveston Island (modified after LeBlanc and Hodgson, 1959) with hypothetical marker bed conforming to the topographic relief. *B*—Same, "hung" on hypothetical marker bed.

which the marker bed has been made horizontal, the sandstone body is very different in shape and might well be considered to be of different origin. The same general effect of initial topography would also be shown in the Mississippi Delta area, where natural levees stand about 15 feet above the adjacent flood plains. The obvious solution is to consider marker beds both above and below the sandstone body. If they are not essentially parallel, the reasons for this must be determined.

Differential compaction may have a somewhat similar effect. Figure 6-*A* shows a flat-bottomed sandstone body between two parallel marker beds; Figure 6-*B* shows the same sandstone body after the enclosing shales have been compacted

50 per cent. This section is "hung" on the upper marker bed. Figures 7-*A* and 7-*B* show a similar pair of sections, except that the sandstone body is flat topped, and the section is "hung" on the lower marker bed. The sandstone bodies in both examples have the same symmetrical lens shape. In constructing cross sections, it seems necessary to use markers both above and below.

As pointed out by Waldschmidt (1941), Heald (1955), and others, extensive internal compaction in sandstone bodies may occur through formation of stylolites and solution of sand grains at points of contact. In general, this internal compaction can be expected to compensate partially for the effects of original topographic relief and compaction of the enclosing shales.

As shown above, an isopach map of an individual sandstone body shows two dimensions but does not give critically needed information about the third dimension. Let us consider what information about sandstone-body geometry is provided by two other types of commonly used maps—net sand thickness and sand/shale ratio. Consider the simple example of uniform thickness and lithology, that is, 50 feet of net sand and 50 feet of shale. The sand/shale ratio is obviously 1:1. Some of the possible sand distributions within this interval are shown in Figure 8. There may be one sand body or many. If there is more than one, the sandstone bodies may be continuous or discontinuous and of uniform thickness, variable thickness, or both; they may be in the top, middle, or bottom of the section, scattered

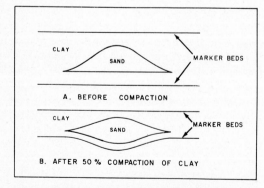

FIG. 6.—Effect of differential compaction of clay on shape of a flat-bottomed sand body.

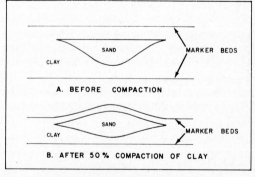

FIG. 7.—Effect of differential compaction of clay on shape of a flat-topped sand body.

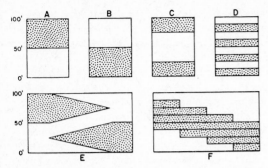

FIG. 8.—Some possible sand distributions in a 100-foot section having 50 feet each of sand and shale (sand/shale ratio=1).

through it, or perhaps even transgressive across it. Figure 8-*E* and -*F* use simple geometric shapes which we, as geologists, would probably reject. These illustrations were purposely drawn to show that although they fulfill the requirements of the maps in a strict geometric sense, our geological experience concerning the shape of sandstone bodies indicates that they should be rejected.

I could present other examples in which the sand content and total thickness of the mapped section could be varied in different ways. However, there is the same lack of definition as to the number of sands present and the shape of the individual sands if more than one sand body is present. Net sand and ratio maps of thick sand-shale sequences have important uses, but they alone cannot be used for reconstruction of the geometry of individual sandstone bodies.

I do not wish to seem discouraging about the reconstruction of sandstone-body geometry, but I do wish to emphasize that problems exist and that these problems must be faced realistically. At the present time, reconstruction of sandstone-body geometry requires the best geologic thinking we can put into it. It is not a mechanical process which in effect will permit us to put data into a machine, turn a crank, and have the answer pop out.

BASIS OF CLASSIFYING SANDSTONE BODIES

Terms such as *shoestring, blanket, lens, finger, tongue,* and *fan,* which have a geometric connotation, have been widely used in the geologic literature. A surprise to me in preparing this paper was that I found only one geometric classification of sedimentary bodies in the literature—that of Krynine (1948, p. 146–148), who used the terms *blanket, tabular, prism,* and *shoestring* for shape, and *large* (or *thick*), *medium,* and *small* (or *thin*) for size. Krynine related his classification to origin, considering blanket shape typical of the orthoquartzite-limestone series of epicontinental deposits, tabular shape typical of the graywackes of geosynclinal deposits, prism shape typical of the arkoses of orogenic deposits, and shoestrings normally as "the smallest building blocks of any of the three preceding types which they form by coalescing."

As indicated previously, geometry of sandstone bodies alone has limited usefulness for prediction, whereas knowledge of origin and of the distribution patterns of sediments of different origins increases the ability to predict. For our use as petroleum geologists, therefore, it seems desirable to aim whatever attempts are made at classification toward a genetic one and to use geometric terminology only until the origin can be determined with a reasonable degree of certainty. For the latter purpose, it seems to me that the terms already available in the literature are adequate and that no development of a geometric hierarchy or classification is necessary or desirable.

What are the genetic types with which we may be concerned? Some years ago, in an advanced course in sedimentation at the University of Cincinnati, my students mapped the distribution of subsurface sandstones in a local area in Illinois. To provide a basis for interpreting the meaning of these sandstone geometries, we listed as many different genetic types of sand bodies as we could think of, and then, from study of the literature and from deduction, we attempted to show how the sands would appear in plan, medial, and longitudinal view and how they would be related to beds above, below, and laterally. As nearly as I can recall now, the genetic types considered were *alluvial fans, river "channels," deltas, beaches, bars, dunes, estuary sands, wave-built terraces, flank sands,* and *shelf-edge sands.* River "channels" were further subdivided into filled-valley and old-age (delta) types. Bars were subdivided into barrier bars and subaqueous bars. Barrier bars, in turn, were further subdivided into those free of tidal influence, those having stationary tidal inlets, and those having migrating tidal inlets (Lucke, 1934). We would now add turbidity-current deposits and would perhaps subdivide them into several subtypes.

These are relatively simple, basic genetic types which represent deposition that might occur during relatively short periods of time under relatively stable conditions. With increased time or gradual change in sea level or in other conditions, gradual migration of some of these genetic types may occur, resulting in a complex that would appear very different from the basic genetic type or types of which it is composed. Lowering of sea level, for example, might result in the development of a blanket sand by gradual migration of a bar.

The simple genetic names are a hodgepodge, referring alone or in combination to shape, agent of deposition, position, and other things, yet they carry to geologists a mental picture of differing genesis, geometry, and physiographic location. As such, they provide a usable basis for classification—one that is practical in the present state of our knowledge and of what our knowledge may be during the next few years. Although a few additional basic genetic types may be added and further subdivisions may be made, the total will not be so large that it will be unwieldy.

Our immediate problem, then, is not one of classification but is one of learning more about these simple genetic types—their three-dimensional geometries, their internal characteristics, and their variations.[3] We must go beyond the descriptive; we must understand how the various types form, for it is only by this understanding that we can make more than picture-book analogies and can understand, or even anticipate, the infinite variations that may result from the interplay of climatic, tectonic, topographic, sediment-source, and water-level controls with various processes of formation.

Much of this knowledge can be obtained by examination of Recent deposits, but such studies will provide only partial answers. It is not enough to know what exists today, but it is also necessary to know what may be preserved, and how, through time and changing conditions, more complex deposits may form. In addition, Recent examples of some genetic types may be limited, and accessibility to others may be difficult. Therefore, extensive and careful studies of ancient rocks will also be necessary. Together, these investigations of Recent and ancient deposits should give us a better understanding of what geometry implies regarding origin and what the distributional patterns of sediments of different origins may be in different depositional situations. The increased ability to predict which will result from this better understanding should enable us to recover more oil and gas at lower cost.

REFERENCES

The following compilation of titles of articles concerned with the classification of sandstone bodies is arranged under two main headings. "References Cited" lists articles to which reference is made in the text; "Selected References" contains supplemental titles grouped under "General" and eleven categories of genetic types.

REFERENCES CITED

Bass, N. W., 1941, Significance of initial daily production of wells in Burbank and South Burbank oil fields, Oklahoma: Am. Assoc. Petroleum Geologists Bull., v. 25, no. 6, p. 1175–1179.

Bernard, H. A., Major, C. F., Jr., and Parrott, B. S., 1959, The Galveston Island barrier island and environs—a model for predicting reservoir occurrence and trend (abst.): Gulf Coast Assoc. Geol. Soc. Trans., v. 9, p. 221–224.

Busch, D. A., 1959, Prospecting for stratigraphic traps: Am. Assoc. Petroleum Geologists Bull., v. 43, no. 12, p. 2829–2843. See also this volume.

Fisk, H. N., 1944, Geological investigation of the alluvial valley of the lower Mississippi River: Vicksburg, Mississippi River Comm., 77 p.

———— and others, 1954, Sedimentary framework of the modern Mississippi Delta: Jour. Sed. Petrology, v. 24, no. 2, p. 76–99.

Heald, M. T., 1955, Stylolites in sandstones: Jour. Geology, v. 63, no. 2, p. 101–113.

Krynine, P. D., 1948, The megascopic study and field classification of sedimentary rocks: Jour. Geology, v. 56, no. 2, p. 130–165.

LeBlanc, R. J., and Hodgson, W. D., 1959, Origin and

[3] The inadequacy of our *geometric* knowledge was again impressed on the writer during preparation of the "Selected References" that appear at the end of this paper. Compiling even six titles on most of the genetic types was not possible, though more time was spent on the reference search than in preparation of the text.

development of the Texas shoreline: Gulf Coast Assoc. Geol. Soc. Trans., v. 9, p. 197–219.

LeRoy, L. W., editor, 1950, Subsurface geologic methods, a symposium: 2d ed., Golden, Colorado School of Mines, 1156 p.

Lucke, J. B., 1934, A study of Barnegat Inlet, New Jersey, and related shore-line phenomena: Shore and Beach, v. 2, no. 2, p. 45–93.

Rich, J. L., 1923, Shoestring sands of eastern Kansas: Am. Assoc. Petroleum Geologists Bull., v. 7, no. 2, p. 103–113.

Waldschmidt, W. A., 1941, Cementing materials in sandstones and their probable influence on migration and accumulation of oil and gas: Am. Assoc. Petroleum Geologists Bull., v. 25, no. 10, p. 1839–1879.

SELECTED REFERENCES

GENERAL

Busch, D. A., 1959, *See* under "References Cited."

Gilbert, G. K., 1890, Lake Bonneville: U. S. Geol. Survey Mon. 1, 438 p.

Guilcher, A., 1958, Coastal and submarine morphology: New York, John Wiley and Sons, Inc., 274 p., English translation.

Hough, J. L., and Menard, H. W., editors, 1956, Finding ancient shorelines—a symposium: Tulsa, Okla., Soc. Econ. Paleontologists and Mineralogists Spec. Pub. 3, 129 p.

Johnson, D. W., 1919, Shore processes and shore line development: New York, John Wiley and Sons, Inc., 584 p.

Johnson, J. W., 1956, Dynamics of nearshore sediment movement: Am. Assoc. Petroleum Geologists Bull., v. 40, no. 9, p. 2211–2232.

Levorsen, A. I., 1954, Geology of petroleum: San Francisco, W. H. Freeman and Co., p. 191–211.

Lobeck, A. K., 1939, Geomorphology, an introduction to the study of landscapes: New York, McGraw-Hill Book Co., Inc., 731 p.

Pirson, S. J., 1950, Elements of oil reservoir engineering: New York, McGraw-Hill Book Co., Inc.; Chart I, facing p. 78.

Pugh, W. E., and Preston, B. G., editors, 1951, Bibliography of stratigraphic traps: Tulsa, Okla., Seismograph Service Corp., 195 p.

Steers, J. A., 1953, The coastline of England and Wales: London, Collins, p. 97–167.

Trask, P. D., editor, 1939, Recent marine sediments— a symposium: Tulsa, Okla., Am. Assoc. Petroleum Geologists, 736 p.; reprinted by Soc. Econ. Paleontologists and Mineralogists as Spec. Pub. 4, 1955.

ALLUVIAL FANS OR CONES

Blissenbach, E., 1954, Geology of alluvial fans in semiarid regions: Geol. Soc. America Bull., v. 65, no. 2, p. 175–190.

Eckis, R., 1928, Alluvial fans of the Cucamonga district, southern California: Jour. Geology, v. 36, no. 3, p. 224–247.

Krumbein, W. C., 1937, Sediments and exponential curves: Jour. Geology, v. 45, no. 6, p. 577–601.

Stokes, W. L., 1954, Some stratigraphic, sedimentary, and structural relations of uranium deposits in the Salt Wash sandstone: U. S. Atomic Energy Comm., RME-3102, 50 p.

Tolman, C. F., 1937, Ground water: New York, Mc-

Graw-Hill Book Co., Inc., p. 365–377.

Trowbridge, A. C., 1911, The terrestrial deposits of Owens Valley, California: Jour. Geology, v. 19, p. 706–747.

BARS

Bass, N. W., and others, 1937, Origin and distribution of Bartlesville and Burbank shoestring sands in parts of Oklahoma and Kansas: Am. Assoc. Petroleum Geologists Bull., v. 21, no. 1, p. 30–66.

Bernard, H. A., and others, 1959, *See* under "References Cited."

LeBlanc, R. J., and Hodgson, W. D., 1959, *See* under "References Cited."

Lucke, J. B., 1934, *See* under "References Cited."

Pepper, J. F., and others, 1944, Map of the second Berea sand in Gallia, Meigs, Athens, Morgan, and Muskingum Counties, Ohio: U. S. Geol. Survey Oil and Gas Inves. Prelim. Map 5.

BEACHES

Bascom, W. N., 1954, Characteristics of natural beaches: 4th Conf. Coastal Eng., Chicago, Ill., Oct. 1953, Berkeley, Calif., Council on Wave Resch. Eng. Found.

Bradley, W. C., 1957, Origin of marine-terrace deposits in the Santa Cruz area, California: Geol. Soc. America Bull., v. 68, no. 4, p. 421–444.

Thompson, W. O., 1937, Original structures of beaches, bars, and dunes: Geol. Soc. America Bull., v. 48, no. 6, p. 723–751.

——— 1949, Lyons sandstone of Colorado Front Range: Am. Assoc. Petroleum Geologists Bull., v. 33, no. 1, p. 52–72.

DELTAS

Barrell, Joseph, 1912, Criteria for the recognition of ancient delta deposits: Geol. Soc. America Bull., v. 23, no. 3, p. 377–446.

——— 1913, 1914, The Upper Devonian delta of the Appalachian geosyncline: Am. Jour. Sci., Pt. 1, v. 36, no. 4, p. 429–472; Pt. 2, v. 37, no. 4, p. 87–109, 229–253.

Busch, D. A., 1954, 1955, Deltas significant in subsurface exploration: World Oil, Pt. 1, v. 139, no. 7, p. 95–98, 106; Pt. 2, v. 140, no. 1, p. 82, 84, 86.

Fisk, H. N., 1944, *See* under "References Cited."

——— and others, 1954, *See* under "References Cited."

Krynine, P. D., 1940, Petrology and genesis of the third Bradford sand: Pennsylvania State Coll. Min. Ind. Expt. Sta. Bull. 29, 134 p.

Rittenhouse, G., 1949, Early Silurian rocks of the northern Appalachian basin: U. S. Geol. Survey Oil and Gas Inves. Prelim. Map 100.

Russell, R. J., 1958, Geological geomorphology: Geol. Soc. American Bull., v. 69, no. 1, p. 1–22.

DUNES

Bagnold, R. A., 1941, The physics of blown sand and desert dunes: London, Methuen and Co., Ltd., 265 p.

Cooper, W. S., 1958, Coastal sand dunes of Oregon and Washington: Geol. Soc. America Mem. 72, 169 p.

Melton, F. A., 1940, A tentative classification of sand dunes, its application to dune history in the southern High Plains: Jour. Geology, v. 48, no. 2, p. 113–174.

ESTUARY SANDS

Ketchum, B. H., 1953, Circulation in estuaries, *in* 3d
Conf. Coastal Eng. Proc., Cambridge, Mass., Oct.
1952: Univ. of California Eng. Found., p. 65–76.
Robinson, A. H. W., 1956, The submarine morphology
of certain port approach channel systems: Inst. of
Navigation Jour., v. 9, p. 20–46.

RIVER "CHANNELS"

Hopkins, M. E., 1958, Geology and petrology of the
Anvil Rock sandstone of southern Illinois: Illinois
Geol. Survey Circ. 256, 49 p.
Lins, T. W., 1950, Origin and environment of the
Tonganoxie sandstone in northeastern Kansas:
Kansas Geol. Survey Bull. 86, pt. 5, p. 108–140.
Nanz, R. H., Jr., 1954, Genesis of Oligocene sandstone
reservoir, Seelingson field, Jim Wells and Kleberg
Counties, Texas: Am. Assoc. Petroleum Geologists
Bull., v. 38, no. 1, p. 96–117.
Pepper, J. F., DeWitt, W., Jr., and Demarest, D. F.,
1954, Geology of the Bedford shale and Berea sand-
stone in the Appalachian basin: U. S. Geol. Survey
Prof. Paper 259, 109 p.
Siever, Raymond, 1951, The Mississippian-Pennsyl-
vanian unconformity in southern Illinois· Am. Assoc.
Petroleum Geologists Bull., v. 35, no. 3, p. 542–581.
Wilson, C. W., Jr., 1948, Channels and channel-filling
sediments of Richmond age in south-central Tennessee: Geol. Soc. America Bull., v. 59, no. 8, p. 733–
766.

SHELF-EDGE SANDS

Rich, J. L., 1951, Three critical environments of deposition, and criteria for recognition of rocks deposited
in each of them: Geol. Soc. America Bull., v. 62, no.
1, p. 1–20.

SUBAQUEOUS BARS

Cloet, R. L., 1954, A hydrographic analysis of the
Goodwin sands and the Brake bank: Geog. Journal,
v. 120, p. 203–215.
van Veen, J., 1950, Eb-en Vloedschaar Systemen in de
Nederlandse getijwatern: T. Kon. Ned. Aard. Gen.,
v. 67, p. 303.

TURBIDITY-CURRENT SANDS

Bell, H. S., 1942, Density currents as agents for transporting sediments: Jour. Geology, v. 50, no. 5, p.
512–547.
Gorsline, D. S., and Emery, K. O., 1959, Turbidity-
current deposits in San Pedro and Santa Monica
basins off southern California: Geol. Soc. America
Bull., v. 70, no. 3, p. 279–290.
Hough, J. L., editor, 1951, Turbidity currents and
transportation of coarse sediments to deep water—a
symposium: Tulsa, Okla., Soc. Econ. Paleontologists
and Mineralogists Spec. Pub. 2, 107 p.
Menard, H. W., Jr., 1955, Deep-sea channels, topography, and sedimentation: Am. Assoc. Petroleum
Geologists Bull., v. 39, no. 2, p. 236–255.

WAVE-BUILT TERRACE SANDS

Barrell, Joseph, 1925, Marine and terrestrial conglomerates: Geol. Soc. America Bull., v. 36, no. 2, p. 279–341.

LABORATORY EXPERIMENTS ON FORM AND STRUCTURE
OF LONGSHORE BARS AND BEACHES[1]

EDWIN D. McKEE[2] AND THOMAS S. STERRETT[2]

Denver, Colorado

ABSTRACT

Beaches and bars have been formed during experiments conducted in a 46-foot wave tank at the Sedimentation Laboratory of the U. S. Geological Survey in Denver. By changing one variable factor at a time, elements responsible for major differences in primary structure and in shape of sand body have been determined. These elements are—differences in slope of sand floor (expressed in terms of water depth), intensity of wave action, and supply of sand. Stages in the growth of the bars and beaches were marked with dark layers of magnetite, and cross sections were preserved on masonite boards coated with liquid rubber, thus recording cross-stratification patterns and sand-body shapes.

Longshore bars are produced at the point of wave break. In very shallow water an emergent bar commonly forms; in somewhat deeper water a submarine bar is built; and in still deeper water no bar forms. Increase in intensity of waves tends to build a bar toward, and even onto, the beach. Weaker waves build bars upward to form barriers, with lagoons to shoreward. Abundant sand furnished on the seaward side of a growing bar simulates conditions caused by some longshore and rip currents, and causes gentle seaward-dipping beds to form. In contrast, a limited sand supply results in growth of bars that characteristically have shoreward-dipping strata of steeper angle.

Beach strata normally dip seaward at low angles from the crest to a point below water level. Offshore, the seaward extensions of these gently dipping beds include fore-set beds with relatively high angles which form a shoreface terrace. The sand body comprised of both sets of bedding builds outward if a large supply of sand is furnished. In shallow water, however, or at moderate depth where waves are strong, the period of beach growth is limited by the deposition of longshore bars which eliminate wave action as they grow into barriers and form lagoons. Under conditions in which no bar is built, growth of the beach and shoreface terrace is controlled by the amount of sand available; the proportion of top-set to fore-set beds is determined by the strength of waves.

INTRODUCTION

In order to determine variations in the form and structure of longshore bars and beaches a series of experiments was conducted in the Sedimentation Laboratory of the U. S. Geological Survey in Denver, during 1959. Various types of bars and beaches were reproduced. Differences in shape and in the cross-stratification of these experimentally formed sand bodies were recorded, establishing criteria useful in the interpretation of similar features preserved in ancient sedimentary rocks.

A metal tank, 46 feet long and $1\frac{1}{2}$ feet wide, with plastic observation windows on one side and an electrically controlled wave generator at one end, was used for the experiments. Waves were formed by the back-and-forth movement of a perforated baffle for which the length of stroke and speed of movement was predetermined according to a table of wave calibration, and set at the beginning of each experiment. The floor of the flume sloped down toward the wave generator at an angle of 0°, 15′, 18″.

Sediment used for wave-tank experiments consisted of well sorted[3] and well rounded, screened sand of fine-grained quartz, showing the following size distribution

$\frac{1}{2}$ mm; coarse.................	7 per cent
$\frac{1}{4}$–$\frac{1}{2}$ mm; medium.............	81 per cent
$\frac{1}{4}$ mm; fine or smaller..........	12 per cent.

At the start of each experiment sand was distributed across the floor of the tank to form a seaward-sloping wedge that tapered to its termination approximately 30 feet from the beach area. At this time and during subsequent stages in the growth and evolution of the sand bodies, thin layers of magnetite were spread over the sand. The magnetite was introduced at regular intervals (15 minutes, 30 minutes, or 60 minutes, depending

---

[1] Read before the Association at Atlantic City, New Jersey, April 25, 1960. Manuscript received, April 26, 1960. Publication authorized by the Director, U. S. Geological Survey.

[2] U. S. Geological Survey.

[3] In experiments to be conducted later, poorly sorted sand will be used for comparison.

on the speed of growth) to serve as markers indicating steps in construction and also to record
details of structure characteristic of the sand
body.

Upon completion of each experiment a permanent record was prepared of the shape and structure formed during investigation. This record
was made by draining water from the tank, cutting
and removing a vertical slice of sand parallel to
the wave direction, and then wedging a masonite
board covered with liquid rubber against the
vertical face. When the rubber hardened and a
surface of sand had adhered to it, excess sand was
removed from the board, leaving a sample cross
section of the sand body. Additional records were
made by tracing structure patterns on transparent
paper through plastic windows of the tank, by
making casts in liquid rubber of surface relief
features such as ripple marks, and by keeping
notes on the evolution of various structures.

Experiments were conducted under the direction of the senior author; details of tank operation
were handled largely by the junior author.

TERMINOLOGY

In this series of experiments the term *beach* is
applied to deposits of the *shore*, which is defined,
following Johnson (1919, p. 160), as the zone over
which the water line, or line of contact between
land and sea, migrates. Extensions of beach
deposits seaward of the low-water level have been
considered a part of the beach by some authors,
but are here referred to as deposits of the *shoreface* and include steeper dipping beds of the
shoreface terrace (Johnson, 1919, p. 163). Sediments seaward of this terrace are referred as as
offshore deposits.

The term *bar* is applied to the sand bodies
formed offshore at the point of wave break and as
a result of wave action. Depending on depth
(variation in slope), amount of wave action, and
availability of sand, these sand bodies may develop as (1) subaqueous masses that do not build
up to water level, (2) masses that build up to but
not above water level, or (3) masses that build to
maximum wave height. All such sand bodies are
termed *offshore bars* by Johnson (1919, p. 259),
and he includes in the term such additional features as beaches and dunes where they are de-

posited on the emergent surfaces during a late
stage.

Those bars that form only as subaqueous types
have been called *balls* (in "lows and balls") by
Evans (1940, p. 476), following earlier usage by
various British geologists, but the inappropriate-
ness of this term has subsequently been shown by
Shepard (1950). The term *offshore bars* as used by
Evans (1942, p. 846) was restricted to those sand
ridges "lying approximately parallel to a shoreline and reaching above the water." Thus, he
would consider two of the types of sand bodies
that were formed in the present laboratory experiments as unrelated and genetically different.

Sand bodies of the types under discussion,
where "submerged at least by high tides," are
designated *longshore bars* by Shepard (1952, p.
1908). In contrast, any sand accumulations above
high-tide level, added to such bodies, cause them
to be termed *barriers*, according to Price (1951,
p. 487–488), and *barrier beaches, barrier islands,* or
barrier spits, depending upon physiographic features, according to Shepard (1952, p. 1905–1906).

Use of the term *longshore bar* in referring to
various experimentally formed offshore sand
ridges seems valid. In some of the higher sand
bodies, especially those resulting from seaward
sand feeding, however, low-angle structures comparable to those of a natural beach and in a
similar position relative to sea level are formed,
thus suggesting that these would be referred to in
nature as *barrier beaches*. A further suggestion is
made that the term *barrier* as used by Price,
Shepard, and others does not represent a single
structural or genetic unit as does a bar, but is a
composite body composed of a longshore bar that
forms its base or core, and a veneer or perhaps
thicker covering of other sand bodies with different structures.

STAGES IN GROWTH OF LONGSHORE
BARS AND BEACHES

Experiments in the series that forms the basis
of this paper were begun, in each case, with a
sand mass representing a shore cliff at one end of
the tank and an even surface of sand sloping
seaward from it toward the opposite end of the
tank. In each experiment the degree of slope of
the sand bottom was regulated by the height of

water level, and thus determining the depth of water at any particular place. The strength of waves to be used was arbitrarily decided in advance and the wave generator was set for the appropriate speed.

After the wave generator was put in motion for an experiment, the variable factors that control sedimentation were not changed, and gradually the deposits became stabilized, terminating the experiment.[4] At that point no further change could be expected without altering one or more of several controls such as depth of water, degree of wave action, or amount of available sediment. Between the beginning of an experiment and the attainment of a stabilized condition, however, a continuous evolution of sedimentary forms and structures took place.

In each experiment, where water was sufficiently shallow for wave-formed orbits of water-particles to impinge on the sand floor, the initial structures to be formed consisted of scattered cusp-type ripple marks on the sand surface. These cusps, which are scattered, crescent-shaped bodies with steep slopes facing shoreward, then changed into parallel-type ripple marks, in series, as a uniform flow movement was brought about by wave motion (Scott, 1945). The ripple marks migrated shoreward, rapidly or slowly according to intensity of wave action, by the normal process of continuous erosion on the seaward side of each crest and deposition to lee (Fig. 1). All ripple marks were asymmetrical because of the forward movement of the waves, but their size varied greatly with changing conditions on the sea floor.

In the evolution of the sea floor, change from an even, ripple-marked surface (Fig. 2-A) to a low mound with rippled surface (Fig. 2-B), signifies the forming of an embryo offshore bar. This change takes place at approximately the point of wave break, as shown by Keulegan (1948, p. 2), and is caused by increased turbulence which tends to disrupt normal ripple-mark production and to pile up sand into a mound. The running time required to start growth of a submarine bar in the laboratory ranged from 4 to 21 hours, depending on each of the several variable factors

concerned. As the bar grows vertically, ripple marks disappear from its surface because turbulence increases and waves of translation carry shoreward the disrupted sand from the ripple marks. The bar then continues to increase in size through the systematic addition of sloping sand layers to shoreward, which may be classed as fore-set beds, or in some bars, as top-set beds.

Vertical and lateral growth of a bar through the accretion of sand in the form of dipping beds is dependent upon an adequate source of sand. In nature this source, according to Davis (1909, p. 708), is the previously developed sand floor to seaward, but according to Gilbert (1890, p. 40), it is shore drift continually being introduced by longshore currents.[5] In the laboratory, sand obtained from the seaward floor alone, being relatively scant, caused growth largely on the lee or shoreward side of the initial mound or bar. This was because removal of sand to seaward with resulting increase of water depth in that direction resulted in shoreward migration of the point of wave break. In contrast, where new sand was constantly being fed artificially[6] to seaward of the bar, as though by a combination of longshore and rip currents, a shoal was produced, resulting in the seaward migration of the point of wave break and the accretion of sand to the seaward side of the bar (Figs. 4-B, 4-D).

In every experiment a series of changes in sand form and in structure evolves in the shore area at the same time that bars are forming to seaward. Beach deposits with strata dipping seaward at low angles form above water level and may be considered as top-set beds; the continuation of the low-angle beds beneath water level and the fore-set beds offshore beyond, dipping at moderately high angles, forms a shoreface terrace (Johnson, 1919, p. 163, 259). The evolution of these related shore and offshore deposits is controlled early in their history by the type and growth of longshore bars that form to seaward.

---

[4] In experiments to be undertaken, rising water level and lowering water level, simulating conditions of transgression and regression, will be introduced.

[5] Validity of the concept of bar growth by the work of longshore currents has been strongly questioned on several grounds by Evans (1942, p. 848); but more recently, Shepard (1950, p. 23) has shown that the combination of shore drift and rip currents feed much sediment to the seaward sides of longshore bars.

[6] Measured quantities were hand fed at regular, timed intervals.

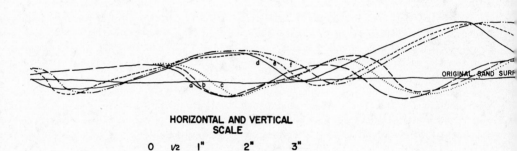

HORIZONTAL AND VERTICAL
SCALE

0   1/2   1"   2"   3"

Fɪɢ. 1.—Migration of sand by wave-formed ripples from offshore toward beach. Tracing
was made on window of tank during early stages of experiment on longshore bar growth.
a, b, c = ripple mark development and migration (early stage); d, e, f = same (late stage).
a, b, c = 3-minute time intervals; d, e, f = 5-minute time intervals.

VARIABLE FACTORS IN WAVE-TANK EXPERIMENTS

In the present series of experiments the growth of longshore bars and beaches took place under controlled conditions. Three variable factors proved to be of major significance—differences in slope of sand floor (expressed in terms of water depth), force or intensity of wave action, and abundance of available sediment. One factor was varied at a time, and after each change the sand body was allowed to evolve until it became completely stabilized with no further growth or change in shape. The time involved ranged from 8 hours where water was shallow and wave action weak, to 70 hours where water was deep and wave action strong.

Three depths of water measured 16 feet from the beach were used—0.4 feet, 0.6 feet, and 0.8 feet; these depths will be referred to hereafter as shallow, moderate, and deep, respectively. Actually they represent differences in slope of the sand floor, and these differences are responsible for major variations in the types of beaches and bars produced.

Intensity of wave action was controlled largely by wave frequency, which ranged from 12 to 48

STATIC WATER LEVEL

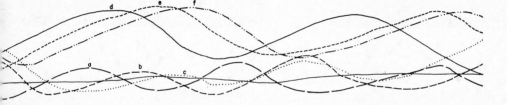

waves per minute, and this frequency was measured in terms of transmission speeds. For convenience in discussion, therefore, wave action is
hereafter referred to as weak when it has a frequency of 16 waves or less per minute; as moderate when 20 to 28 waves per minute; as strong
when 32 waves or more per minute.

Sources of sand were of two types (1) sediment
derived from normal, sloping floor and from erosion of the shore, and no new sand introduced, and
(2) sand fed artificially at constant rate into an
area seaward of growing submarine bar or at base
of shoreface terrace when no bar formed, conditions intended to simulate those resulting from
introduction of sand by a combination of longshore and rip currents.

SHAPE AND STRUCTURE OF LONGSHORE BARS

Experiments 1 and 2—Water depth, shallow
(gentle floor slope). *Wave action,* moderate. *Sand,*
none added. Figures 2-C, 4-C.

Longshore bars form readily under these conditions. They start near the point of wave break,
which is relatively far from shore, and build both
upward and shoreward (Fig. 2-C). The resulting
structure in cross section is a series of fore-set
beds dipping shoreward at 20°–30° (Table I). For
some reason, not full understood, the cross-strata
normally are concave downward. Forward growth
of the bar commonly buries the shoreward,
ripple-marked surface on which it advances;
vertical growth soon reaches water level and
above, attaining a height equal to that of the
maximum wave height, thus forming a lagoon to
shoreward and terminating deposition in that
direction. Sand bars formed under these conditions are relatively high in relation to their width;
those formed experimentally have ratios of 1 to 11
(Table II; Fig. 4-C).

Experiments 3, 4, and 5—Water depth, shallow
(gentle floor slope). *Wave action,* strong. *Sand,*
none added. Figures 2-E, 3-A.

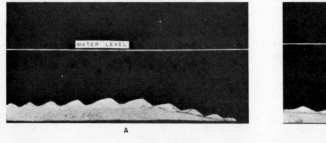

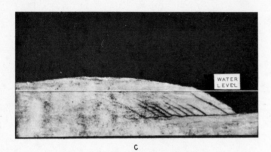

Fig. 2.—Cross sections of longshore bars formed in laboratory. Shore to right.

A, B—Low mounds formed during early stages of bar growth on flat, ripple-marked sand floor.
   C—Bar formed with shallow water and moderate wave action; sand derived from seaward floor only.
   D—Bar formed with moderate water depth and weak wave action; sand derived from seaward floor only.
   E—Bar formed with shallow water and strong wave action; sand derived from seaward floor only.
   F—Bar formed with moderate water depth and moderate wave action; derived from seaward floor only.
   G—Bar formed with deep water and strong wave action; sand derived from seaward floor only.

Where shallow depth is maintained but intensity of wave action is increased to "strong," a longshore bar begins to form farther from shore than in the preceding experiment—a result of the point of wave break being in deeper water. The bar builds upward and shoreward, but mostly shoreward because of stronger wave action than before. Commonly, the upper surface of the bar barely attains water level, but the bar builds shoreward all the way to the beach and even buries the lower part of the foreshore. The resulting structure in cross section consists of a series of relatively long fore-set beds, dipping shoreward at 10°–20°, and concave downward (Figs. 2-E, 3-A; Table I). Its ratio of height to width as determined in the laboratory is about 1 to 28 (Table II).

Experiment 6—Water depth, moderate (moderate floor slope). *Wave action,* weak. *Sand,* none added. Figure 2-D.

Under these conditions a longshore bar will accumulate only after considerable time, and it will remain as a submarine mound, rising but a short distance above the original sand floor. Intensity of wave action apparently is too slight to allow further accumulation and the bar moves back and forth locally by alternate erosion and deposition along its margins. Its structure consists of shoreward-dipping strata with angles of 28°–30° (Fig. 2-D). Its ratio of height to width is 1 to 9.

Experiments 7 and 8—Water depth, moderate (moderate floor slope). *Wave action,* moderate. *Sand,* none added. Figures 4-A, 2-F.

At moderate depth as in the preceding experiment, but with stronger wave action (moderate strength), longshore bars will grow to water level and advance shoreward, much like those formed in shallow water when wave action is strong. Thus, an effect similar to that caused by increasing wave action in shallow water is obtained at greater depth where a submarine bar builds upward and shoreward because of an increase in

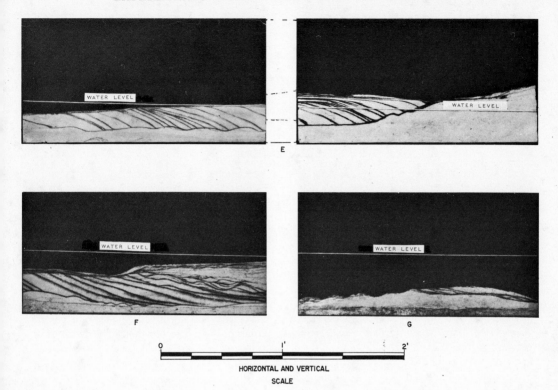

HORIZONTAL AND VERTICAL
SCALE

wave action (Figs. 4-*A*, 2-*F*). Such bars advance to and over the lower part of the beach; their structure includes fore-set beds that are concave downward and that dip 23°–30° shoreward. The height-to-width ratio of this type of bar as formed in the laboratory is 1 to 21.

Experiments 9 and 10—Water depth, deep (steep floor slope). *Wave action,* weak to moderate. *Sand,* none added. No figure.

In deep water with weak to moderate wave action no bar forms, regardless of the time involved.

Experiment 11—Water depth, deep (steep floor slope). *Wave action,* strong. *Sand,* none added. Figure 2-*G*.

Under these conditions submarine bars commonly form. In structure and shape (Fig. 2-*G*) they resemble those formed in water of moderate depth with weak wave action, and like them, never mature into any more than low mounds well below water level. Fore-set beds dip 20°

shoreward and the ratio of height to width in the sand body is 1 to 12 (Tables I and II).

Experiment 12—Water depth, shallow (gentle floor slope). *Wave action,* moderate. *Sand,* artificial seaward feeding. Figure 4-*B*.

With new sand constantly being furnished artificially on the seaward side of a growing submarine bar, conditions are attained which simulate natural bar growth from the introduction of sand by longshore and rip currents. In shallow water, with wave action moderate, sand-feeding to seaward results in building a bar upward and slightly seaward until it reaches water level where it becomes stabilized (Fig. 4-*B*). Cross sections normal to the shore show an original core or nucleus composed of relatively steep, shoreward-dipping beds like those of preceding experiments. Superimposed on this core are low-angle beds dipping gently to seaward (Table I). The overall shape of the bar is represented by a height-to-width ratio of 1:10.

TABLE I. ANGLE OF DIP OF CROSS-STRATA IN BARS[a]

Exp. No.	Environment			Seaward-dipping Strata (degrees)	Shoreward-dipping Strata (degrees)
	Water Depth	Intensity of Wave Action	Sand Available		
1	Shallow	Moderate	Bottom only	None	28–30
2	Shallow	Moderate	Bottom only	None	20
3	Shallow	Strong	Bottom only	Horizontal	10–15
4	Shallow	Strong	Bottom only	None	14–20
5	Shallow	Strong	Bottom only	None	15–20
6	Moderate	Weak	Bottom only	None	28–30
7	Moderate	Moderate	Bottom only	None	23–30
8	Moderate	Moderate	Bottom only	None	25–30
9	Deep	Weak	Bottom only	No bar	No bar
10	Deep	Moderate	Bottom only	—	—
11	Deep	Strong	Bottom only	None	20
12	Shallow	Moderate	Seaward feeding	6–7	16–25
13	Shallow	Strong	Seaward feeding	4–6[b]	17–25
14	Deep	Moderate	Seaward feeding	No bar	No bar
15	Deep	Strong	Seaward feeding	—	—

[a] In fifteen experiments completed, not every possible combination of the three variables could be included, but data for experiments omitted probably can be estimated reasonably well on the basis of the combinations selected.
[b] Terrace front—30°.

Experiment 13—Water depth, shallow (gentle floor slope). *Wave action,* strong. *Sand,* artificial seaward feeding. Figure 4-*D.*

Under these conditions, the resulting structure is relatively complicated (Fig. 4-*D*). The waves move some sand forward over the original submarine core to form shoreward-dipping strata; the remaining sand accumulates as nearly horizontal beds on top, or is deposited to seaward and dips gently in that direction. Thus, the bar grows larger in three directions until it reaches sea level and can build farther only in a seaward direction. On the seaward side of the bar the beds dip 4°–6°; on the shoreward side they dip 17°–25°. Height-to-width ratio is 1:19.

Experiments 14 and 15—Water depth, deep (steep floor slope). *Wave action,* moderate to strong. *Sand,* artificial seaward feeding. No figure.

TABLE II. HEIGHT-TO-WIDTH RATIOS OF LONGSHORE BARS AS DETERMINED IN LABORATORY EXPERIMENTS

Exp. No.	Environment			Dimensions		Ratio H:W
	Water Depth	Intensity of Wave Action	Sand Available	Height (feet)	Width (feet)	
1	Shallow	Moderate	Bottom only	0.35	3.8	1:11
2	Shallow	Moderate	Bottom only	0.4	4.6	1:12
3	Shallow	Strong	Bottom only	0.25	7.0	1:28
4	Shallow	Strong	Bottom only	0.25	7.0	1:28
5	Shallow	Strong	Bottom only	0.25	7.0	1:28
6	Moderate	Weak	Bottom only	0.2	1.8	1:9[a]
7	Moderate	Moderate	Bottom only	0.42	8.8	1:21
8	Moderate	Moderate	Bottom only	—	—	—
9	Deep	Weak	Bottom only	None	None	None
10	Deep	Moderate	Bottom only	—	—	—
11	Deep	Strong	Bottom only	0.2	2.3	1:12[a]
12	Shallow	Moderat	Seaward feeding	0.6	6.2	1:10
13	Shallow	Strong	Seaward feeding	0.5	9.5	1:19
14	Deep	Moderate	Seaward feeding	None	None	None
15	Deep	Strong	Seaward feeding	—	—	—

[a] Submarine bar.

TABLE III. ANGLE OF DIP OF TOP-SET BEDS ON BEACHES
AND FORE-SET BEDS ON SHOREFACE TERRACES

Exp. No.	Environment			Top-set Beds Beach (degrees)	Fore-set Beds Shoreface Terrace (degrees)
	Water Depth	Intensity of Wave Action	Sand Available		
4	Shallow	Strong	Bottom and shore	7–9	27–28
6	Moderate	Weak	Bottom and shore	9–10	29–30
7	Moderate	Moderate	Bottom and shore	9–11	27–30
9	Deep	Weak	Bottom and shore	8–12	29–31
10	Deep	Moderate	Bottom and shore	11–13	28–31
15	Deep	Strong	Seaward feeding	12–15	30

In deep water, even with strong wave action and with considerable offshore sand-feeding, no bar accumulates. All sand moves steadily into the beach area.

SHAPE AND STRUCTURE OF BEACHES AND ADJACENT SHOREFACE TERRACES

Experiment 4—Water depth, shallow (gentle floor slope). *Wave action*, strong. *Sand*, none added. Figure 3-*B*.

Beaches in shallow water areas (gently sloping floors) normally have only a short period of growth because longshore bars build up rapidly to seaward and change those factors responsible for beach accumulation. Where wave action is weak the bars form barriers, thus eliminating wave action to shoreward and causing lagoons to be formed; where wave action is strong, the bars build shoreward and sometimes partly bury the beach. In laboratory experiments shallow-water beaches washed by strong wave action are built up largely as top-set beds with gentle seaward dips of 7°–9°. Shorter but steeper dipping (27°–28°) fore-set deposits are formed in the shoreface area to seaward, but they cannot be considered a part of the beach proper (Fig. 3-*B*; Table III), for they are below low water level.

Experiment 6—Water depth, moderate (moderate floor slope). *Wave action*, weak. *Sand*, none added. Figures 3-*E*, 3-*C*.

Under these conditions a complex structure pattern is formed. It consists of relatively long, high-angle fore-set beds below water level and low-angle top-set beds partly above and partly below (Fig. 3-*E*). The beach grows seaward relatively far because no longshore bar of sufficient height to eliminate wave action is formed. Stabilization is attained, however, when sand advances shoreward in the form of migrating ripple marks and mingles with the sand of fore-set beds that are building seaward. This mingling results in a zone where opposing forces produce alternations in deposition and erosion, and it results in complex interfingering structures (Fig. 3-*C*). In the laboratory such composite sand bodies have height-to-width ratios of approximately 1 to 12 (Table IV).

TABLE IV. HEIGHT-TO-WIDTH RATIOS OF SAND BODIES COMPOSED OF
BEACH AND SHOREFACE TERRACE DEPOSITS COMBINED

Exp. No.	Environment			Dimensions		Ratio H:W
	Water Depth	Intensity of Wave Action	Sand Available	Height (feet)	Width[a] (feet)	
4	Shallow	Strong	Bottom and shore	0.09	1.5	1:17
6	Moderate	Weak	Bottom and shore	0.30	3.5	1:12
7	Moderate	Moderate	Bottom and shore	0.28	3.0	1:11
9	Deep	Weak	Bottom and shore	0.46	4.0	1:9
10	Deep	Moderate	Bottom and shore	0.57	6.0	1:10
15	Deep	Strong	Seaward feeding	0.45	4.5	1:10

[a] Measured horizontally from base of terrace fore-sets to approximate shoreward pinchout.

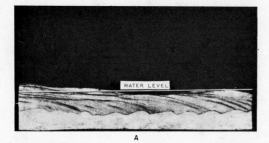

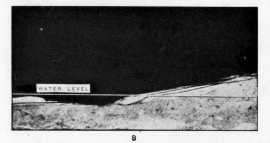

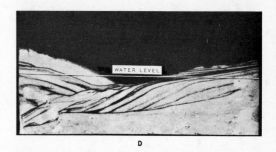

FIG. 3.—Cross sections of beaches, shoreface terraces, and a longshore bar formed in laboratory. Shore to right.

A—Bar formed with shallow water and strong wave action; sand derived from seaward floor only.
B—Beach formed with shallow water and strong wave action; sand derived from shore.
C—Shoreface deposits formed with moderate depth and weak wave action; sand derived from sea floor.
D—Beach (with fore-set beds of bar to left) formed with moderate depth and moderate wave action; sand derived from shore.
E—Beach and shoreface deposits formed with moderate water depth and weak wave action; sand derived from shore.
F—Beach and shoreface deposits formed with deep water and weak wave action; sand derived from shore.

Experiment 7—Water depth, moderate (moderate floor slope). *Wave action*, moderate. *Sand*, none added. Figure 3-*D*.

Beaches formed in the laboratory under these conditions contain structure patterns resembling, in most respects, those formed by weaker waves in the preceding experiment. Because of greater wave strength, however, top-set beds here build to a greater thickness and at a higher angle (9°–11°). Further, the ultimate seaward growth of these associated beach and shoreface deposits is limited by advancing sand of a longshore bar that approaches and overrides them (Fig. 3-*D*). The height-to-width ratio of the beach and shoreface deposits upon stabilization is about 1 to 11 (Table IV).

Experiment 9—Water depth, deep (steep floor slope). *Wave action*, weak. *Sand*, none added. Figure 3-*F*.

In this environment the process of forming gently dipping top-set beds on the beach proper and steeper dipping fore-set beds in shoreface areas (Fig. 3-*F*), is similar to that described for other environments. Only a relatively thin series of top-set beds is formed because the waves are weak and both top-set and associated fore-set beds dip at lower angles than those formed under conditions of stronger wave action. Because longshore bars, which eliminate wave action near shore, do not form under conditions of deep water, beach extension seaward continues longer than otherwise and is terminated only when waves can

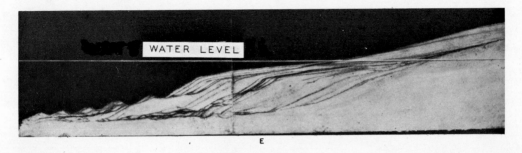

E

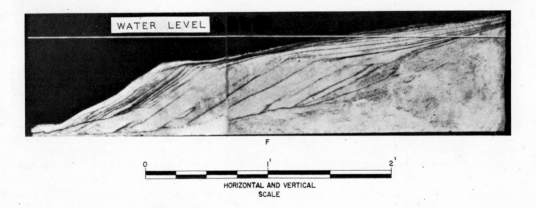

F

0   1'   2'

HORIZONTAL AND VERTICAL
SCALE

no longer obtain a supply of sand from the shore. The ratio of height to width in this type of sand body is 1 to 9 (Table IV).

Experiment 10—Water depth, deep (steep floor slope). *Wave action*, moderate. *Sand*, none added. Figure 4-*E*.

A final experiment in beach construction with no sand introduced offshore was in deep water (steeply sloping floor) with moderate wave action. The resulting sand body shows, in cross section normal to the strand (Fig. 4-*E*), a very thick series of top-set beds. Both top-set and fore-set beds have relatively steep dips—11°–13°, and 28°–31°, respectively. The height-to-width ratio obtained in the laboratory was 1 to 10.

Experiment 15—Water depth, deep (steep floor slope). *Wave action*, strong. *Sand*, artificial seaward feeding. Figure 4-*F*.

Continuous feeding of sediment at base of the shoreface terrace, intended to simulate conditions of sand introduction by longshore and rip currents, results in a complex form and structure pattern (Fig. 4-*F*). Experiments with deep water (steeply sloping floor) and with strong wave action result in a conflict of forces in which advancing waves move sand shoreward to meet other sand carried seaward by backwash. Top-set beds on the beach, which are comprised of shore-derived sand, dip seaward at 12°–15° and form a landward-thickening wedge. To seaward, meanwhile, newly introduced sand advances landward forming a complicated ripple and scour-and-fill structure. This deposit builds up as rapidly as the sand supply permits. Much of the new sand, moreover, is carried farther shoreward, ultimately contributing to construction of fore-set beds as the

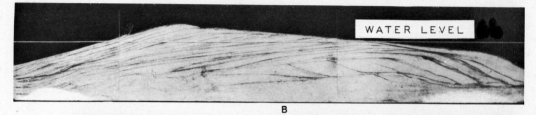

B

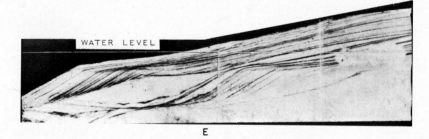

E

FIG. 4.—Cross sections of longshore bars, shoreface deposits, and beaches formed in laboratory. Shore to right

A—Bar formed with moderate depth and moderate wave action; sand derived from seaward floor only.
B—Bar formed with shallow water and moderate wave action; sand fed to seaward.
C—Bar formed with shallow water and moderate wave action; sand derived from seaward floor only; illustrates shape but not structure.
D—Bar formed with shallow water and strong wave action; sand fed to seaward.
E—Beach and shoreface deposits formed with deep water and moderate wave action; sand derived from shore.
F—Beach and shoreface deposits formed with deep water and strong wave action; sand fed to seaward.

backwash redeposits this sand in the form of a shoreface terrace.

The wedge shape of top-set beds seems to result from the continuous compression of the seaward parts of these beds. This compression results from the force of waves which break near shore because of deep water (steeply sloping floor) and which exert greatest pressure in the area referred to. Intensity of the force increases as the fore-set beds build out from shore, causing the point of wave break to be progressively farther to seaward.

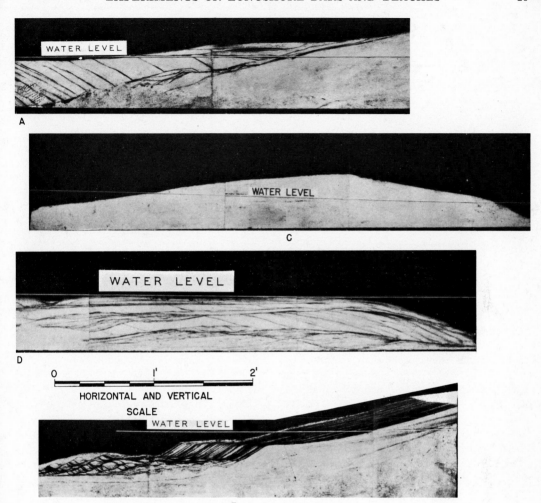

STRUCTURES IN SOME MODERN BEACHES AND BARS

A comparison of foreshore beach structures formed during laboratory experiments with those formed on modern beaches at several localities shows a close similarity. In both actual and experimental beaches the strata dip gently seaward with long, even slopes; in both, the structure pattern as shown in cross section is due largely to slight differences in the dip of strata in adjacent sets (Thompson, 1937, p. 732). Only in degree of dip is any noticeable difference detected; those

strata formed in the experimental laboratory are, in general, somewhat steeper than those of natural beaches. Studies of foreshore beach strata on the Gulf Coast of Texas, for example, show a range from 2° to 5°, and on the coast of southern California between 7° and 10° (McKee, 1957, p. 1708–1715). By way of comparison, foreshore beach strata deposited in laboratory experiments dip from 7° to 15° (Table III).

No data are available, insofar as the writers know, concerning structures on modern shoreface terraces. In the laboratory, as shown in Table III,

Seaward

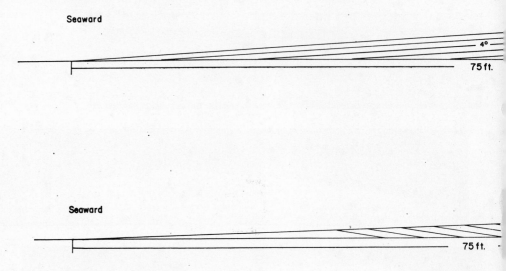

4°

75 ft.

Seaward

75 ft.

strata on the front of this terrace dip 27° to 31° seaward, forming in cross section a pattern which in most respects is not unlike that made by fore-set beds of a delta. Differences in beach strata formed under similar conditions, suggest that these dips probably are somewhat greater than those formed in nature. Confirmation of this comparison, however, must await field investigations.

Stratification of some longshore bars formed in the laboratory may be compared with that in bars examined by the senior author and C. Teichert in 1959 off the north coast of Bimini in the Bahama Islands. The Bimini bars lie roughly parallel to the shore; they stand above low-tide level and are barely awash during high tide. Cross sections trenched normal to the shoreline during low tide showed that large parts of the bars were formed mainly of strata dipping shoreward at 16° to 20°, but in some places, seaward of the bar crest, upper strata dipped seaward at 4° to 5° (Fig. 5). Thus, the structures in these modern bars resemble those formed in the experimental laboratory under conditions of shallow water (gently sloping floor), artificial sand feeding to seaward, and moderate wave action (Fig. 4-B).

Longshore bars, other than the type just discussed that builds to the surface and advances shoreward, have been described by numerous geologists, but no information concerning their structure seems to be available. Submarine bars that have accumulated on the relatively steep slopes off southern California (Fig. 6) have been examined by Shepard (1950), and those that have accumulated in Lake Michigan have been studied by Evans (1940) and others.

Bars that have built above high water level in the shallow waters of the Texas coast and that have compound structures resulting from the accretion of beach and dune deposits, are discussed by Shepard and Moore (1955) and by Fisk (1959). On the basis of sample data from many borings, most of the sediment underlying Padre Island, for example, is considered (Fisk, 1959, Fig. 13; Table 2) to be shoreface sand; overlying the shoreface sand on the present barrier is beach sand, and above it dune sand, indicating a seaward advance of these facies (Fig. 7). Unfortunately, data describing stratification in this sequence of sands are meager.[7]

The present general lack of information concerning primary structures both in modern shoreface deposits and in longshore bars makes impossible any detailed or systematic comparison

[7] The volume "Recent Sediments, Northwest Gulf of Mexico," edited by Shepard, Phleger, and van Andel (1960, Am. Assoc. Petroleum Geologists, Tulsa, Okla.), appeared as this paper *was* in press.

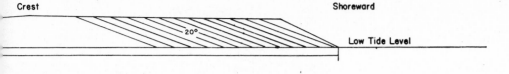

FIG. 5.—Cross sections of longshore bars off north shore of North Bimini Island showing stratification above low tide level. Horizontal and vertical scale approximately equal.

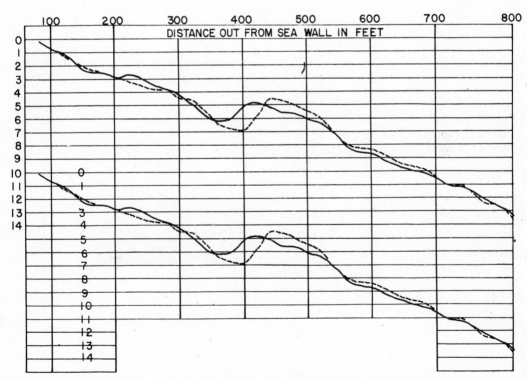

FIG. 6.—Profiles of submarine, longshore bars off coast at La Jolla, California. From Shepard, 1950.

LAGOONAL AREA   PADRE ISLAND   GULF

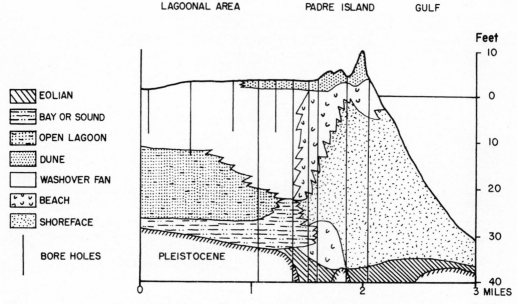

FIG. 7.—Cross section of post-Pleistocene shore and nearshore deposits at
Padre Island, Gulf Coast of Texas. From Fisk, 1959.

between them and their supposed counterparts formed in the laboratory. Thus, the suggestion is clear that an important field for future investigation lies in a precise recording of details concerning structure patterns that are representative of these sand environments. The obvious next step, then, is the interpretation of ancient sand bodies through comparison with the modern and with the laboratory examples.

REFERENCES

Davis, W. M., 1909, Geographical essays: Boston, p. 708.
Evans, O. F., 1940, The low and ball of the eastern shore of Lake Michigan: Jour. Geology, v. 48, no. 5, p. 476–511.
———— 1942, The origin of spits, bars, and related structures: Jour. Geology, v. 50, no. 7, p. 846–865.
Fisk, H. N., 1959, Padre Island and the Laguna Madre flats, coastal south Texas: 2nd Coastal Geog. Conf., Coastal Studies Inst., Louisiana State Univ., Baton Rouge, p. 103–151.
Gilbert, G. K., 1890, Lake Bonneville: U. S. Geol. Survey Mon. 1, 438 p.
Johnson, D. W., 1919, Shore processes and shore-line development: New York, John Wiley and Sons, Inc., 584 p.
Keulegan, G. H., 1948, An experimental study of submarine sand bars: U. S. Beach Erosion Board Tech. Rept. 3, 40 p.
McKee, E. D., 1957, Primary structures in some Recent sediments: Am. Assoc. Petroleum Geologists Bull., v. 41, no. 8, p. 1704–1747.
Price, W. A., 1951, Barrier island, not "offshore bar": Science, v. 113, p. 487–488.
Scott, Theodore, 1945, Sand movement by waves: U. S. Beach Erosion Board Tech. Mem. 48, 37 p.
Shepard, F. P., 1950, Longshore-bars and longshore-troughs: U. S. Beach Erosion Board Tech. Mem. 15, 32 p.
———— 1952, Revised nomenclature for depositional coastal features: Am. Assoc. Petroleum Geologists Bull., v. 36, no. 10, p. 1902–1912.
———— and Moore, D. G., 1955, Central Texas coast sedimentation: characteristics of sedimentary environment, recent history, and diagenesis: Am. Assoc. Petroleum Geologists Bull., v. 39, no. 8, p. 1463–1593.
Thompson, W. O., 1937, Original structures of beaches, bars, and dunes: Geol. Soc. America Bull., v. 48, no. 6, p. 723–751.

BAR-FINGER SANDS OF MISSISSIPPI DELTA[1]

H. N. FISK[2]
Houston, Texas

ABSTRACT

Recent core tests in the Mississippi bird-foot delta provide additional information on the geometry and facies characteristics of bar-finger sands. These elongate lenticular sand bodies underlie the 15- to 20-mile-long major distributaries of the river and are characterized by a branching pattern with inter-branch areas widening gulfward. Originating as distributary-mouth bar deposits, the fingers reach maximum widths comparable to those of the present-day bars—approximately 5 miles. Their lenticular form and maximum thickness of more than 250 feet result largely from displacement of water-rich delta-platform clayey silts by the mass of accumulating bar sands. Each finger comprises three zones—a central zone of "clean" sand with minor amounts of silt and clay; a relatively thin upper transition zone, with more silt and clay, which grades upward into natural-levee and delta-plain deposits; and a lithologically similar, but relatively thick, lower transition zone which grades downward and laterally into delta-front deposits. Typical internal features of the fingers include—thin layers with unidirectional cross-bedding in the upper transition and central zones, and thin festoon cross-beds throughout; laminae of plant fragments and scattered laminae of clayey silt; minor faults and contorted beds in the lower transition zone; and an absence of both microfauna and macrofauna. Locally, the bar fingers have been deformed by upward movement of mud lumps. The lower Pennsylvanian Booch sand of the greater Seminole district, Oklahoma, provides an excellent example of ancient bar-finger deposits.

INTRODUCTION

Sand bodies capable of serving as reservoirs for petroleum are present in deltaic deposits that make up a substantial part of the filling of many sedimentary basins. Recognition of such sands in ancient rocks can be facilitated through an understanding of the nature and occurrence of similar facies in modern deltas. Distinctive features of the bird-foot delta of the Mississippi River are thick lenticular bodies of sand and silt underlying the principal distributaries or passes. These lithologic units, which were described in a report to the President of the Mississippi River Commission prepared under the supervision of the writer (Fisk, 1952), were named bar-finger sands in reference to their origin and distribution. Originating as distributary-mouth bar deposits, the fingers mark long-continued seaward lengthening of the passes which branch from the Mississippi at Head of Passes and extend gulfward for distances ranging from 15 to 20 miles. Diagnostic features of the bar-finger sands and their relationships to other facies making up the sedimentary framework of the delta have been discussed in other articles by the writer and his collaborators (Fisk and others, 1954; Fisk, 1955).

This paper brings up to date the information presented in earlier articles dealing with the origin and distribution of bar fingers. New data used in this study include lithologic logs of 64 cored foundation test borings made at drilling-platform sites located in various parts of the delta and adjacent gulf waters. This additional information has made it possible to locate the margins of

[1] Read before the Association at Atlantic City, New Jersey, April 25, 1960. Manuscript received, December 1, 1960.

Many of the logs and samples of foundation test borings were made available by Eustis Engineering Company and McClelland Engineers. Approval for their release was secured from The California Oil Company, Continental Oil Company, and Freeport Sulphur Company. Additional logs of foundation test borings were supplied by Humble Oil & Refining Company and Shell Oil Company. Electric logs indicating characteristics of near-surface deposits penetrated by exploratory wells drilled in various sections of the delta were contributed by Gulf Oil Corporation.

The writer is greatly indebted to his associates of the Humble Oil & Refining Company for their assistance in developing critical information. John V. Byrne made a detailed study of cores from the Southeast Pass boring and assembled petrologic data. The faunal content of samples from borings drilled in the delta region was identified by Duane O. LeRoy, who also made interpretations of environmental conditions based on faunal assemblages. E. McFarlan, Jr., re-examined samples from the U. S. Corps of Engineers core-test boring at Burrwood, Louisiana, and compiled information on the regional distribution of bar fingers. Radiocarbon analyses were supplied by the Geochemical Group, and grain-size analyses were made by the Service Laboratory of the Company.

[2] Humble Oil & Refining Company.

the bar fingers and to determine the depth to their upper surfaces more accurately than has been previously possible. Identification of the faunal content and lithologic characteristics of core samples from several key borings has permitted a more accurate interpretation of facies relationships and of environments of deposition represented in the sequence of delta-platform deposits. An extensive suite of cores from a Humble Oil & Refining Company geologic test boring on the natural levee of Southeast Pass provided critical details of the bar-sand facies. These details include variations in lithology and texture, types of sedimentary structure, and gradational relationships with underlying and overlying beds; they may provide additional criteria for recognition of ancient sand facies.

BAR FINGERS AND THE DELTA PLATFORM

Construction of the Mississippi River bird-foot delta has been accomplished by long-continued deposition in deep water near the edge of the continental shelf. The deltaic accumulation has created an extensive platform with a relatively steep frontal slope, averaging approximately $\frac{1}{2}°$, built forward across the 240-foot gulf-floor contour (Fig. 1-A). Deposits making up the bird-foot-delta platform reflect the fine-grained sediment load of the Mississippi River; suspended silts and clays constitute more than 75 per cent of the load, and fine and very fine sands, which make up the bed load, form the remainder (Fisk and others, 1954). Most of the suspended load is carried beyond the mouths of the passes to settle along the delta front or farther offshore in the prodelta zone. These deposits make up the bulk of the platform. The bed-load sands are swept to distributary-mouth bars at the delta front and are built forward across the fine grained delta-front deposits. Some of the river's load is laid down during flood to form the natural levees which flank distributary channels or to accumulate in the marshes and shallow bays of the interdistributary troughs. Some of the sands are swept from the bars into shallow waters of the troughs by waves and gulf currents to form spits, bars, and beaches.

Interdistributary troughs make up most of the area of the upper surface of the platform—the delta plain. The troughs are arbitrarily separated

from the delta-front environment by the 18-foot gulf-floor contour (Fig. 1-B). The delta front and the prodelta zone are transitional features which are separated by a slight break in slope at a depth of approximately 240 feet below sea level.

The distributary-mouth bars are shallow-water features located a mile or more offshore from the bell-shaped mouths of the passes. Prior to the construction of the Southwest Pass jetties in 1908, the bar of this distributary provided a typical example. Figure 2-A presents the configuration of the bar as contoured at approximate 30-year intervals in 1838, 1867, and 1898. As shown on the series of profiles (Fig. 2-B), the bar advanced gulfward at a rate of approximately 250 feet per year. The Southwest Pass bar maintained a lunate form during its advance, and its crest was crossed by minor channels that radiated from the mouth of the pass (Fig. 2-A). Sands were transported through these channels to the steep frontal zone of the bar, which formed an arc approximately 3 miles long, directly in front of the river mouth. Some of the sands were shifted laterally by gulf currents, widening the bar to slightly more than 5 miles. With completion of jetty construction in 1908, river flow was confined largely to a single channel, and the configuration of the bar was radically changed. The bar now forms a narrow gulf-floor bulge, slightly more than a mile in width, which extends more than 2 miles gulfward of the jetties.

Studies of gulf-floor sediment samples by Trowbridge (1930) and by Fisk and others (1954) show that well-sorted "clean" sands make up the crests of the Southwest Pass, South Pass, and Southeast Pass bars. An increasing percentage of silt and clay is mixed with the sand at progressively greater depths along the frontal slope of the bars; in sediment deposited in water more than 150 feet deep, less than 5 per cent sand is present. Shepard (1956) recorded a high percentage of sand and silt in samples from the channel side of the crests of the North Pass and Pass a Loutre bars, but in the same general area other samples contained a high percentage of silt and clay.

The bar fingers developed in response to progressive gulfward building of the distributary-mouth bars and the settling of the bar sand mass in the delta-front muds. The width of a bar finger

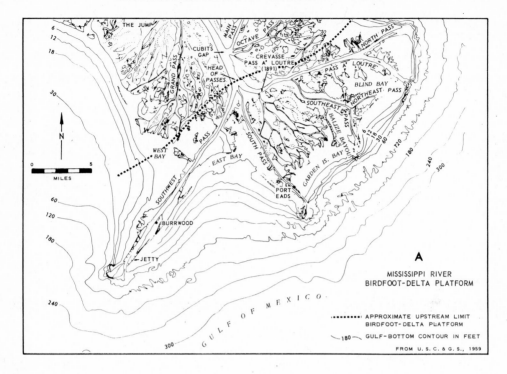

A

MISSISSIPPI RIVER
BIRDFOOT-DELTA PLATFORM

••••••••• APPROXIMATE UPSTREAM LIMIT
BIRDFOOT-DELTA PLATFORM

—180— GULF-BOTTOM CONTOUR IN FEET

FROM U. S. C. & G. S., 1959

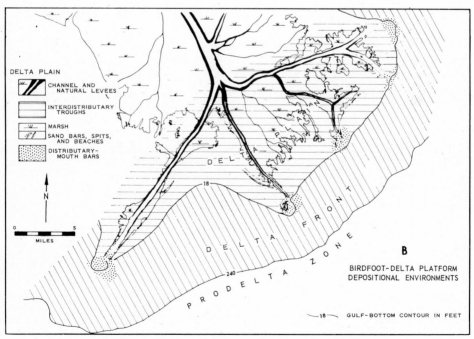

B

BIRDFOOT-DELTA PLATFORM
DEPOSITIONAL ENVIRONMENTS

—18— GULF-BOTTOM CONTOUR IN FEET

FIG. 1.—Mississippi bird-foot delta and its depositional environments.

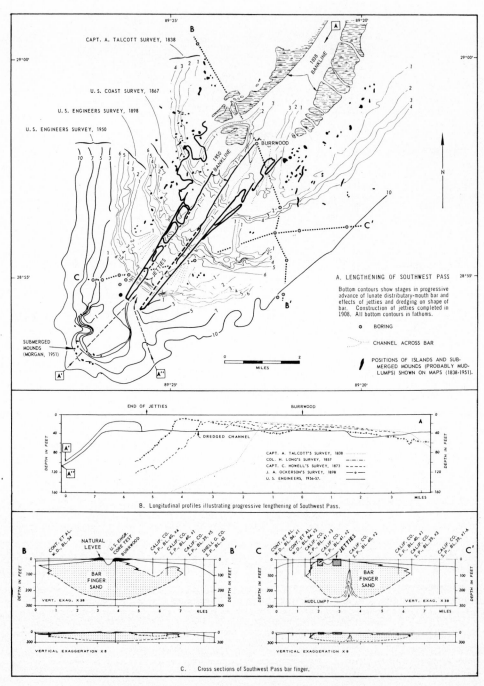

FIG. 2.—Historic development of Southwest Pass bar finger.

for each pass is comparable to that of the bar at the mouth of the distributary, and the sand deposits of the finger exhibit the same general grain size and sorting characteristics as do the present-day bar deposits. Composed mainly of well sorted, unfossiliferous fine and very fine sands and silts, with local thin layers of clayey silt, the bar fingers grade downward and laterally into massive delta-front clayey silts. As previously indicated, sands are largely absent on the Southwest Pass bar below 150 feet, but the base of the bar finger at Burrwood, 5 miles upstream, rests at 251 feet below sea level. (See cross section B-B', Fig. 2-C.)

A logical explanation for the excessive sand thicknesses in the bar fingers involves settlement of the bar sand masses during deposition. Settlement occurs in response to displacement by flowage, and secondarily to compaction, of underlying water-rich silts and clays through pressure exerted by the accumulating sand mass. Data from borings and hydrographic surveys provide evidence that settlement is a rapid process. Figures 2-A and 2-B illustrate the historic advance of the Southwest Pass distributary-mouth bar, and Figure 2-C shows the thickness of the Southwest Pass bar finger as determined by the U. S. Corps of Engineers core-test boring at Burrwood. The Burrwood boring is near the position of the center line of the Southwest Pass channel as mapped in 1838 and is approximately 1 mile upstream from the bar crest of that date (Fig. 2-A). Based on the historic rate of bar advance, the basal bar-finger sands penetrated in the boring were laid down at the toe of the bar front about 1750; by 1800, the crest of the bar had advanced to the position of Burrwood, and the entire bar-finger section had been deposited. Because the upper surface of the bar sands presently rests at a depth of 15 feet below sea level and is overlain only by natural-levee deposits, little settlement has taken place since 1800. It must be concluded, therefore, that settlement and deposition of bar sands are contemporaneous processes, and that the bar crest shifts seaward only when the pressure of the bar sand mass no longer exceeds the bearing capacity of underlying silts and clays.

Bar fingers occur only beneath the major passes, or branches of these passes, which existed for extended periods near the margin of the delta platform. Some of these branches were abandoned as the major passes lengthened. A typical example is Old Balize Bayou, which until 1900 was an active distributary leading from Southeast Pass. This abandoned distributary branch is underlain by a well-defined finger more than 200 feet thick. A similar minor distributary, Grand Pass, branched from South Pass and extended southward across East Bay for more than 5 miles. Grand Pass carried flow from South Pass until around 1880 when a dam was constructed across its head, causing its channel to deteriorate. Since then, subsidence and the lack of local deposition have permitted the entire land area along the pass to revert to the gulf. The outlines of this abandoned pass are dotted on Figure 3. A boring in East Bay about a mile south of the former mouth of Grand Pass, at an appropriate position for its distributary-mouth bar, penetrated sands more than 50 feet thick (Fig. 4). Minor bar-finger branches probably underlie the abandoned Pass Cheval distributary system on the north flank of Pass a Loutre, but no subsurface information is available for that area.

The fingers are not associated with the minor distributary branchwork systems which have formed in historic time on the bird-foot-delta plain and above Head of Passes. Such branchworks have been created by continuing discharge of river waters through crevasses—breaches in the natural levees—including The Jump (1839), Cubits Gap (1862), and the crevasse of Pass a Loutre (1891). (See Fig. 1-A.) These minor distributary systems have developed in interdistributary troughs or in areas marginal to the main stream and have created shoal-water deltas distinct from the deep-water bird-foot delta (Fisk, 1955). In the shoal-water deltas, sands carried to the mouth of an enlarging pass form a bar that divides the stream into branches, each of which lengthens and bifurcates to form a part of a complicated branchwork. With continued increase in flow through a branchwork system, sands are shifted from the many small stream-mouth bars by waves and currents to form a thin widespread sheet deposit upon which finer marsh and bay deposits accumulate. Compaction of the underlying deposits by the prograding sand sheet has been negligible

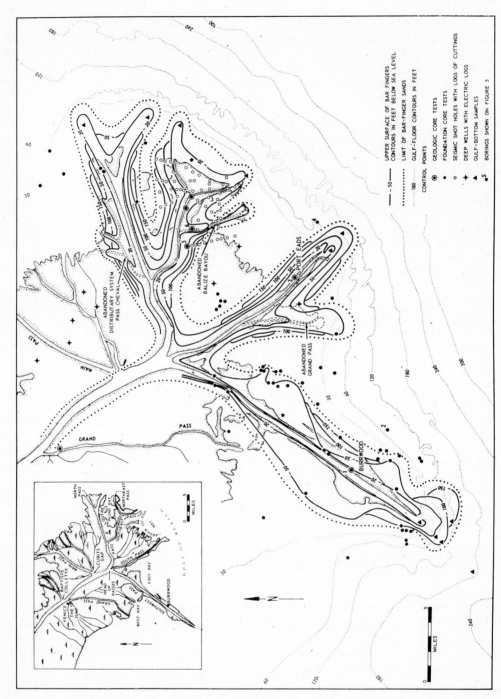

FIG. 3.—Outline of bar fingers, Mississippi bird-foot delta, and depths to upper surfaces.

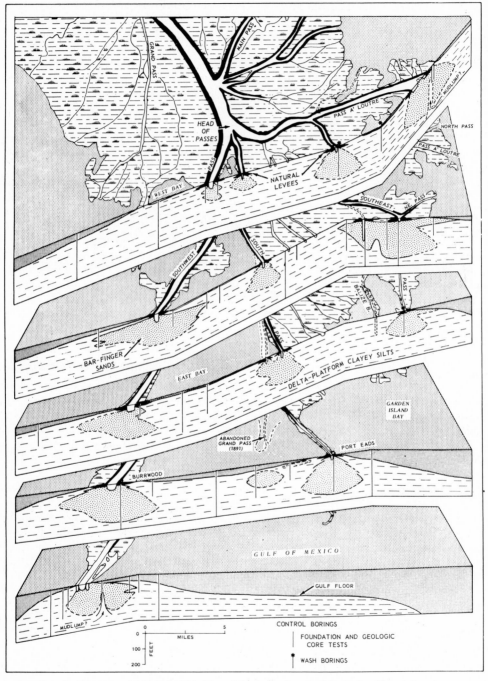

Fig. 4.—Diagram of Mississippi bird-foot delta indicating spatial relationships of deposits.

because of the thinness of the sands. No abnormal thickness of sands in the region of the rapidly advancing Main Pass distributary branchwork system which heads at Cubits Gap (Fig. 1-*A*) has been recorded. Data from three borings in this area presented by Shepard and Lankford (1959) indicate the possibility of a thin sand sheet at a depth of approximately 10 feet. Core tests in the Garden Island Bay interdistributary trough have penetrated the sequence of deposits laid down by the Pass a Loutre crevasse distributary branchwork. A thin silty-sand layer is locally present at a depth of approximately 15 feet.

GEOMETRY OF BAR FINGERS

Knowledge of the three-dimensional characteristics of bar fingers is based on study of lithologic logs and samples of borings, the locations of which are shown on Figure 3. The outlines of the fingers, their lenticular shape, thickness, relationship to enclosing deposits, and the configuration of their upper surfaces shown on Figures 3 and 4 are based on these subsurface data. Control for delineating the fingers is generally sparse; only a few borings provide information on the nature and distribution of the deposits along Pass a Loutre and South Pass. In the Southwest Pass and Southeast Pass areas, however, control is relatively closely spaced, and several cored borings and a few wash borings have completely penetrated the bar fingers and provide accurate information concerning their thickness and width. The widest bar finger underlies Southwest Pass and reaches a width of more than 5 miles near Burrwood. Maximum thicknesses recorded are—Southwest Pass finger at Burrwood, approximately 235 feet; Southeast Pass finger near junction of Southeast and Northeast Passes, approximately 250 feet; and South Pass, underlain by the thickest known section of sands, more than 270 feet at Port Eads.

A distinctive geometric feature of the bar fingers is their branching pattern, with a gulfward increase in the distance between adjacent branches (Fig. 3). Although subsurface data are widely scattered, the relatively small size of each finger for a few miles downstream from Head of Passes (Fig. 4) appears to be another distinctive feature and reflects the relatively small volume carried by each distributary during its initial stage of development. The narrow and thin upstream end of the Southwest Pass finger suggests that this distributary was slightly more than 5 miles long before it developed to a size comparable with the present stream. In its lower reaches, each finger increases in thickness but maintains a characteristic average maximum width. This relationship results from deposition of the bar sands upon a progressively gulfward thickening section of bird-foot-delta-platform silts and clays. This thickening marks the progradation of the platform into progressively deeper water.

Although bar fingers are thickest directly beneath distributary channels, the decrease in thickness toward their lateral margins is not regular nor progressive. Depth to the upper surface of the fingers (Fig. 3) indicates that in several places sands are shingled beyond normal lateral limits. This condition probably reflects abnormal depositional activity along the flanks of stream-mouth bars for short periods. A similar shingling effect can be noted in the gulfward overlap of contours in the area of the present-day distributary-mouth bars (Fisk and others, 1954).

INCORPORATING PLATFORM FACIES

Bar-finger sands are enclosed by the clayey-silt deposits (Fig. 4) which constitute most of the delta platform. Accumulating contemporaneously with bar sands, the fine deposits were laid down in the interdistributary troughs of the delta surface, along the delta front, and farther offshore in the prodelta environment (Fig. 1-*B*). Borings in interdistributary troughs penetrate a sedimentary sequence which marks stages in the progradation of the delta (Fig. 5). The relationships which the sands bear to the incorporating fine-grained facies, together with the variations in depositional environments represented by these facies, provide a basis for distinguishing similar sand bodies in ancient rocks.

The thick central section of a bar finger is transitionally overlain by natural-levee deposits made up of silty sands and clayey silts, which grade laterally into the complex of dominantly fine-grained interdistributary-trough deposits laid down in marsh and shallow-bay environments. These trough deposits interfinger with the upper part of the bar-finger sands. Incorporated within

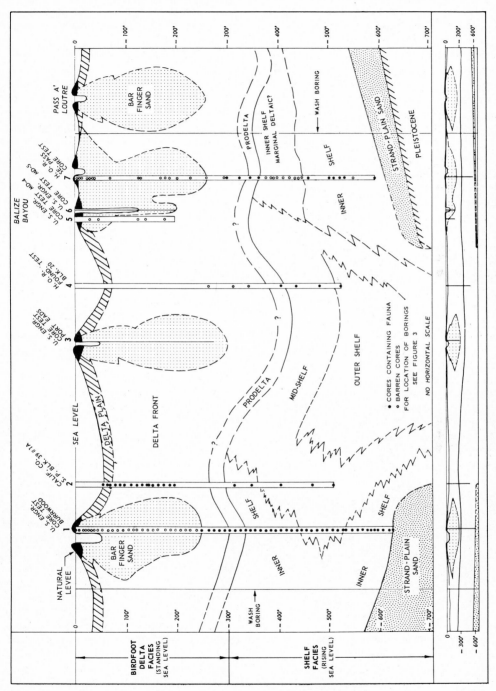

Fig. 5.—Sequence of delta-platform facies and underlying older Recent shelf facies.

the fine-grained trough deposits are thin silty-sand bodies laid down as beaches, spits, and bars (Fig. 1-*A*). The bar fingers grade downward into delta-front clayey silts which in turn grade into prodelta clays. These units, unlike the trough deposits which overlie them, are devoid of sand bodies.

The sequence of delta-platform facies and underlying shelf deposits penetrated by core tests is interpreted in terms of depositional environments on Figure 5. This interpretation is based largely upon comparison of the microfaunal and macrofaunal content of core samples with faunas in modern local environments. Genera and species of faunas recovered from cores in the course of this investigation and those recorded in the literature for modern environments are listed in Table I.

A significant feature of bar-finger sands is the absence of faunas. In marked contrast, the overlying interdistributary-trough deposits, laid down in shallow bays, lakes, and marshes, or as spits and bars in shallow open gulf water, contain a generally sparse but varied microfauna and macrofauna. The overlying natural levees locally also contain a distinctive, sparse fauna. Delta-front deposits underlying the bar sands and marginal to them generally contain sparse assemblages of inner-neritic (0–60 feet) and mid-neritic (60–250 feet) faunas. Some cores from the middle part of the delta-front section were barren; the local absence of faunas in these deposits may reflect either unfavorable conditions for life or destruction of shell material after burial. Clays of the prodelta zone contain abundant mid-neritic and outer-neritic (250–600 feet) microfaunas and are readily distinguished on this basis from the overlying delta-platform deposits. They rest upon older Recent shelf deposits, locally sandy in character, which are marked by distinctive faunal assemblages.

SEDIMENTARY CHARACTERISTICS
OF BAR FINGERS

Identification of ancient bar-finger sands requires not only geometric and stratigraphic data but also an understanding of sedimentary characteristics of similar modern deposits. Oriented cores taken from the Humble Oil & Refining Company geologic core test in the Southeast Pass bar finger provide useful details of lithology, texture, and sedimentary structure. Nine cores, each 5 feet long and 5 inches in diameter, were taken in the bar-finger sands; data from these and other cores are presented on Figure 6. Also, re-examination and additional analyses of core samples from the U. S. Corps of Engineers Southwest Pass core test at Burrwood provide new data on bar-finger sands. (See Fig. 7.) Less detailed information on samples from this boring has been previously reported (Fisk, 1952; Fisk and others, 1954). Both the Southwest Pass and Southeast Pass borings completely penetrated bar fingers and underlying delta-front and prodelta facies of the bird-foot-delta platform and bottomed in the thick section of underlying older Recent shelf deposits. Data from cores taken from the various facies below the bar fingers (Figs. 6, 7) provide a basis for comparison.

General features.—Both the Southwest Pass and Southeast Pass bar fingers are distinguished by the small size of the sand particles—no grains being larger than fine-sand size, by an absence of faunas, by the presence of scattered lignite grains within the sands and of thin layers of finely divided plant fragments, and by the laminated nature of the deposits. Sand and silt laminae are intercalated with ones made up largely of plant fragments; together these form thin beds which, in turn, are interbedded with thin cross-bedded layers. Thin layers of silty clay and clayey silt, ranging from 1 mm to 2 feet in thickness, are widely scattered in the deposits and become more abundant near the base.

On the basis of the ratio of sand to silt and clay, the bar-finger deposits are separated into three distinct zones. An upper zone of silty sands and sandy silts is transitional with the overlying natural-levee deposits. A central clean-sand zone comprises well sorted fine and very fine sands with less than 20 per cent silt and little or no clay. A lower zone of alternating thin layers of sand, silt, and clayey silt is transitional with the underlying delta-front deposits. Plates 1 and 2 include photographs of cores illustrating these general features.

Grain size and sorting.—Sands of the bar fingers are of fine to very fine sand size and are angular to subangular. Analyses indicate that many of the

TABLE I. Distribution of microfauna and macrofauna, Mississippi bird-foot delta and adjacent shelf environments.

MACROFAUNA

Facies columns — DELTA: CHANNEL FILL, NATURAL LEVEE, BAR FINGER, MARSH, INTERDISTR. TROUGH, DELTA FRONT, PRODELTA; SHELF: INNER NERITIC, MID-NERITIC, OUTER NERITIC; REFERENCE.

MACROFAUNA	REFERENCE
MOLLUSCA	
GASTROPODA	
NERITINA RECLIVATA	2,3,4
LITTORINA IRRORATA	2,3,4
LITTORIDINA SPHINCTOSTOMA	3
ANACHIS OBESA	3
POLINICES DUPLICATUS	2,3
ANACHIS AVARA SIMILIS	3
NASSARIUS ACUTUS	3
CREPIDULA SP.	2,3
FASCIOLARIA SP.	2
NATICA SP.	2,3
OLIVELLA SP.	2,3
TURBONILLI HEMPHILLI	4
TEREBRA PROTEXTA	3,4
RETUSA CANILICULATA	4
PELECYPODA	
MACOMA MITCHELLI	3
RANGIA FLEXUOSA	6
PETRICOLA PHOLADIFORMIS	6
QUADRANS LINTEA	6
MACOMA TAGELIFORMIS	3
RANGIA CUNEATA	3
CRASSOSTREA VIRGINICA	3
MULINIA LATERALIS	2,3,4
MYTILUS SP.	2
NUCULANA EBOREA	2,3,4
ABRA LIOCA	3,4
NUCULANA ACUTA	2,3,4
CARDIUM SP.	2,3,4
CHIONE SP.	3,4
PHACOIDES SP.	2
CRASSINELLA SP.	3,4
CORBULA SWIFTIANA	3,4
ANADARA SP.	3,4
NUCULA PROXIMA	4
SCAPHOPODA	
DENTALIUM TEXASIANUM	3,4
CADULUS SP.	3,4
PTEROPODA	
CAVOLINA SP.	3,4
ECHINODERMATA	
UNIDENTIFIED SPINES & PLATES	3,4
COELENTERATA	
HEXACORALLA	
DENDROPHYLLIA SP.	4

MICROFAUNA

MICROFAUNA	REFERENCE
BENTHONIC FORAMINIFERA	
PALMERINELLA GARDENISLANDENSIS	1
AMMOASTUTA INEPTA	1
ARENOPARRELLA MEXICANA	1
TROCHAMMINA INFLATA	1,2
MILIAMMINA FUSCA	1
AMMOTIUM SALSUM AND VARS.	1
ELPHIDIUM DELICATULUM	1,2,4
ELPHIDIUM GUNTERI	1,2,4,5
STREBLUS BECCARII VARS.	1,4
HANZAWAIA STRATTONI	1,4,5
BOLIVINA LOWMANI	1,4,5
BULIMINELLA CF. BASSENDORFENSIS	1,4
EPISTOMINELLA VITREA	1,4,5
NONIONELLA OPIMA	1,2,4,5
BULIMINA MARGINATA	1,4,5
VIRGULINA PONTONI	1,4,5
BOLIVINA SP.	1,4,5
QUINQUELOCULINA SP.	1,4,5
TEXTULARIA MAYORI	1,4,5
TEXTULARIA SP.	1,2,4
BIGENERINA IRREGULARIS	1,2,4,5
REUSSELLA ATLANTICA	1,4,5
ROBULUS CF. CULTRATUS	4
ROBULUS SP.	2,4
ROBULUS IOTUS	4
CIBICIDES SP.	2,4,5
NONION SP.	1,2,4
MARGINULINA MARGINULINOIDES	4,5
EPONIDES ANTILLARIUM	4,5
UVIGERINA PARVULA	1,4,5
PENEROPLIS SP.	4,5
SARACENARIA LATIFORMIS	4
ARCHAIAS SP.	4,5
AMPHISTEGINA LESSONI	4,5
LIEBUSELLA SOLDANII	4,5
TEXTULARIELLA BARRETTI	4,5
VAGINULINONSIS SP.	4,5
LENTICULINA CF. CONVERGINS	4
NODOSARIA SP.	4
PLANKTONIC FORAMINIFERA	
GLOBIGERINA SP.	4
ORBULINA UNIVERSA	4
GLOBOROTALIA SPP.	2,4
GLOBIGERINOIDES SPP.	4
PULLENIATINA SP.	4

REFERENCES: (1) LANKFORD, 1959; (2) FISK ET. AL., 1954; (3) PARKER, 1956; (4) PRESENT INVESTIGATION; (5) LUDWICK AND WALTON, 1957; (6) SHEPARD, 1956.
ABUNDANCE OF FORMS DETERMINED FROM THIS STUDY; A, ABUNDANT; C, COMMON; R, RARE.

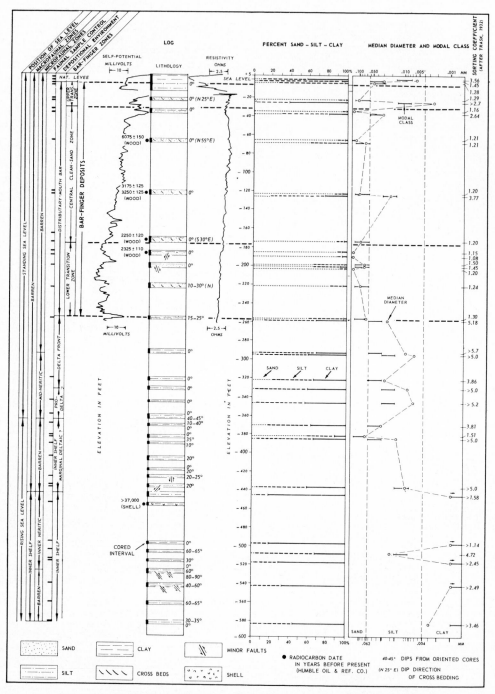

Fig. 6.—Analyses and interpretations of cores from Humble Oil & Refining Company Southeast Pass geologic core test. For location see Fig. 3, boring 7.

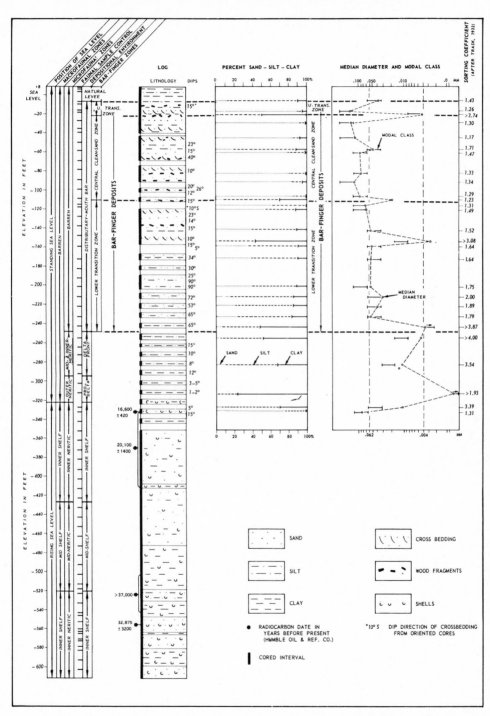

FIG. 7.—Analyses and interpretations of cores from U. S. Corps of Engineers Southwest Pass geologic core test, Burrwood, Louisiana. For location see Fig. 3, boring 1.

sand layers have a high percentage of silt, but the proportion of interstitial clay is less than 10 per cent. Where clay is more abundant, it is mixed with silt and occurs in thin beds. Grain size is expressed in terms of median diameter and modal class (Figs. 6, 7), and the degree of sorting is illustrated by cumulative grain-size curves (Fig. 8) and by numerical representation of the sorting coefficient (Figs. 6, 7). A total of 43 grain-size analyses were made of core samples from the Southeast Pass boring, and 27 core samples were analyzed from the Southwest Pass boring at Burrwood. Each sample analyzed was selected from a distinct lamination or thin bed; analyses representative of the various lithologies sampled are presented on the graphs of Figures 6 and 7. These analyses indicate the presence of scattered thin laminae of clayey silts within the bar-finger section.

The modal-class representation of delta-platform samples from Southeast Pass shows a systematic variation downward from the natural-levee deposits through the bar finger into the underlying delta-front facies. Fine silt is dominant at the top of the natural levees, with coarse silt at the base; very fine sand and fine sand characterize the bar fingers; and medium to coarse silt is dominant in the underlying delta-front clayey silts. As indicated by the cumulative curves and sorting coefficients, the bar-finger sands are better sorted than either the overlying natural-levee deposits or the underlying delta-front facies.

The relative proportions of sand, silt, and clay throughout the bar fingers and the transitional relationships of the bar sands with the overlying natural-levee facies and with the underlying delta-front facies are major diagnostic features. Both influence the character of electric-log patterns by affecting porosity and permeability. Sands of the central clean-sand zone form the most permeable part of the bar-sand section. In the Southeast Pass finger, the clean-sand zone is 140 feet thick (Fig. 6); its average composition is 88 per cent sand, 11 per cent silt, and 1 per cent clay. At Burrwood, this zone in the Southwest Pass finger is 89 feet thick; the average composition of the sediment is 83 per cent sand, 15 per cent silt, and 2 per cent clay (Fig. 7).

The transition zone between the bar-finger sands and the overlying natural levees is thin relative to the thickness of the underlying central clean-sand and lower transition zones. At Burrwood, the upper transition zone is 14 feet thick (Fig. 7), and consists of layers of silty sand (averaging 81 per cent sand, 16 per cent silt, and 3 per cent clay), and clayey silts (averaging 50 per cent silt, 49 per cent clay, and 1 per cent sand). The overlying natural-levee deposits, at a depth of 7 feet below sea level, are made up of only 11 per cent sand with 79 per cent silt and 10 per cent clay. At Southeast Pass, the upper transition zone is 30 feet thick and is made up of well-sorted sands with scattered thin beds of silty clay averaging 62 per cent clay, 36 per cent silt, and 2 per cent sand. The overlying basal deposits of the natural levees, at a depth of 3 feet below sea level, comprise 25

EXPLANATION OF PLATE 1

A—Natural-levee silts and clayey silts with incorporated root fibers and plant fragments. Top of core 1 foot below sea level.

B—Laminated sands and silts of the bar-finger central clean-sand zone. Darker laminations consist of finely divided plant fragments. Top of core 121 feet below sea level.

C—Base of bar-finger deposits showing transition with underlying delta-front clayey silt. Top of core 257 feet below sea level.

D—Massive prodelta clay. Top of core 291 feet below sea level.

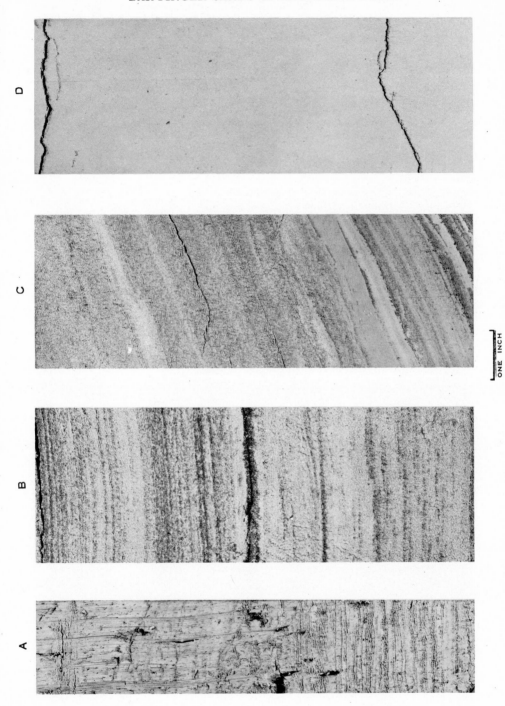

PLATE 1.—Cores of delta-platform facies. Humble Oil & Refining Company Southeast Pass geologic core test.

H. N. FISK

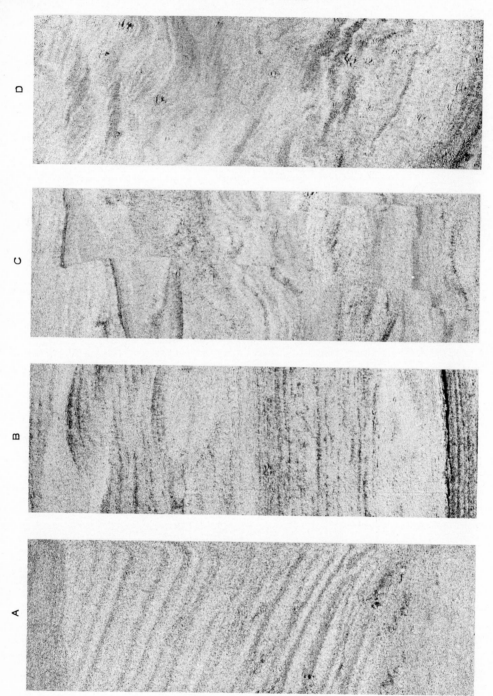

ONE INCH

PLATE 2.—Cores of bar-finger deposits. Humble Oil & Refining Company Southeast Pass geologic test.

per cent sand, 73 per cent silt, and 2 per cent clay. At sea level, the levees consist of 8 per cent sand, 50 per cent silt, and 42 per cent clay.

The lower transition zone, between clean sands and underlying delta-front deposits, is thicker than the upper transition zone. In the Southwest Pass boring, it is 137 feet thick. Its sand content gradually decreases to 22 per cent near the base of the finger, and there is a corresponding increase in silt content to 61 per cent, and of clay to 17 per cent. The underlying delta-front clayey silts contain less than 10 per cent sand; they hold approximately equal amounts of silt and clay, with silt predominating in one sample. The prodelta facies from a sample at a depth of 313 feet is sand free; the sample consists of 77 per cent clay and 23 per cent silt. At Southeast Pass, the lower transition zone is 84 feet thick. At the base of the bar finger, 257 feet below sea level, the sand content is approximately 46 per cent and is associated with 43 per cent silt and 11 per cent clay. The delta-front deposits beneath the Southeast Pass finger are made up of 13 per cent sand, 57 per cent silt, and 30 per cent clay. Similar proportions are maintained to the base of the delta-platform section at about 350 feet below sea level.

The transitional relationships of the central clean-sand and lower transition zones in the bar fingers reflect the distribution of sediment on the active distributary-mouth bars. In these bars the cleanest sands occur at the crest, and the percentage of silt and clay increases with depth on the front slope.

An attempt to obtain an electric log of the Southeast Pass boring was not entirely successful. Caving of the hole made it impractical to log the fine-grained deposits beneath the bar finger. Resistivity and self-potential curves for the upper part of the boring are shown on Figure 6.

Sedimentary structures.—The characterizing sedimentary structures of the bar fingers, including bedding (Pl. 1-*B*, -*C*), like grain size and sorting characteristics, reflect depositional conditions and also give evidence of slumping within the sand mass brought about by settling during deposition. Both the laminated and the cross-bedded character of the bar fingers reflect sand deposition in the distributary-mouth-bar environment. Most of the laminae probably were laid down below wave base on the bar front; the cross-beds were formed in the wave zone near the bar crest.

A striking feature of the entire section of bar-finger sands is the occurrence of thin cross-bedded layers, generally less than 2 inches thick. The thickest cross-bed cored was only 9 inches thick; it was recovered at a depth of 22.5 feet below sea level in the Southeast Pass boring. Two types of cross-bedding are present. The more distinctive of these types is composed of thin laminae, which in a given bed, dip in a constant direction (Pl. 2-*A*). This type of cross-bedding is found only in the clean sand and upper transition zones. In the oriented cores from the Southeast Pass boring, the direction of dip of the cross-beds varied for different layers, but was confined either to the north-

---

EXPLANATION OF PLATE 2

A—Large-scale unidirectional cross-bedding in upper transition zone. Laminae dip 25° to the northeast. Top of core 22.5 feet below sea level.

B—Festoon cross-bedding in sands and silts of the central clean-sand zone. Note upward convexity of some laminae. Dark material is finely divided plant fragments. Top of core 121 feet below sea level.

C—Small-scale faults in lower transition zone resulting from subsidence of the bar-finger sand mass. Top of core 189 feet below sea level.

D—Contorted beds in lower transition zone resulting from slumping during deposition associated with small-scale faulting, developed contemporaneously with deposition. Top of core 222 feet below sea level.

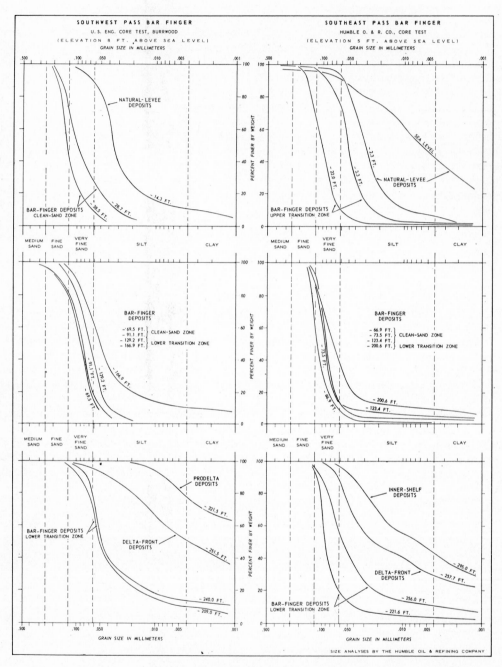

FIG. 8.—Grain-size cumulative-frequency curves of delta-platform deposits from core samples.
(Depths on curves are measured from sea level.)

east or southeast quadrants; in oriented cores from the Southwest Pass boring, the observed dip directions were to the south. In both bar fingers, therefore, the dip of laminae in this type of cross-bedding radiates gulfward from the direction of flow in the distributary. The other type of cross-bedding consists of minor festoons (Pl. 2-B) and is found in all three zones of the bar fingers. These cross-beds consist of extremely thin, curved laminae confined to beds less than 2 inches thick; some of the laminae are convex upward.

Small-scale faults (Pl. 2-C) and associated thin contorted layers (Pl. 2-D) were noted in several of the cores. Displacement along most of the faults ranged from a fraction of an inch to less than 3 inches, and some of the faults were confined to a single 5-foot core. These structures all appear to be internal features of the bar sands and probably result from slumping brought about by settling of the bar during its formation.

RADIOCARBON DATES AND AGE OF SOUTHEAST PASS BAR FINGER

Sufficient quantities of plant material interlaminated with sands and silts were obtained from four of the Southeast Pass cores to permit radiocarbon analysis. The ages of 5 samples from these cores (Fig. 6) range from $2,250 \pm 120$ years old, at approximately 170 feet below sea level, to $6,075 \pm 150$ years old, at a depth of 70 feet below sea level. At a depth of 190 feet below sea level, a date of $2,350 \pm 110$ years was obtained; two dates—$3,175 \pm 125$ years and $3,250 \pm 125$ years—were obtained from a core taken 120 feet below sea level. The inversion of radiocarbon dates with younger ages near the base of the sands in the Southeast Pass boring suggests that the plant material was derived upstream from older deltaic and flood-plain deposits by scouring action of the Mississippi River.

The radiocarbon dates are not significant with respect to time of bar-sand deposition; historic evidence supports this conclusion. Plotting of the location of the Southeast Pass boring on historic maps indicates that the bar-sand section penetrated by this boring accumulated prior to 1764 and probably around 1600. The Lords Commissioners of the Admiralty map, 1764–1771, shows Southeast Pass as the principal distributary of the Mississippi. The pass gradually widened to approximately 1 mile at its mouth, and its flow was discharged across a broad submerged bar upon which were scattered mud-lump islands. Well defined subaqueous channels, including both Northeast and Southeast Passes, radiated from the distributary mouth and carried sediment to the bar crest at the edge of deep water, approximately 2 miles offshore. When plotted on the 1764–1771 map, the Southeast Pass boring is a short distance offshore near the point of bifurcation of the subaqueous channels. By 1838, when the delta was surveyed by Capt. A. Talcott for the War Department, both Southeast Pass and Northeast Pass were subaerially defined for approximately 1 mile beyond the 1764 shore. The bar crest had also advanced 1 mile seaward at a rate of 70 feet per year. Assuming this rate to have been constant, the bar crest in 1600 would have been slightly inland from the location of the Southeast Pass boring. It seems certain, therefore, that the entire bar-finger section encountered in the boring had been laid down by this date.

UNDERLYING DEPOSITS

The floor across which the bird-foot-delta platform prograded consists of older Recent deposits, genetically unrelated to those of the delta (Fig. 5). Characteristics of these deposits provide information concerning local geologic history and serve to emphasize the distinctive nature of the bar-finger sands. Accumulating during the rise in sea level which accompanied melting of the Wisconsin glacial-stage ice masses, the older Recent beds comprise strand and shelf facies laid down in the inner-neritic, mid-neritic, and outer-neritic zones. The section penetrated in the Burrwood boring (Fig. 7) is largely sand; it contains abundant molluscan fossils, many of which are waterworn. A short distance east of this boring, an abrupt facies change occurs between the sands and the massive shelf clays that were penetrated in borings Nos. 2 and 4 (Fig. 5). Microfaunas in the upper part of the clay section in boring No. 4 indicate accumulation in a mid-shelf environment. Farther east and north, in the Southeast Pass boring, the clay section directly beneath the delta platform is barren of fossils, suggesting shallow-water marginal deltaic deposition. Faunas recorded from throughout the shelf section are listed in Table I.

The locally sharp break between the prodelta facies and underlying shelf deposits is emphasized by the radiocarbon dates. The shelf deposits range in age from approximately 16,000 years to more than 37,000 years (Figs. 6, 7), whereas the delta platform has been created in the last 450 years (Fisk and others, 1954). The radiocarbon ages of shells from shelf deposits in the Burrwood boring are—16,600 ± 420 years, core sample from 330 feet below sea level; 20,100 ± 1,400 years, composite sample from a depth of 330–410 feet below sea level; more than 37,000 years (dead), composite sample from 500–540 feet below sea level (anomalous date); and 32,875 ± 3,200 years, core sample from 550 feet below sea level. These dates provide evidence as to the time of rising sea level and the rate of the rise. A sample from a thin sandy shell-bearing bed at 455 feet below sea level in the Southeast Pass boring contained an assemblage of mollusks, echinoids, and coral fragments, all of which were dated as being older than 37,000 years. Coral fragments in the shell detritus and the age of the material suggest accumulation in close proximity to a Pleistocene coral reef such as has been described along the shelf margin east of the Mississippi Delta by Ludwick and Walton (1957).

DEFORMATION OF BAR FINGERS BY MUD LUMPS

Mud lumps are structural features unique to the Mississippi bird-foot delta and are closely associated with the distributary-mouth bars. They are deformed masses of clays, silty clays, and clayey silts which intrude the bars and extend to the surface, forming submerged mounds and offshore islands which rise only a few feet above sea level and which cover areas generally less than an acre. Wave attack soon destroys the islands; the few that have survived are incorporated in pro-grading marshlands. These diapiric structures develop during distributary-mouth bar deposition and provide empirical evidence of the displacement of fine-grained delta-platform deposits by the mass of accumulating bar sands. Morgan (1951) indicates that in their initial stage, mud lumps occur as low subaqueous mounds around the bar front. The pressure of the mass of accumulating bar sands deforms the underlying water-rich deposits and forces them upward during bar growth. Microfaunas from several of the mud lumps indicate that the structures originated at varying depths (Andersen, 1951). The mud lump off Pass a Loutre (Fig. 5) contains older Recent shelf faunas similar to those found in the Southeast Pass boring between depths of 460 and 500 feet.

Upward movement of mud lumps creates local structures in the bar sand mass which can serve as additional criteria for recognition of bar fingers in ancient sediments. Dips ranging from 53° to 90° were noted in cores taken from the basal 50 feet of the Southwest Pass finger (Fig. 7). Beds at the base of the Southeast Pass finger exhibit dips of 15°–25° (Fig. 6; Pl. 1-C). Although these dips are not as great as those in the Southwest Pass finger, they far exceed dips to be expected as depositional features.

Anomalous occurrences of clay penetrated by borings within the areas of the bar fingers are represented as mud lumps on the cross sections (Figs. 2-C, 4). Future drilling will no doubt encounter an increasing number of such clay masses because the series of detailed maps by the U. S. Corps of Engineers indicates that a large number of mud lumps have formed in the vicinity of distributary-mouth bars. Each of the maps shows a group of new offshore islands which are probably mud lumps; together these maps show that a succession of mud-lump structures marks the lengthening of each distributary. The positions of offshore islands, and of submerged mounds mapped by Morgan (1951), which developed around the Southwest Pass bar between 1838 and 1950, are indicated on Figure 2-A. One or two of the mud lumps remain stranded in the marshes west of Burrwood, but the majority were destroyed by wave action soon after their formation. Although surface indications of the mud lumps are generally absent, their "stocks" remain as features of the bar fingers.

SUMMARY OF CRITERIA FOR RECOGNITION OF BAR FINGERS

A wealth of information demonstrates that thick sand bodies associated with distributaries of the Mississippi River bird-foot delta originated as distributary-mouth-bar deposits. Irrefutable evi-

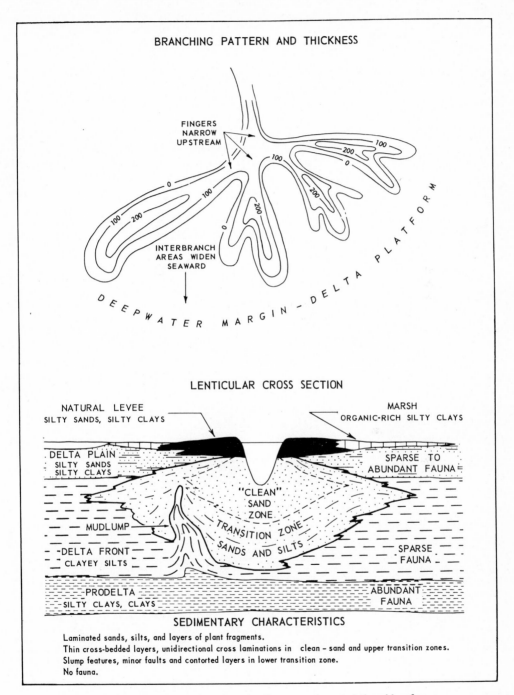

FIG. 9.—Distinguishing geometric and sedimentary characteristics of bar fingers.

dence lies in historic maps which show that the gulfward ends of some of the thick sand fingers now occur in areas which were formerly open gulf along, or beyond, the delta front. The transitional lithologic characteristics of the sands making up the fingers and the incorporation of the sand bodies within thick fine-grained delta-platform facies substantiate the interpretation of their distributary-mouth-bar origin. There is a lack of evidence to support the contention of Shepard and Lankford (1959) that these sands originated in part as stream-channel deposits, including point bars, and in part as barrier-island sands.

Criteria which should prove useful in the recognition of bar-finger sands in ancient deltaic deposits are diagrammatically presented on Figure 9 and include the following.

1. *Distribution and form*—elongate, lenticular shape; upstream narrowing and thinning; thickest accumulation at center of finger with irregular lateral decrease in thickness; branching pattern with interbranch width increasing seaward.

2. *Facies relationships*—transitional boundaries with surrounding fine-grained deposits; upper transition zone thinner than basal zone; sands free of faunas and grading into fine-grained facies bearing faunas.

3. *Sedimentary characteristics*—central zone of sand bodies made up of clean, well sorted, laminated sands; thin layers of unidirectional cross-beds limited to the central clean sand and upper transition zones, but festoon cross-beds common throughout; dip of unidirectional cross-beds is away from axis of bar; entire section characterized by laminae of plant fragments and by scattered laminae and thin layers of silt and clayey silt.

4. *Structures developed penecontemporaneously with deposition*—intruded mud-lump "stocks" with bordering zone of steep dips within the sands; minor faults and contorted beds in sands, due to slumping.

Ancient bar fingers can be expected to differ in thickness and width, reflecting the size and character of load of their parent streams, the depth of water into which the delta platform was prograded, and the thickness of the fine-grained deposits upon which the bar sands accumulated. Bar fingers can also be expected to be of different

lengths in accord with stability of the distributary system and with rate of delta-front advance which is affected by sea-floor configuration. Present knowledge of Mississippi bar fingers indicates an average maximum width of approximately 5 miles at the delta front and a thickness of from 250 to possibly more than 300 feet. The system has been stable for at least 450 years, permitting bar fingers to attain lengths of approximately 15 miles under the major distributaries. Progressive lengthening of these distributaries has been accompanied by abandonment of minor branches which may also be underlain by bar fingers.

ANCIENT BAR-FINGER SANDS

Application of the criteria listed indicates that the Booch sand of the lower Pennsylvanian McAlester formation, greater Seminole district, Oklahoma, includes thick bar fingers (Fisk,1955). The thickness map of the Booch sand (Fig. 10-*A*) and the cross section (Fig. 10-*B*) are modified from ones published by Busch (1953), who recognized the deltaic origin of the sand. The isopach pattern is similar to that of the Mississippi bird-foot-delta bar fingers; each main finger of Booch sand is more than 200 feet thick, and the smaller branches locally attain comparable thicknesses. Interbranch areas widen seaward toward a line of flexure and contain thick shales which, in most areas, are overlain by thin Booch sands. The electric-log pattern of the thick sand finger penetrated in well No. 89 (Fig. 10-*B*) indicates greater porosity near the top of the sand. It also records a thin transition zone with overlying shales and a much thicker basal transition zone. Although the thick Booch sands were interpreted by Busch as fillings of erosional channels, their width and downward convexity strongly suggest depositional fingers. Additional details of lithology and faunal content of the section in which the sands occur will be required for more accurate interpretation.

No published maps show the pattern of distribution of locally abnormally thick sand bodies which are known to be present within various Tertiary formations of the Gulf basin. Eocene Wilcox sands which produce oil in the Nebo field, La Salle Parish, Louisiana, locally exhibit characteristics of bar fingers. Attaining thicknesses of more than 150 feet, these sand bodies grade

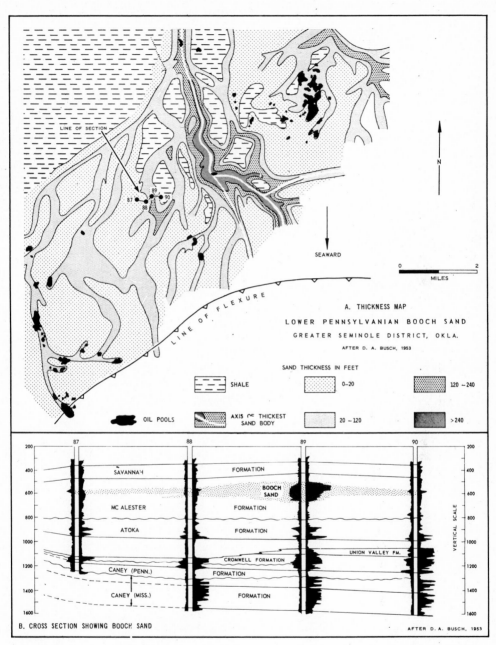

FIG. 10.—Ancient deltaic deposits illustrating pattern of bar fingers and cross section of minor finger.

laterally into sand-shale sections of similar thicknesses within distances of 2–3 miles. Oil production comes from porous zones near the top of the thick sands; an abrupt transition with overlying shales and a thicker transition zone with underlying deposits are indicated by electric logs.

Judging from electric-log patterns and facies relationships, the down-dip Eocene Sparta and Cockfield formations in central Louisiana also contain bar fingers, as do the thick Oligocene and Miocene deposits of coastal sections of Texas, Louisiana, and Mississippi. Exploration for bar-finger stratigraphic traps within these formations will require detailed regional lithofacies and thickness studies, as well as careful examination of samples for diagnostic faunas and lithologies.

REFERENCES

Andersen, H. V., 1951, Report on the mudlumps at the mouths of the Mississippi River—Part II, Foraminiferal faunules from the mudlumps and environments in the vicinity of the mouths of the Mississippi River: unpub. report, U. S. Corps of Engineers, New Orleans District, 214 p.

Busch, D. A., 1953, The significance of deltas in subsurface exploration: Tulsa Geol. Society Digest, v. 21, p. 71–80.

Fisk, H. N., 1952, Geological investigations of the Atchafalaya basin and the problem of Mississippi River diversion: U. S. Corps of Engineers, Waterways Expt. Sta., Vicksburg, 145 p.

———— 1955, Sand facies of Recent Mississippi delta deposits: 4th World Petroleum Cong. (Rome) Proc., Sec. 1-C, p. 377–398.

———— McFarlan, E., Jr., Kolb, C. R., and Wilbert, L. J., Jr., 1954, Sedimentary framework of the modern Mississippi Delta: Jour. Sed. Petrology, v. 24, no. 2, p. 76–99.

Lankford, R. R., 1959, Distribution and ecology of Foraminifera from east Mississippi Delta margin: Am. Assoc. Petroleum Geologists Bull., v. 43, no. 9, p. 2068–2099.

Ludwick, J. C., and Walton, W. R., 1957, Shelf-edge calcareous prominences in northeastern Gulf of Mexico: Am. Assoc. Petroleum Geologists Bull., v. 41, no. 9, p. 2054–2101.

Morgan, J. P., 1951, Mudlumps at the mouths of the Mississippi River, Chap. 11 of Johnson, J. W., ed., proc. 2nd Conf. Coastal Engineering, Houston, Texas: p. 130–144.

Parker, R. H., 1956, Macro-invertebrate assemblages as indicators of sedimentary environments in east Mississippi Delta region: Am. Assoc. Petroleum Geologists Bull., v. 40, no. 2, p. 295–376.

Shepard, F. P., 1956, Marginal sediments of Mississippi Delta: Am. Assoc. Petroleum Geologists Bull., v. 40, no. 11, p. 2537–2623.

———— and Lankford, R. R., 1959, Sedimentary facies from shallow borings in lower Mississippi Delta: Am. Assoc. Petroleum Geologists Bull., v. 43, no. 9, p. 2051–2067.

Trask, P. D., assisted by Hammar, H. E., and Wu, C. C., 1932, Origin and environment of source sediments of petroleum: Houston, Texas, Gulf Pub. Co., 323 p.

Trowbridge, A. C., 1930, Building of Mississippi Delta: Am. Assoc. Petroleum Geologists Bull., v. 14, no. 7, p. 867–901.

BAHAMIAN OÖLITE SHOALS[1]

EDWARD G. PURDY[2]

Houston, Texas

ABSTRACT

In the Bahamas the post-Wisconsin rise in sea level flooded an irregular limestone surface which super-imposed local increases and decreases in current velocity on the regional tidal regimen. The calcium carbonate supersaturated bank waters of the shoaler unsheltered rock areas were characterized by considerable current agitation and consequent oölite formation. The rate of oölite accumulation kept pace with or exceeded the rate of sea level rise, thereby resulting in the formation of extensive oölite shoals. The distribution of these shoals reflects the distribution of the limestone prominences which underlie them. The form variation exhibited by the shoals is apparently a product of the continuous or discontinuous nature of the underlying rock ridges.

INTRODUCTION

Southeast of the Florida mainland the North American continental shelf is characterized by a number of shallowly submerged limestone platforms which are separated from each other and from Florida, Cuba, and Hispaniola by relatively deep water (Fig. 1). These platforms have attracted considerable geologic interest in that they are mantled by nearly pure calcium carbonate deposits, terrigenous noncarbonate grains being virtually absent. Among these several platforms none has received more attention than the Great Bahama Bank, and of the several types of calcium carbonate sediment which have been recognized on this platform, none is more impressive than the vast areas of brightly illuminated oölite shoals. The problem of the origin of Bahamian oölite has been considered by a number of workers (Illing, 1954; Newell, Purdy, and Imbrie, 1960), but the related problem of the origin of the oölite shoals has been neglected. It is the purpose of this paper to consider briefly the nature and genesis of these carbonate sand bodies.

PREVIOUS INVESTIGATIONS

The extensive submarine ridges of carbonate sand occurring on many parts of the Great Bahama Bank were described first by Agassiz (1894, p. 37–39) who referred to them as "sand bores,"

[1] Manuscript received, December 1, 1960.
[2] Rice University. The writer is indebted to Norman D. Newell, of the American Museum of Natural History, for the photographs of Fig. 7, which had been previously published by Newell and Rigby (1957). Appreciation is also expressed to William Kanes, of Humble Oil and Refining Company, who kindly provided information on the relief of the limestone surface beneath the South Cat Cay-Browns Cay oölite shoal.

a term which he apparently obtained from the various hydrographic office charts of the area. Agassiz noted that the bores were frequently more or less subaerially exposed at low tide and commented further on the distribution and form of the bores, but he made no mention of their composition or origin. Rich (1948, p. 768, 770) suggested that some of the bores might be composed of oölite and speculated that the pattern of bars which he observed along the western margin of the bank might " . . . well be a product of a combination of wave and current action." Subsequently several publications have documented not only the considerable form variation exhibited by these sand bodies, but also the oölitic composition of many of them (Newell, Rigby, Whiteman, and Bradley, 1951; Newell and Rigby, 1957). Those bores occurring in shallow, strongly current-agitated waters have been found to contain oöids in excess of 90 per cent (Purdy, 1960), and hence can be referred to as oölite shoals, a designation which emphasizes their two most obvious characteristics.

DISTRIBUTION AND FORM OF OÖLITE SHOALS

It is convenient to discuss the distribution of oölite shoals with respect to the four bathymetric provinces generally recognized in the Bahamas. These have been termed the marginal escarpment, the outer platform, the barrier rim, and the shelf lagoon (Newell, 1955; Newell and Imbrie, 1955). The steeply sloping marginal escarpment bordering the Great Bahama Bank descends to depths of 100 fathoms or more, and is succeeded at depths of approximately 20 fathoms by a more gently sloping surface—the outer platform—which shoals bankward toward a marginal line of islands and shoals termed the barrier rim. Bankward of the

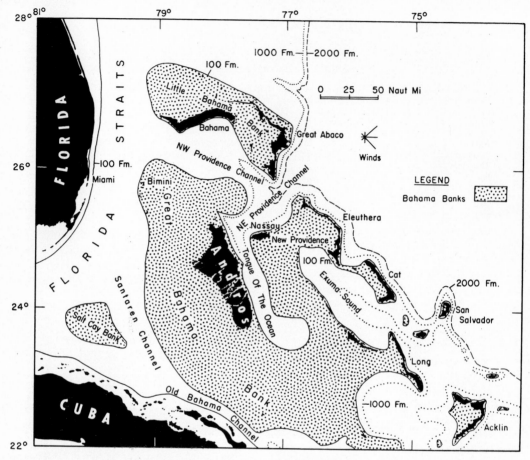

FIG. 1.—The Bahama Banks and environs. Modified from Newell, 1955.

barrier rim the platform generally is depressed to depths of 3 fathoms or less, and is designated as the shelf lagoon. These relationships are indicated in the generalized bank profile of Figure 2.

The oölite shoals generally occur at or slightly bankward of the barrier rim; however there are many places along the barrier rim where oölite deposits are absent. Moreover, there are occasional occurrences of oölite shoals some distance within the shelf lagoon (Fig. 3).

The form of the oölite shoals is less subject to generalization than the distribution of these

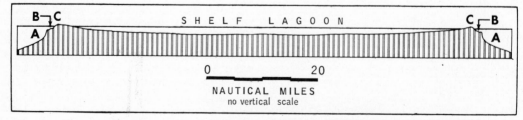

FIG. 2.—Generalized Bahamian bathymetric profile. *A*. Marginal escarpment. *B*. Outer platform. *C*. Barrier rim. Modified from Newell and others, 1959.

deposits. In the South Cat Cay-Browns Cay area (Figs. 4 and 5) the oölite shoal occurs as a single ridge, 1–3 kilometers wide, in which the long axis of the ridge is oriented approximately normal to the direction of tidal flow. In contrast, the oölite shoals at the head of the Tongue of the Ocean (Figs. 6 and 7-A) are displayed in a series of parallel sand ridges several kilometers in length, but here the long axes of the ridges generally parallel the direction of tidal flow. Finally, there are the intriguing submarine barchans (Fig. 7-B), which are best developed along the southeastern

edge of the Tongue of the Ocean (Newell and Rigby, 1957, p. 57). Here the crescentic dunes are 90–210 feet wide and are convex eastward (Illing, 1954, Pl. 7.4; p. 90). "They are grouped together into distinct zones, commonly in the middle of the big sand spreads. Toward the edges of the latter, the barchans merge into linear dunes, both being controlled by ebbing tidal currents directed westward toward the Tongue of the Ocean" (Illing, 1954, p. 90).

Optimum conditions for oölite formation in the Bahamas apparently occur only where sea water

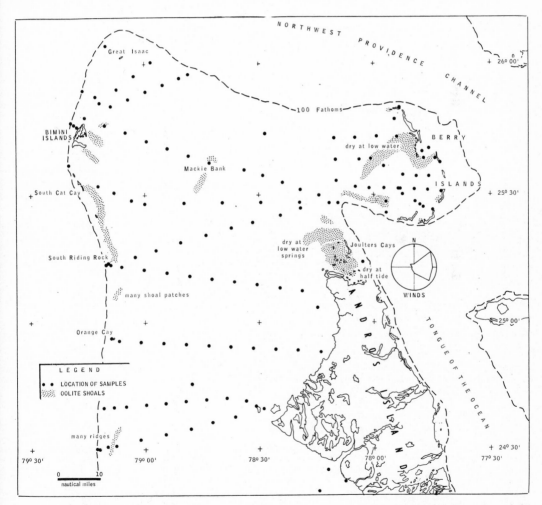

FIG. 3.—Distribution of oölite shoals on the northern part of the Andros platform. The dimensions of the shoals are approximate; their indicated position and form are based on one or more of the following sorts of information—field observations, aerial photographs, petrographic data, and the bathymetric information provided by U. S. Hydrographic Office Chart 26a.

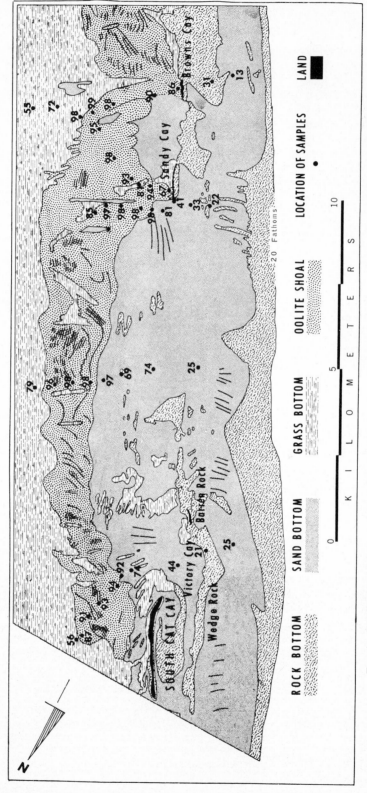

Fig. 4.—Distribution and form of the oölite shoal in the South Cat Cay-Browns Cay area. The percentage of oölitically coated grains in the sediment is indicated at each sample locality. Modified from Newell and others, 1959.

ROCK BOTTOM   SAND BOTTOM   GRASS BOTTOM   OOLITE SHOAL   LOCATION OF SAMPLES   LAND

KILOMETERS
0   5   10

:20 Fathoms:

N

Browns Cay
Sandy Cay
South Cat Cay
Victory Cay
Barica Rock
Wedge Rock

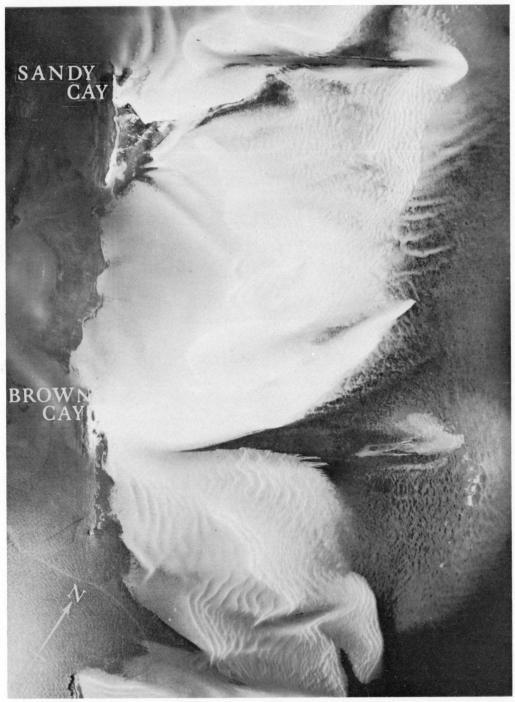

Fig. 5.—Vertical aerial photograph of part of the South Cat Cay-Browns Cay oölite shoal. Not visible in the photograph are the Florida Straits, located to the southwest. Note the abundance of para-ripples and the grass-covered depression east of the northern end of Sandy Cay. Part of the extensively para-rippled area is awash at low tide. The northeast-southwest elongated depression north of Sandy Cay is a tidal channel doubly terminated by small deltas. The photograph also shows that the low escarpment bordering either side of the shoal has greater relief on the seaward side. Approximate scale: 4 cm = 1 km. U. S. Navy Hydrographic Office photograph. Compare with Fig. 4.

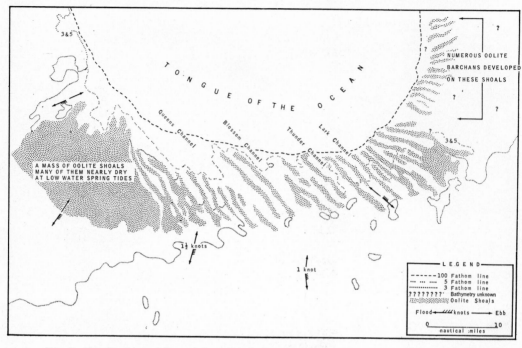

FIG. 6.—Distribution and form of the oölite shoals at the south end of the Tongue of the Ocean. Modified from U. S. Hydrographic Office Charts 26b, c, d.

supersaturated with calcium carbonate is subjected to relatively great current agitation (Newell, Purdy, and Imbrie, 1960; Purdy, 1960). The abundance of non-skeletal grain types at and bankward of the barrier rim (Purdy, 1960) indicates that sea water in this region is supersaturated with calcium carbonate. Consequently the distribution of oölite in the Bahamas must be related to sites of relatively great current agitation. The unsheltered shoals of the Bahamas constitute such sites, because these shoals cause local increase in tidal current velocity, an effect similar to that resulting when a submerged barrier is placed across the width of a stream. The increased current agitation, in turn, causes the precipitation of oölitic laminae. This relationship explains the high oölite content of the shoals, but it does not account for the origin of the shoals themselves.

SOUTH CAT CAY—BROWNS CAY OÖLITE SHOAL

The South Cat Cay-Browns Cay oölite shoal of Figure 4 is one of the few oölite areas which have been studied in any detail (Newell, Purdy, and Imbrie, 1960), and consequently it seems appropriate to use the features of this shoal as a basis for extrapolation concerning the genesis of oölite shoals in general.

The depth of water overlying the shoal ranges from intertidal exposure at low tide to an observed maximum of 10 feet. The average depth is less than 6 feet. The shallowest areas, subaerially exposed at low tide, generally occur on or near the seaward margin of the shoal. The oölite sand on the ridge is in nearly constant motion as evidenced by the rapid shifting of small sand ripples. Giant ripples, termed para-ripples, are also in evidence on the bottom (Fig. 5). These have an amplitude of approximately 3 feet and an estimated wave length of 100 feet. In places, depressions occur on the oölite ridge. These are typically floored by dense growths of the marine grass *Thalassia testudinum*, producing a dark coloration which contrasts markedly with the brilliantly white oölite bottom of the surrounding area. In some regions the oölite shoal is margined both on its seaward and bankward sides by a low escarpment beyond which the depth of water increases

A

B

FIG. 7-*A*.—Oblique aerial photograph of oölite shoals at the south end of the Tongue of the Ocean. The brilliantly white oölite shoals are separated from each other by the darker colored waters of relatively deep channels. View toward the southwest from an approximate altitude of 2,500 feet. From Newell and Rigby, 1957, Pl. XIII, Fig. 2. (Compare Fig. 6.) *B*.—Oblique aerial photograph of oölite barchans at the southeast end of the Tongue of the Ocean. Note how the barchans grade into para-ripples. The oölite shoal in the background has a ridge-like form, and both barchans and para-ripples have been developed on its surface. The arrow indicates the direction of trade wind drift. View south-southwest from an approximate altitude of 1,500 feet. From Newell and Rigby, 1957, Pl. X, Fig. 1.

abruptly to 8 or 11 feet. The increase in water depth is generally greater by 2 or more feet on the seaward margin, as compared to the bankward margin. The seaward escarpment is commonly absent where cays are present. In these instances the cays themselves appear to constitute the seaward border of the ridge. Bankward of the oölite ridge, the bottom is covered by a dense growth of *Thalassia testudinum*. The dense vegetative cover and the lack of ripple marks indicate bottom stability. Seaward of the shoal the bottom is strongly rippled and supports a sparse floral cover. The local occurrence of sea whips (plexaurids) on this bottom suggests that the sediment in places forms only a thin veneer over a rock platform.

The development of the South Cat Cay-Browns Cay oölite shoal, and indeed of oölite shoals elsewhere on the bank, is related to the uneven surface of the underlying Pleistocene limestone. Subaerial exposure of the Great Bahama Bank during times of glacially lowered sea level caused the induration of previously formed submarine carbonate deposits (Illing, 1954, p. 48). Prior to the induration accompanying the Wisconsin emergence of the bank, some of the subaerially exposed carbonate sands were heaped into aeolian dunes, many of which project above the present sea surface as the cross-bedded limestones of the Bahama Islands (Newell, 1960). Subsequent to the induration a karst topography was developed on the Pleistocene limestone surface (Newell and Rigby, 1957). The product of this combination of events is the uneven limestone surface which presently underlies the recent unconsolidated Bahamian carbonate sediments. Purdy (1960) speculated that as sea level rose to its present position, the uneven rock surface superimposed local increases and decreases in current velocity on the regional tidal regimen, the shoaler unsheltered areas being characterized by considerable current agitation and consequent oölite formation. According to this interpretation, each of the oölite shoals should have a limestone ridge beneath its unconsolidated sediment surface. Confirmation of this hypothesis has been obtained in the South Cat Cay-Browns Cay area where William Kanes of the Humble Oil and Refining Company has located a rock ridge beneath the shallowest areas of oölite accumulation.[3]

The sequence of events leading to the development of this particular oölite shoal can now be tentatively reconstructed. As sea level rose, the uneven Pleistocene limestone surface induced local increases and decreases in current velocity. The shallowly submerged rock ridge was attended by considerable current agitation resulting in the precipitation of oölitic laminae. The rate of oölite accumulation evidently exceeded the rate of sea level rise so that oölite was transported bankward and seaward from its site of origin at the intertidally maintained sediment depositional surface above the limestone ridge. The initial optimal environment for oölitic accretion expanded concomitantly with the expansion of the oölite shoal, and as a result the rate of expansion of the shoal probably was accelerated progressively.

Flood tidal currents on the bank are stronger than ebb currents (U. S. Navy Hydrographic Office Chart 26a); consequently, more oöids were transported bankward from their site of origin than seaward. This discrepancy in the competency of flood as compared to ebb tidal currents is reflected in the present distribution of typical ridge oöids. Bankward of the shoal the oöids are similar to those occurring on the shoal in that they characteristically consist of an elliptically shaped cryptocrystalline nucleus surrounded by a large number of oölitic laminae. In contrast, most of the oöids seaward of the shoal have a relatively large, irregularly shaped, cryptocrystalline nucleus coated by few concentric laminations. Thus, the distribution of typical ridge oöids is also in accordance with the hypothesis of greater bankward than seaward expansion of the prototype oölite shoal. Viewed in this context, the steep marginal slopes of the oölite shoal are probably analogous to foreslopes of tidal deltas (Newell, Purdy, and Imbrie, 1960, p. 485). In some cases the sheltering effect of cays decreased the competence of flood tidal currents, so that in these areas the oölite shoals were extended appreciably seaward as well as bankward. Apparently this is the case in some parts of the South Cat Cay-Browns Cay area of Figure 4, where locally the cays themselves appear to constitute the seaward border of the shoal.

The relationship between the limestone ridge and the development of the oölite shoal in the

_____
[3] The location of this ridge is based on data collected from 125 core holes.

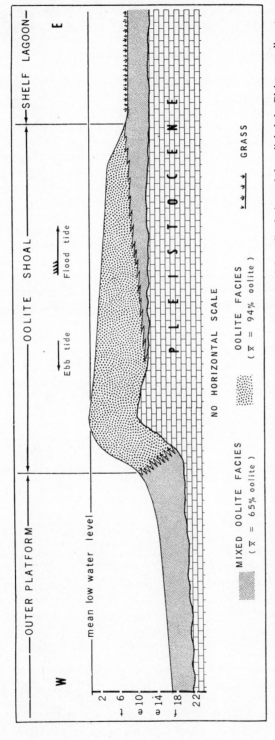

FIG. 8.—Idealized relationships in the South Cat Cay-Sandy Cay oölite shoal. The thickness of the oölite facies and the relief of the Pleistocene limestone ridge have been generalized from data gathered by Kanes in the Sandy Cay-Browns Cay oölite shoal. The steepness of the western slope of the limestone ridge may be due, in part, to the cliffing action of the sea as it rose to its present level.

South Cat Cay-Sandy Cay area is shown in idealized form in Figure 8. It should be emphasized
that this diagram is an oversimplification of a
complex developmental sequence. For example,
Kanes (personal communication) has found that
the depth to the limestone surface in the grass
covered, isolated depressions occurring within this
shoal is approximately the same as that beneath
the adjacent oölite deposits. This fact and the
isolated nature of these depressions (Fig. 4)
strongly suggest that the present South Cat Cay-
Browns Cay oölite shoal is a composite one resulting from the coalescence of several smaller shoals.
The grass-covered depressions, then, represent
areas where this coalescence has not, as yet, been
completed.

The nature of the limestone surface beneath
other oölite shoals has not been ascertained. The
characteristics noted for the South Cat Cay-
Browns Cay oölite area, however, are similar to
those of oölite shoals observed elsewhere in the
Bahamas, and therefore it seems likely that limestone prominences will also be found beneath
these deposits.

CONCLUSIONS

The prevalence of oölite shoals at or slightly
bankward of the barrier rim is best explained at
present by the interpretation that these shoals
have developed on drowned, indurated, aeolian
dunes. The distribution of the Bahama Islands,
which are composed mainly of lithified dune
material, suggests that extensive dune development occurred in the vicinity of the present
barrier rim during the Pleistocene. As sea level
rose to its present position, many of the dunes
were submerged, and those that were drowned
and attended by strong current agitation became
the sites of oölite shoal development. The limestone ridge or ridges underlying the shoals occurring within the shelf lagoon may be of aeolian
origin or, perhaps more likely, may represent
residual karst prominences.

Little is known concerning the causes of form
variation among oölite shoals; however, it may be
speculated that a continuous rock ridge or a series
of closely spaced rock ridges oriented approximately parallel to the bank's edge would result in
an oölite shoal similar to that of the South Cat

Cay-Browns Cay area. Here the long axis of the
shoal would be normal to the prevailing tidal
currents. In contrast, widely spaced limestone
ridges occurring in areas of vigorous tidal flow
would be expected to produce oölite shoals similar
to those observed at the head of the Tongue of the
Ocean (Fig. 6). In this case, the long axes of the
shoals would parallel the direction of tidal movement. The barchan-like shoals along the southeastern edge of the Tongue of the Ocean (Fig.
7-B) are analogous to the para-ripples of the South
Cat Cay-Browns Cay area in that both appear to
be features which are superimposed upon a general sand sea of oölite. Evidently the occurrence of
barchans and/or para-ripples on various oölite
shoals is related more to local current conditions
than to any peculiarity in the underlying limestone surface.

REFERENCES

Agassiz, A., 1894, A reconnaissance of the Bahamas
    and of the elevated reefs of Cuba in the steam yacht
    "Wild Duck," January to April, 1893: Harvard Coll.
    Mus. Comp. Zoology Bull., v. 26, p. 1–203.
Illing, L. V., 1954, Bahaman calcareous sands: Am.
    Assoc. Petroleum Geologists Bull., v. 38, no. 1, p.
    1–95.
Newell, N. D., 1955, Bahamian platforms, in Polder-
    vaart, A., ed., Crust of the earth—a symposium:
    Geol. Soc. America Spec. Paper 62, p. 303–315.
——— 1960, Marine planation of tropical limestone
    islands: Science, v. 132, p. 144–145.
——— and Imbrie, J., 1955, Biogeological reconnais-
    sance in the Bimini area, Great Bahama Bank: N. Y.
    Acad. Sci. Trans., v. 18, ser. 2, p. 3–14.
——— Purdy, E. G., and Thurber, D. L., 1959,
    Organism communities and bottom facies, Great
    Bahama Bank: Am. Mus. Nat. Hist. Bull., v. 117, p.
    177–228.
——— Purdy, E. G., and Imbrie, J., 1960. Bahamian
    oölitic sand: Jour. Geology, v. 68, no. 5, p. 481–497.
——— and Rigby, J. K., 1957, Geologic studies on the
    Great Bahama Bank, in Regional aspects of car-
    bonate deposition: Soc. Econ. Paleontologists and
    Mineralogists Spec. Pub. 5, p. 15–79.
——— ——— Whiteman, A. J., and Bradley, J. S.,
    1951, Shoal-water geology and environments, eastern
    Andros Island, Bahamas: Am. Mus. Nat. Hist. Bull.,
    v. 97, p. 1–29.
Purdy, E. G., 1960, Recent calcium carbonate facies of
    the Great Bahama Bank: unpub. Ph.D. dissertation,
    Columbia Univ., 174 p.
Rich, J. L., 1948, Submarine sedimentary features on
    Bahama Banks and their bearing on distribution pat-
    terns of lenticular oil sands: Am. Assoc. Petroleum
    Geologists Bull., v. 32, no. 5, p. 767–779.
U. S. Hydrographic Office, Charts 26a, b, c, and d, Great
    Bahama Bank, northwestern, northeastern, south-
    western, and southeastern parts.

TURBIDITES IN OIL EXPLORATION[1]

HAROLD H. SULLWOLD, JR.[2]
North Hollywood, California

ABSTRACT

The rapid accumulation of data, mainly from field observations and oceanographic research in the past few years, has forced the conclusion that turbidites are not freaks of nature but are very common-place, especially in environments of deep-water sedimentation. Billions of barrels of oil have been produced from turbidites in the Los Angeles basin alone. A thorough knowledge of their characteristic features and mode of origin would be of great use in petroleum exploration and development in areas where turbidites exist. By virtue of their mode of deposition, turbidites have peculiar syngenetic structures which serve as useful recognition clues and as indicators of current direction and sea-bottom topography. Much more data collecting is necessary before these potential clues can be fully utilized in predicting shape, size, and trend of turbidites from isolated well data, but the possibilities are enormous. Turbidites are deposited in low places on the sea floor, and their over-all geometry is controlled by the shape of these low places. Channel, fan, and blanket-like shapes have been observed. Descriptions in the literature of entire turbidites, showing their complete geometry, are lacking, but four incomplete or generalized examples are given from the California Tertiary.

INTRODUCTION

A *turbidity current* is a muddy current which is able to move, even in still water, by virtue of its own muddiness, and the sediment which it deposits is a *turbidite*. Turbidity currents as a common mechanism for the deposition of sandstones have received recognition only in the last decade. In this time much has been written describing the internal and external features of turbidites, both as recognition clues and as evidence for mode of deposition. The increasing tempo of study of turbidites on the modern sea floor has provided valuable data as to their present habitat and over-all shape. Directions of ancient turbidity current flow have been established in many areas from oriented structures observed on outcrops. As yet, however, there is a severe lack of descriptions in the literature of the over-all shape of individual turbidites. It is hoped this situation will soon be remedied.

Because turbidites are potential oil and gas reservoirs, the importance of predicting their shape and size in the prospecting or early field development stage is obvious. Internal distribution of porosity and permeability in turbidites also appears to have some peculiarities of importance. In relatively deep water of subsiding basins, deposi-tion of sands by turbidity currents is now believed to be the rule rather than the exception. This dumping is in contrast to the winnowing and re-working which takes place on stable shelves. Most turbidites have the property of displaying their directions of transport by virtue of their con-tained syngenetic, oriented structures. This is an extremely useful tool in working out paleogeog-raphy—an obvious asset in the search for oil.

It now appears that virtually all the oil sands in the prolific Los Angeles basin are turbidites; this basin has produced nearly 5 billion barrels of oil. Turbidite oil sands are common in other areas in California also. More and more clastic forma-tions are taking their places on the list of recorded turbidites, both in and out of the oil country. Examples include sandstones of the Permian Delaware Mountain group of Texas and New Mexico (Hull, 1957), Pennsylvanian Atoka forma-tion of Oklahoma (E. V. Winterer, personal com-munication), Ordovician Martinsburg and Reeds-ville formations of the Appalachian Mountains (McBride, 1960; Van Houten, 1954), and Devon-ian Portage facies in the Appalachian Mountains (McIver, 1960). The Gulf Coast Tertiary becomes progressively deeper water in character toward the Gulf (Lowman, 1949) and should contain tur-bidites in its deeper water facies, for such are now being deposited in the modern gulf (Bates, 1953). Caution is advised in accepting all "turbidite" labels, however, for some descriptions have ap-

[1] Manuscript received December 1, 1960.
[2] George H. Roth and Associates, consulting geolo-gists.

peared in the literature which do not fit the turbidity-current concept, especially those reported
from shallow water on stable shelf areas.

This paper is a brief review of turbidites with
emphasis on their geometry and their significance
in oil exploration. The examples were hurriedly
assembled, mostly from unpublished work of
others, and represent the best that could be obtained in the time available and in the present
state of knowledge of the subject. The responsi-
bility for all statements herein rests entirely with
the writer.

PRINCIPLES OF TURBIDITE DEPOSITION

Turbidity currents have been recognized for
years under such names as density currents and
suspension currents, but it was not until 1950,
when Kuenen and Migliorini demonstrated that
graded bedding was a natural consequence of
turbidity currents, that their importance as a
mechanism for sediment transport in the sea came
to be recognized. Since then, many studies have
been made of marine sedimentary rocks, modern
sediments on the sea floor, and deposits in experimental tanks, which marshal evidence that these
currents are common now, and were common in
the past. Indeed, they constitute a very important
sedimentation mechanism. Under certain conditions, transport of materials by these currents is
probably the dominant process in operation.

A turbidity current is opaque and muddy (by
definition) because of its load of suspended material (hence, *suspension current*) which gives the current greater density than the surrounding water
(hence, *density current*). The mechanism for get-
ting the material into suspension could be heavily
loaded flood waters or a submarine slump in unconsolidated sediments at the edge of the continental shelf or delta or at the head of a submarine
canyon. The trigger action causing the slump
could be an earthquake, unusually severe storm,
excess local deposition by other sorts of currents,
or submarine seeps. Once the sediments begin to
slump they mix with the surrounding water, and
the resulting turbid mixture, because of its increased density, can move as a unit down the
slope. Thus, even in bodies of standing water, a
current is born. One can create miniature turbidity currents by poking one's finger into a
water-filled footprint in muddy soil.

A turbidity current is capable of transporting
rock and mineral particles in some proportion to
its density, velocity, and viscosity. Velocity depends on the slope of the sea bottom for a given
current. The current moves downward along the
bottom. On smooth slopes it should spread widely;
on irregular floors it should follow low areas,
probably meandering much like streams on land.
Where the balance between density and velocity
of the current and texture of the bottom sediment
permits, the current may erode. It is becoming
increasingly evident that the great submarine
canyons, thousands of feet deep and tens of miles
long, have been cut by these turbidity currents.
All turbidity currents must eventually lose velocity as the slope lessens. Where this occurs,
deposition begins. Deposition is generally accompanied by sorting as the heavier particles settle
out first along with entrapped portions of the finer
material (matrix?), resulting in a graded bed or
lamina. Sorting may also take place while the current is moving, with the heavier particles advancing toward the toe of the current. As the material
within the current is generally a mixture of many
particle sizes, the resulting turbidite will, on the
whole, be poorly sorted; yet, because of the particle selection during deposition, sorting at any
particular level within the deposit will differ from
the average for the turbidite, and sorting will
improve upward in the deposit because of the
decrease in coarse particles.

Turbidites differ from most other deposits in
that they are nearly instantaneous. These sandstones do not accumulate at a steady rate, but a
single deposit, possibly tens of feet thick, may
require only a few hours or a few days, and it may
be followed by a thin pelagic deposit representing
many years or centuries of accumulation. A single
turbidite, therefore, will not grade laterally into
an equivalent thickness of lutite but will sharply
disappear into a bedding plane. In areas of rapid
subsidence and active upland erosion, turbidites
may follow one another rather rapidly with intervening pelagic deposits thin or missing. In at
least one area, repetition of thin turbidites has
been related to annual cycles of organic growth
and rainfall (Riveroll and Jones, 1954).

Turbidites should thus be expected in geosynclinal sequences in fairly deep to very deep water, on or below slopes. They would not be expected in shallow water within wave-base depths, for here they would be destroyed by reworking and winnowing if, indeed, there were sufficient slope for turbidity currents to get started.

In recent years the quickening pace of oceanographic research has resulted in a growing body of evidence which undeniably demonstrates the great importance of turbidity currents as a mechanism for erosion and transportation on the modern sea floor. Especially active along these lines have been the Lamont Geological Observatory, U. S. Naval Electronic Laboratory, Scripps Institution of Oceanography, and Allan Hancock Foundation. Their findings include sand deposits with shallow-water organic remains on the abyssal plains hundreds of miles from land; submarine canyons with well developed sandy deltas in water more than 10,000 feet deep; sudden evacuation of large volumes of sediment from heads of submarine canyons; breakage of a series of submarine cables by something that was travelling at the rate of 50 knots along a front 210 miles wide, and left a deposit of silt behind; natural levees bordering some of the more prominent channels; and topographic control of deposition wherein nearshore basins trap the sediment and fill up before more distant low places receive sediment. These phenomena are no longer surprising to the oceanographers, but are now expected as a matter of course. Heezen (1959) has very ably summarized early and recent thinking on deep-sea sedimentation.

RECOGNITION FEATURES

Because turbidites are deposited in a manner markedly different from the traditionally accepted sedimentary mechanisms, they have characteristic properties and structures which might be considered their "signature." These structures and textures are not all unique to turbidites, but, considered as a group and in the light of the rapidly accumulating experimental and sea-floor observations, they now appear to fit into a logical and well documented genetic pattern. These features have been discussed by Kuenen (1953), Kuenen and Carozzi (1953), and Crowell (1955), and there is now a large body of literature on the

genesis of individual features, features in certain stratigraphic units, and features in modern sediments. European geologists have been especially active in this respect. There is no need to describe these features here again in detail, but they must be discussed briefly inasmuch as they form part of the geometry of these sandstone bodies.

GENERAL FEATURES

Perhaps most significant of all (though difficult to prove in older formations) is the presence of these sands in deep water. The great abyssal plains of the oceans are now thought to be built by turbidity currents (Heezen, Tharp, and Ewing, 1959). Miocene and Pliocene sandy and pebbly turbidites in California are interbedded with shales containing Foraminifera indicating water depths of 2,000–8,000 feet. Multiple repetitions of sands and deep-water shales rule out a shallow-water origin for the sands. Care must be taken to avoid associating coarse sands and conglomerates, cross-bedding, scour and fill, and even shallow-water fossils, wholly with a shallow-water environment, for these features may be imparted by turbidity currents in deep water. Turbidites need not. be confined to deep water, however.

Poor sorting is an expected feature in turbidites. This, of course, depends upon the type of material included in the original slump which started the current. It would be an unusual situation that would provide well-sorted sand without a significant proportion of clay and silt becoming involved in the slumping or transportation process. A problem arises in that sorting of sands is commonly expressed in terms of Trask's sorting coefficient which compares the grain sizes of the first and third quartiles of the cumulative grain-size curve. These quartiles do not take into account the tails which may consist of coarse sand grains or pebbles at one end and clay at the other; these portions constitute half of the rock. Thus, a well-sorted sand in the Trask system may be classified as poorly sorted by some other system such as that of Payne's (1942, p. 1707). The large percentage of silt and clay in these sands has caused them to be termed wackes and graywackes by most workers. This poor sorting strongly suggests rapid dumping and lack of winnowing and reworking—a suggestion generally supported by grain angularity and high feldspar content. The turbidity-current origin of any well-sorted sand should be viewed with suspicion. Sorting is directly related to porosity, and turbidites must therefore have less original porosity than shallow-water sands which have had the benefit of winnowing. That this decrease in porosity is not a serious handicap to the oil industry is illustrated by the Los Angeles basin.

Repetition of similar sandstone beds separated by normal pelagic finer grained clastics is common. It stands to reason that once the conditions on the sea floor become favorable to the development of turbidity currents, these conditions will persist long enough to permit many repetitions. A slight change in conditions may be reflected in the structural and textural characteristics of the turbidites. These conditions include sea-bottom slope, sea-bottom cohesiveness, type of material in the source area, and type and frequency of triggering mechanisms. The quantitative relating of certain structures and textures to certain conditions must await additional fact gathering.

A turbidity current is clearly not an ideal habitat for any kind of life. Fossils in growth position are lacking in turbidites. Fossils are rare, and those found can commonly be shown to have been transported. The writer spent 110 days in the field examining outcrops of Miocene deep-water turbidites near Los Angeles and found only one mega-fossil, a thoroughly worn oyster shell; Foraminifera were abundant in the enclosing shales, but those in the sands were clearly transported, as evidenced by mixed faunas and their presence in cross-bedding (Sullwold, 1960a, p. 441). Modern turbidites containing shallow-water faunas have been found at a depth of nearly 12,000 feet, 120 miles from the nearest appropriate biotope (Phleger, 1951). Others have been found with green grass at a depth of 4,500 feet (Heezen, 1956). Algae, requiring life-giving sunlight, have been found in turbidites at 26,000 feet in the bottom of the Puerto Rico Trough (Ericson, Ewing, and Heezen, 1952). Turbidity currents can not only transport living or recently deceased creatures from their natural habitat into deeper waters in wholesale lots, but can also erode fossil-bearing rocks, thus introducing older, perhaps extinct, forms into the fauna. The implications of this

willy-nilly mixing of ages and environments are enormous in working out fossil time ranges and paleoecology, and, especially, in detailed paleontologic correlation. The writer has the utmost admiration for the ability of those paleontologists who have endeavored, and largely succeeded, in bringing some sort of order out of this chaos.

INTERNAL FEATURES

Graded bedding is the most characteristic internal feature of turbidites. A single graded bed must have been deposited as a single depositional unit reflecting a definite beginning and end of the supply or the transporting agent. A series of graded beds could not have been deposited by normal oceanic currents with a continuous supply of material. Turbidity currents are the most logical explanation for the great bulk of marine graded beds. Reservoir characteristics clearly differ vertically within a single graded bed. A single core analysis would not necessarily be representative, and might be the source of considerable error in calculating fluid volume, even in a relatively thin bed. Studies of the relationship of porosity and permeability to graded bedding in turbidites are needed.

Other internal features include convolute bedding, current bedding, shale inclusions, charcoal fragments, oriented grains, and imbricate arrangement of larger clasts. These are less significant than graded bedding in reservoir calculations, but have varying degrees of utility in recognition of turbidites and orientation of flow directions.

EXTERNAL FEATURES

The most characteristic external feature of a turbidite is the sharp basal contact—a natural consequence of dumping an exotic mixture of sediment upon the sea floor. No gradational contact can be envisioned here, nor do such exist, in the writer's experience. Conversely, the upper contact is commonly seen to grade imperceptibly upward into normal pelagic lutites—a consequence of the similarity in grain size of last-deposited particles in the turbidite and later lutites. This gradation may be locally destroyed by erosion by subsequent currents, hence it is not as universal as the sharp base.

Sole markings of various sorts are very distinctive and have received much attention partly because of speculation as to their origin and partly because of their great usefulness as current indicators. Birkenmajer (1959) has classified bed surface structures into 18 categories and provided an excellent bibliography. Sole markings or hicroglyphs may be subdivided into a few major groups. (1) One group is a result of load deformation wherein the sudden application of the load (turbidite) on a muddy bottom causes the mud to deform. The deformation takes the form of load folds in the mud, load casts on the under surface of the sandstone, load pockets within the sandstone, and load waves of mud squirting up into the sandstone (Sullwold, 1959 and 1960b). (2) Another group consists of tracks or grooves cut into the sea floor by objects dragged by the current. They were observed, illustrated, and correctly interpreted by James Hall (1843) nearly 120 years ago, and more recently dealt with in detail by Dzulynski and Radomski (1955). (3) A third group, also erosional, includes those markings made by the current itself in the sea floor without the benefit of "tools," including flow markings and flutes.

Where these markings are seen on the base of the sandstone, as is commonly the case, rather than at the top of the underlying shale, they are raised casts of the original impression of the mud on the sea floor, and the word "cast" is consequently combined with the structural term, as *flute-cast* and *load-cast*. These markings are nearly all linear features providing excellent bearings of the current, and some, by pointing upstream, even provide absolute direction of the current. A careful examination of bedding planes in cores could provide valuable data on current directions when related to known attitude of the strata.

The top surface of a turbidite is generally planar; the upper part of the turbidite is commonly laminated and gradational with the overlying lutites. Perhaps the most significant departure from this situation is the common presence of ripple marks at the top. As the sand is deposited from a current traveling along the sea floor, it is not surprising that occasionally the relationship of grain size to velocity is such that ripple marks (and associated current bedding) form. These too, are excellent current indicators. In the

California Tertiary ripple marks are more common at the top of thin beds, from a fraction of an inch to 6 inches, than in thicker beds.

All these relatively small elements in the geometry of turbidite bodies have their significance in the science of petroleum geology. They serve as valuable tools, first, in recognizing turbidites as such, then in determining the direction of travel. With this latter knowledge paleogeography can be worked out in much finer detail—an obvious asset in the search for oil. Furthermore, much promise is offered that by these studies, the trend of a turbidite sand body may be predicted from examination of cores in a single well. It is too soon yet, but studies are under way with this goal in mind. These structures are also useful in differentiating top and bottom of beds in complex structural areas such as in California. Once the current directions have been established in a given area at a given horizon, a core in a wildcat well could be oriented, provided it contained a recognizable, oriented feature. Prior to that, the data for fixing current directions would have to come from outcrops or from cores where the attitude was known by structural position or by oriented dips.

Calculation of volume of recoverable oil in place in turbidites should be tempered with considerations of the sharp basal and lateral contacts of each turbidite, the change in porosity and permeability within each turbidite corresponding to the grading, and the probable presence of thin impermeable pelagic lutite layers between the individual turbidites.

GROSS GEOMETRY

The geometry of special interest in this volume is the over-all shape of sandstone bodies. Unfortunately, published detailed descriptions of complete turbidites are lacking. However, sufficient observations have been made in the field and on the sea floor to permit reasonable statements as to the expected shapes of complete ancient turbidites—a necessary and significant approach in cases where the ancient ones are oil bearing.

The typical situation on the modern sea floor is for a turbidity current to flow down a submarine canyon, debouch over a fan at the mouth of the canyon, then spread out over a wide front on the basin floor, seeking out the lowest path, avoiding the topographic highs. Variations of this pattern may be caused by levee topping, deflections due to oceanic currents, centrifugal forces at curves, or momentum at slope reversals. The current may deposit all or part of its load at any part of its course, depending on the density, velocity, and load of the current. Several tentative conclusions may be reached from this hypothetical situation.

It is clear that a single turbidite will not have a gradual change-of-facies relationship, laterally, with the enclosing normal pelagic sediments (Fig. 1). It will either fill a low area on the sea floor whose mud surface forms a continuous bed en-closing the bottom and sides of the turbidite, or it will fill a channel eroded into the sea floor by the forward part of the same current or by a previous current. Upward, a turbidite may grade into finer and finer clastics eventually inseparable from subsequent pelagic sediments. These single turbidites may be from less than an inch to many feet in thickness. The writer has seen single sedimentation units up to 10 feet thick in the California Tertiary, and turbidites more than 20 feet thick are reported from 15,000 feet in the Atlantic (Ericson and others, 1951).

As it is the habit of turbidites to follow one another in relatively rapid succession once the proper conditions prevail, outcrop sections com-

FIG. 1.—Bundle of sandstone turbidites (light) overlain by a shale unit (dark). Prominent sandstone in the right center of the shale unit is a single graded bed containing shale flakes. At featheredge it passes between the enclosing shale laminae without any evident erosion; no facies change is present. Individual turbidites in sandstone bundle were either deposited in sufficiently rapid succession to preclude deposition of normal pelagic shales, or any lutites that were deposited were stripped off by intervening turbidity currents. Shale slabs may be seen in sandstone near shovel handle. Shovel (lower right) is $3\frac{1}{2}$ feet long. Horizontal streaks are man made. Modelo formation, upper Miocene, Santa Monica Mountains, Los Angeles, California.

monly show a series or "bundle" of sandstone beds with the intervening normal pelagic strata (shale) very thin, or missing altogether (Fig. 1). Where not well exposed, the bundle of sands would appear gradually to shale out at the edges. This would be particularly true in the subsurface where well spacing would preclude a detailed study of the edges of the deposit. Too often such a boundary is interpreted as a single body of sand with either a sharp buttressing or truncated edge, or a gradational facies change to shale. The accompanying diagram (Fig. 2) shows the stratigraphic relationships in a hypothetical bundle of turbidites, and indicates the sort of correlation problems that might exist in an oil field. Obviously a clear understanding of turbidity-current deposition would greatly facilitate geologic interpretations of the geometry of turbidite bodies; treating them as offshore bars, blanket sands, deltas, or some other more traditional and familiar form would lead to erroneous results.

It is axiomatic that the bottom surface of any sedimentary body must coincide with the surface on which it is deposited. As turbidites fill hollows in the sea floor, their bottoms should ideally be concave upward. This shape will not always be discernable in widespread deposits because of the scale. Concavity may be absent in the case of deposition on an abyssal plain, engulfment of a low eminence on the sea floor, or levee topping.

The areal dimensions and shape in plan view of turbidites are perhaps of greatest interest to the petroleum industry. Unfortunately, it is here that information is weakest. The writer knows of no isopach map of an entire turbidite. Portions of turbidite deposits no doubt are included in the many isopach maps of sandstone stratigraphic traps in the literature, though positive accompanying evidence of their turbidity-current origin is lacking. Our understanding of the mode of deposition of turbidites gives us a basis upon which to postulate several regimes in which they might be deposited and in which characteristic geometry might develop. A tripartite grouping would include *channel* or submarine canyon deposits, *fan* deposits, and *basin-floor* deposits.

Channel deposits would be linear with bottoms concave upward in cross section and truncating the subjacent strata. They would contain the coarsest grains of the three groups; gravel is commonly found in modern canyon bottoms. The gross size of a channel deposit would be relatively limited compared to a basin floor deposit. Directional features within the deposit would indicate current direction parallel to the axis of the channel. A single core may be of great significance in determining the trend of suspected channel deposits by means of lithologic studies and careful observation of syngenetic structures. Slump structures might be associated with channel deposits because of the relatively steep adjacent slopes. During erosion of the channel or canyon its sedimentary fill would be local and temporary, but a change in conditions—such as a rise in sea level—would permit relatively permanent deposition.

In a *submarine fan* individual turbidites might be linear because of deposition in minor channels, or might be blanketlike. The relative volume of the turbidite compared to the microtopography of the fan surface would be important in this respect. Slopes and shapes of fan surfaces might vary widely and thus control the shapes of the sands therein. A radial pattern would be displayed by the current-direction indicators in the deposit as a whole, with the currents radiating from a point source—the mouth of the submarine canyon. Here, too, slumps might develop should the slopes be sufficiently steep. Average grain size would be smaller than in the canyons, but gravels still might exist. The entire deposit would be equidimensional rather than linear, conforming to the topography below and convex upward in cross section, thinning abruptly in the up-current direction and gradually in the down-current direction, perhaps coalescing with other fans, especially laterally. If a fan were relatively isolated rather than being sandwiched between other bundles of turbidites, it would constitute a bulge on the sea floor partly enclosed by much thinner normal pelagic strata, thus potentially forming the core of a compaction fold.

Menard (1960) has supplied us with a pictorial representation of a group of fans off the coast of central California (Fig. 3). Here a group of three submarine canyons heading near shore have huge fans at their mouths in water 9,000–12,000 feet

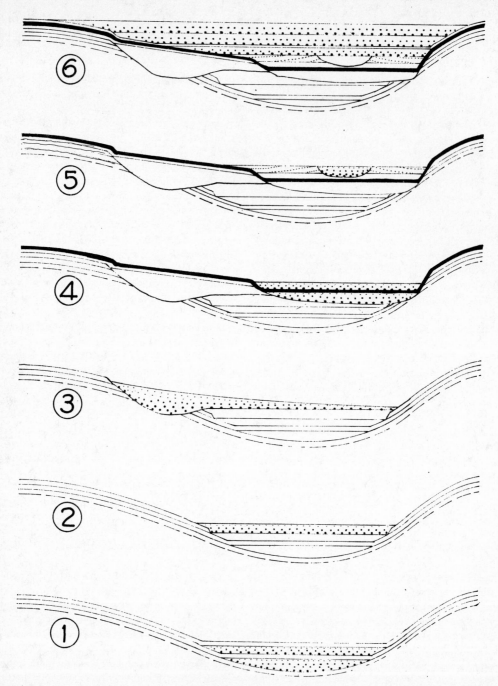

Fig. 2.—Hypothetical sequence in deposition of bundle of turbidites. No scale intended, but vertical is exaggerated probably by between 10 and 1,000. Assume view is in down-current direction and read the diagram from the bottom up. (1) A natural hollow, perhaps produced by tectonics or differential compaction (could also be erosional), receives two turbidites, each followed by a layer of pelagic lutite; no erosion involved. (2) The top pelagic layer is eroded off the floor by a turbidity current, and the third turbidite is deposited on the second. (3) A channel is eroded along the left side of the basin and filled to overflowing by a current under some sort of lateral stress permitting an asymmetric deposit. (4) The sloping surface is covered with pelagic sediment. A new channel is eroded in the new trough created by the sloping deposit. This channel is filled with two turbidites and an intervening pelagic layer (black). (5) A new channel is cut, and conditions are such that natural levees form, permitting the finer material at the top of the currents in the channel to spill over and dump their fine-grained loads (sloping dots) to the side of the main channel. Main channel then fills with a single deposit. (6) Three more graded beds are deposited, the first followed by a pelagic layer and the second followed by the third, without time for a pelagic layer; no erosion involved.

deep. The areal shape and bottom contour of these fans are clearly influenced by the pre-existing topography of the sea floor; for some ridges and fault scarps are buried, and others act as dams. The Monterey fan has a radius of about 200 miles. The two larger fans appear to have engulfed hills 1,000 feet high, and extrapolation of topography beneath the fans suggests a thickness at their apices of more than 4,000 feet.

Basin-floor turbidites differ from the first two types in being blanketlike, thinner, more extensive, and finer grained. Silt is the most common grain size on modern abyssal plains. Current-direction indicators would be more consistent than those on fans, and less consistent than those in channels. Variations in current directions would ensue from superposition of turbidites coming from different sides of the basin and also from meanderings of currents owing to slight tec-

tonic tilts or bulges on the extensive floor. Relatively confined basins might act much like large canyons with the currents flowing down the axis of the trough. The possible huge areal extent of a turbidite on an abyssal plain is suggested by the turbidity current triggered by the Grand Banks earthquake of 1929, which travelled over an area in excess of 80,000 square miles and left a bed of graded silt one meter thick containing shallow-water microfossils.

Gorsline and Emery (1959) have described the turbidites on the sea floor off Los Angeles in the partially filled San Pedro and Santa Monica basins and their associated canyons and fans. Most of the basin-floor sediment is green clayey silt (in the top few feet studied), but contains interbeds of fine sand. Sand becomes coarser, thicker bedded, and more abundant toward the fans. Gravel is present on the fans and in the canyons. The basin

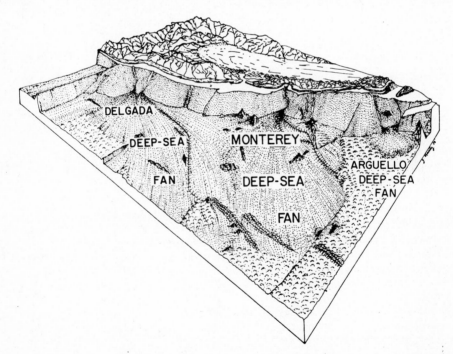

Fig. 3.—Deep-sea fans at mouths of Delgada, Monterey, and Arguello submarine canyons off coast of central California. The scarps from north to south (left to right) reflect the Mendocino, Pioneer, and Murray fracture zones. The Monterey fan has a radius of about 200 miles, and the sea floor lies at maximum depths of 14,000 feet. Sea-floor topography initially influences distribution, and is later engulfed by the vast quantities of sediment carried by turbidity currents. Canyons which do not head near shore and thus cannot trap sediment carried by long-shore currents on the shelf, have very small fans. From Menard, Geol. Soc. America Bull., Vol. 71, No. 8, 1960.

floors lie at a depth of about 3,000 feet and slope less than 0°11'. The areal shape of the entire sequence may be seen on the map (Fig. 4). Insufficient cores have been taken to map individual turbidites, nor is the total thickness known. The sediment is clearly filling a structural trough on the sea floor much like the already filled Los Angeles and Ventura basins on land. The shape of the basins is controlled in part by fault scarps.

EXAMPLES OF TURBIDITE GEOMETRY

The writer has not seen in the literature any isopach maps of entire sandstone bodies identified as turbidites. There is a great need for publication of studies of this sort. In lieu of ideal examples of complete single turbidites, the present paper includes a few incomplete or generalized examples of bundles of turbidites. These will serve the purpose of demonstrating some of the grosser aspects of size and shape of turbidity-current deposits. These illustrations are all from California, where the writer feels a certain amount of familiarity with the geology.

TARZANA FAN

The Tarzana fan (Sullwold, 1960a) is a clear-cut case of turbidity-current deposition. It is of upper Miocene age and is exposed on the north flank of the Santa Monica Mountains, in Southern California. Its thickness ranges from zero to 4,000 feet in a distance of 16 miles, with sandstone comprising about half, and siliceous shale and siltstone the other half. Foraminifera in the shales attest to water depths of about 3,000 feet, and the sands contain abundant syngenetic structures and textures characteristic of turbidites—such as graded bedding, poor sorting, convolute bedding, load deformation, slump structures, shale slabs, cross-bedding, ripple marks, sharp bottoms, gradational tops, charcoal fragments, transported faunas, and lack of indigenous faunas. A northern source is suggested by the radiation of abundant current indicators from a point source to the north; this is supported by the cross sectional lens shape of the deposit in outcrop, and by a tentative identification of its provenance area to the north. Figure 5 is a geologic map of the fan, redrawn to emphasize the shape and distribution of the mappable sandstone bodies or turbidite

bundles. As the rocks here are generally dipping about 20° northward, a down-dip view of the map provides one with a simulated cross section more detailed and accurate than could be constructed by conventional means. One finds it difficult to detect a pattern here which could be applied generally to other subsurface fans. Perhaps the very lack of pattern and the random distribution of sand offer hope that hitherto unsuspected sands in similar environments, elsewhere, may suddenly appear in the section at a favorable structural position.

STEVENS SAND, SAN JOAQUIN VALLEY

The Stevens sand, of late Miocene age, underlies an area 30 by 50 miles in the southern San Joaquin Valley, California, where it is a very important producer of oil in more than 20 oil fields. Its maximum thickness is more than 3,000 feet, of which two-thirds is sand. It is a series of turbidites alternating with normal marine organic shales whose fauna indicates a water depth of approximately 1,000 feet.[3] The deep-water Stevens grades eastward to shallow-water Santa Margarita sand (mostly non-turbid), and the latter to the nonmarine Chanac formation. Sand dominates in the central portion of the Stevens, but shale gradually increases to the north, west, and south until the sand disappears altogether. The sand is described as poorly sorted, silty to coarse to pebbly, locally containing siltstone pebbles, arkosic, subangular, unfossiliferous, lenticular, with silty to clayey matrix, and with rapid changes in permeability both vertically and horizontally.

Figure 6 is an isopach map of net sand in the combined Stevens-Santa Margarita facies, and the cross section (Fig. 7) further clarifies an understanding of its distribution and geometry. The writer is indebted to Ted L. Bear, consulting geologist, and Rollin Eckis, Richfield Oil Corporation, for access to unpublished manuscripts on the Stevens sand. Natland (1957, Pl. 6) has implied a turbidity current origin, and Eckis (unpublished manuscript) concluded as early as 1940 that deposition must have been by currents moving along the ocean floor (but without using the

---

[3] Water depth supplied by Manley L. Natland, Richfield Oil Corporation, Los Angeles.

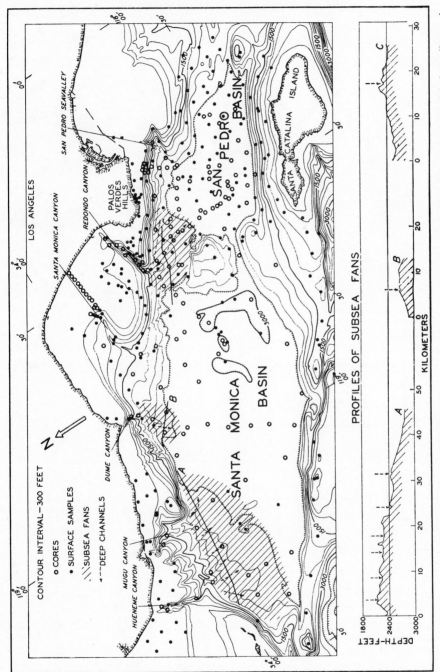

Fig. 4.—San Pedro and Santa Monica basins off coast of southern California. Basin floors are very flat and are underlain by sediment deposited in part by turbidity currents. The fans are reflected in topographic expression and in their coarser and thicker sands. Mineralogy of sands is very similar to sands being carried along shore on the shelf. From Gorsline and Emery, Geol. Soc. America Bull., Vol. 70, No. 3, 1959.

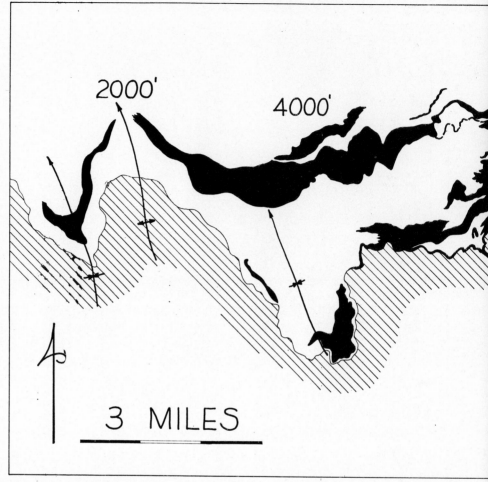

F<small>IG</small>. 5.—Simplified geologic map of Tarzana fan, bathyal upper Miocene, Los Angeles County, California. Mappable sandstone bodies (bundles of turbidites) are indicated in solid black. Older subjacent rocks are diagonally lined. Much of white area between sandstone beds is also sandstone, but finely laminated and inter-bedded with shale. Figures at top indicate total measured thickness of fan sediment at various places. Rocks are generally dipping about 20° north, so down-dip view simulates a cross section, providing some insight as to shape and size of turbidite bundles. Some minor irregularities are caused by topography, and some by folding, and one important fault interrupts the continuity, probably repeating the eastern portion of the fan. Base of diatomite marks approximate top of fan to east; top to west is less distinct. Adapted from Sullwold, 1960a.

magic words, turbidity current). The writer's only first-hand knowledge of the formation is an inspection of a single core that contained many typical syngenetic structures. No published work has been devoted to the Stevens sand as a turbidite, taking full advantage of the hitherto unused clues awaiting the worker who is willing to go a step farther than routine subsurface work. The evi-

dence is sufficiently strong to assume that the Stevens sand is a bundle of turbidites, and its gross geometry is here presented as an example.

LOWER PLIOCENE, LOS ANGELES BASIN

Few areas in the world have produced so much oil from so small an area as the Los Angeles basin. Cumulative production is 4.9 billion bar-

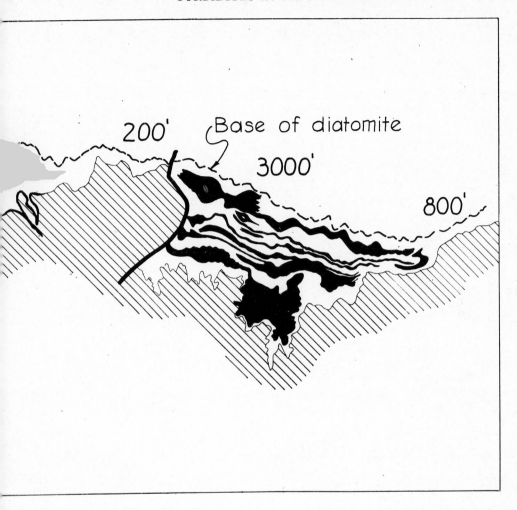

rels of oil from about 63 square miles of productive area, and nearly all of this oil comes from upper Miocene and lower Pliocene turbidites. About 20,000 feet of strata accumulated in this basin from middle Miocene to Recent time in a more or less continuous cycle of clastic sedimentation. Its general geology has been described by Wissler (1943), Driver (1948), and Barbat (1958), and countless papers have been written describing individual oil fields. Still, there are no published data on the detailed geometry of the turbidites.

More than half the oil produced from this area has come from the lower Pliocene Repetto "formation." This part of the section has recently been studied by Slosson (1958) and Conrey (1959) but the complete work has not yet been published. Repetto strata range from zero to 5,000 feet in thickness, and approximately half is sandstone. These sandstones were deposited in water depths of 6,000–8,000 feet, and are arkosic, silty to conglomeratic, laminated to massive, with graded bedding, sharp basal contacts, and local imbrication. It is generally agreed by all recent students of these deposits that the sandstones are turbidites. The gross geometry of the lower Pliocene Repetto sandstones is shown on the isopach map (Fig. 8) taken from Conrey. This map clearly shows a northeast source with a spread and

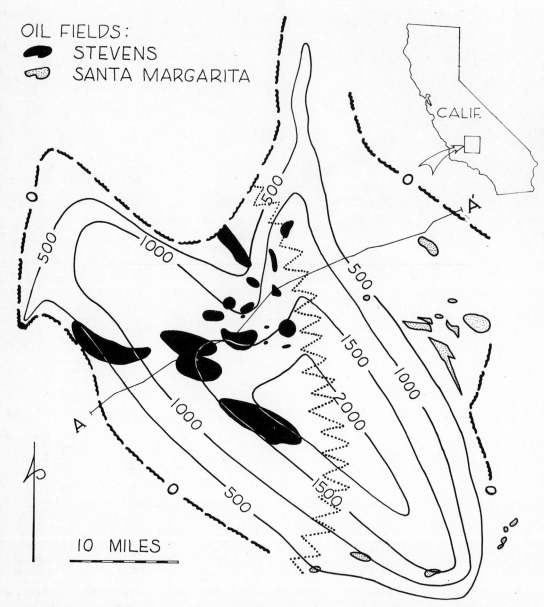

FIG. 6.—Net-sand isopachs, Stevens-Santa Margarita sand facies of the upper Miocene, San Joaquin Valley, California. Portion west of dotted line is the Stevens sand, a deep water turbidite facies; portion to east is shallow-water Santa Margarita sand. Nature of the facies change between the Stevens and Santa Margarita is not yet documented. See cross section *A-A'* (Fig. 7) for further elucidation. Adapted from unpublished reports of Rollin Eckis and Ted L. Bear.

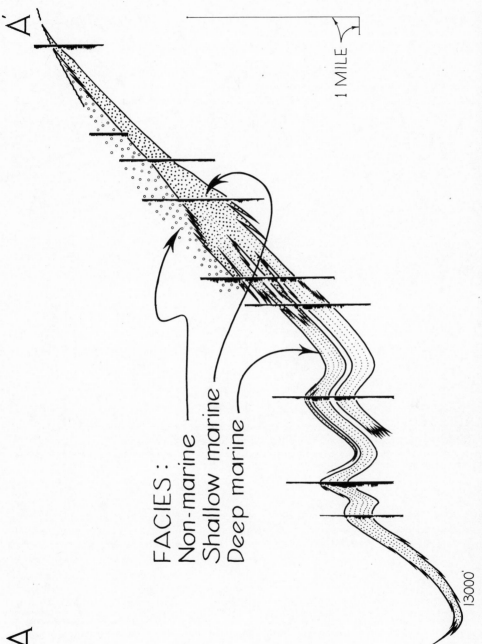

A   A'

1 MILE

FACIES:
Non-marine
Shallow marine
Deep marine

13000'

FIG. 7.—Section *A-A'*, Stevens and Santa Margarita sands, upper Miocene, San Joaquin Valley, California. The Stevens sand is the deep-water facies (fine parallel rows of dots), the Santa Margarita, the shallow-water facies (coarse dots), and the Chanac formation, the nonmarine facies (open circles). Self-potential curves indicate the sands by excursions to the left on the electric logs. Adapted from a cross section in an unpublished manuscript of Ted L. Bear. Trace is line *A-A'*, Fig. 6.

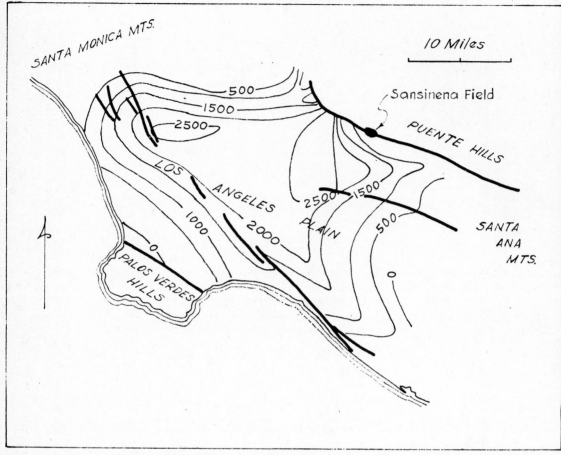

FIG. 8.—Isopach map of net sand in the Lower Pliocene Repetto "formation" in the Los Angeles basin, California. These sands are turbidites deposited in water 6,000–8,000 feet deep. Heavy lines are faults. From Conrey, 1959. Location of Sansinena oil field is shown as orientation for Fig. 9.

diminishing thickness away from that point. It is unfortunate that no detailed maps of individual turbidites or local bundles of turbidites are available.

EAST SANSINENA

The upper Miocene A-10 sand in the East Sansinena field is a more detailed example of a turbidite in the Los Angeles basin. The field has been described by A. F. Woodward (1958), and he and R. Miller kindly permitted the writer to study the Union Oil Company cross sections and to construct therefrom the accompanying isopach

map (Fig. 9). In an effort to achieve detail, only the upper part of the A-10 sand is included. Inasmuch as the wells are directionally drilled from three drilling "islands," corrections for true thickness had to be made for the attitude of the boreholes as well as for the strata. The map is still a distortion, for although true thicknesses are shown, the plan view was not stretched out to undo the post-depositional structure, which is considerable. The field is small, 1 mile by ½ mile, yet its structural relief is more than 2,000 feet.

The isopach map clearly delineates a channel or portion of a small basin. Its apparent trend agrees reasonably well with a northerly source area, generally considered valid for this part of the Los Angeles basin. The southern extension is unknown, for the sand plunges beyond the down-dip edge of the field into a deep syncline where well control is lacking. The sand was cored in five wells, but the core descriptions are not sufficiently detailed to provide proof of turbidite origin, nor have the cores been saved for further inspection. Descriptions show variations from sandy silt-stone to conglomerate, thinly laminated to massive, arkosic, gritty, poorly sorted—adequately fitting the qualifications for a turbidite. Furthermore, ecologic data (supplied by Manley Natland) indicate a depositional water depth here of 1,000–2,000 feet, and the depth increases southwestward in the general direction in which the isopachs also suggest deepening.

IMPORTANCE OF TURBIDITE STUDIES

The many billions of barrels of oil already found in turbidites testify to the importance of these rocks to the oil industry. Perhaps the significance of turbidites as oil reservoirs lies not in a superiority of reservoir characteristics, but in their environment of deposition. They are typically dumped into low places on the sea floor—areas low in oxygen—and are surrounded by muds rich in pelagic organic remains. The turbidity currents themselves may also enrich the organic content of the sea floor by introducing vast quantities of plant material. Thus, the reservoir is inserted directly into ideal source sediment, and the distance of primary migration of oil is greatly reduced.

Clearly, a full understanding of the genesis, lithology, and geometry of turbidites will greatly facilitate both oil development and oil exploration in relatively unstable parts of the earth's crust. The textural relationships within the sandstones should be taken into account in calculating reserves and reservoir mechanics. The geometry of the individual turbidites and bundles of turbidites constituting petroleum reservoirs is important for the same reasons. Oriented syngenetic structures serve to indicate direction of transport, and this, in turn, greatly enhances the understanding of paleogeography—an esteemed tool in oil exploration. For example, identification of a submarine fan in the subsurface would be an excel-

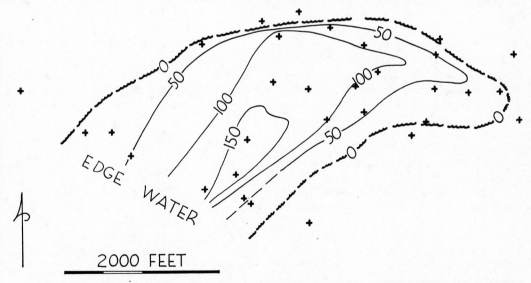

FIG. 9.—Isopach map of the upper part of the upper Miocene A-10 sand, principal producing zone in the East Sansinena field, Los Angeles County, California. Crosses indicate location of control points where slant-drilled wells penetrate sand. It appears that the turbidites were deposited in a southwest-sloping channel in water 1,000–2,000 feet deep. The geometry of this sandstone body makes its own trap. Constructed by the writer from data provided by A. F. Woodward and R. Miller, Union Oil Company of California. True sandstone thickness in feet. Location of East Sansinena field shown in Fig. 8.

lent guide toward finding the associated channel or canyon with its coarse-grained fill—an ideal reservoir. Furthermore, current indicators in the cores of an exploratory well may suggest the trend of a channel-type sand and reduce the risk on a follow-up well. These indicators may be used to orient cores and thus their contained dips. The mere routine correlations of electric logs, and construction of cross sections can be done with much more realism when the worker has a feeling for the genesis and geometry of the sands under study. And, too, a widespread turbidite constitutes a time marker fully as significant as an ash bed.

At the present time there appears to be more potential than actual use in the application of a knowledge of turbidites, for a large amount of observational data must be gathered before firm conclusions can be reached. The science is yet young. Even in California, where turbidites abound, there is a surprising lack of recognition of the utility of this new tool; its study is generally relegated to a few research workers.

Adequate coring is necessary fully to utilize the information locked up in subsurface turbidites, for it is visual inspection of the sandstones that provides the significant data. Various wireline devices are a poor substitute for geologic observation. Detailed outcrop studies are also of first-priority importance. Turbidite features have been completely overlooked in conventional geologic mapping, with a few recent exceptions. Old oil fields and cores should be reworked in the light of this new concept; perhaps unsuspected current trends will appear that will point to extensions and new pools. All of this will, of course, require more geologic labor, but the labor is largely geologic observation and footwork, and thus relatively inexpensive.

It is becoming increasingly obvious that turbidites are very common on the sea floor and in the geologic record—a fact little known and rarely taught when most of us were being educated. Surely the volume of turbidites in the modern sea must equal or exceed the volume of nearshore shallow-water sands. Although these volumes are not yet measurable, nor could they be projected quantitatively into the past, they certainly justify acceptance of ancient turbidites on a large scale, perhaps in a pre-eminent volumetric position.

REFERENCES

Barbat, W. F., 1958, The Los Angeles basin area, California, *in* Habitat of Oil, Am. Assoc. Petroleum Geologists, p. 62–77; also *in* A guide to the geology and oil fields of the Los Angeles and Ventura regions, Pacific Section, Am. Assoc. Petroleum Geologists, p. 37–49.

Bates, C. C., 1953, Rational theory of delta formation: Am. Assoc. Petroleum Geologists Bull., v. 37, no. 9, p. 2119–2162.

Birkenmajer, K., 1959, Classification of bedding in flysch and similar graded deposits: Studia Geologica Polonica, v. 3, 128 p.

Conrey, B. L., 1959, Sedimentary history of the early Pliocene in the Los Angeles basin, California: unpub. Ph.D. dissertation, Univ. Southern Calif., 273 p. Brief résumé published *in* A guide to the geology and oil fields of the Los Angeles and Ventura regions: Pacific Section, Am. Assoc. Petroleum Geologists, p. 51–54, 1958.

Crowell, J. C., 1955, Directional-current structures from the Prealpine Flysch, Switzerland: Geol. Soc. America Bull., v. 66, no. 11, p. 1351–1384.

Driver, H. L., 1948, Genesis and evolution of Los Angeles basin, California: Am. Assoc. Petroleum Geologists, v. 32, no. 1, p. 109–125.

Dzulynski, S., and Radomski, A., 1955, Origin of groove-casts in the light of turbidity current hypothesis: Acta Geologica Polonica, v. 5, p. 47–66.

Ericson, D. B., Ewing, M., and Heezen, B. C., 1951, Deep-sea sands and submarine canyons: Geol. Soc. America Bull., v. 62, no. 8, p. 961–966.

———— and ————, 1952, Turbidity currents and sediments in the North Atlantic: Am. Assoc. Petroleum Geologists, v. 36, no. 3, p. 489–511.

Gorsline, D. S., and Emery, K. O., 1959, Turbidity-current deposits in San Pedro and Santa Monica basins off southern California: Geol. Soc. America Bull., v. 70, no. 3, p. 279–290.

Hall, James, 1843, Geology of New York; Part IV, Comprising the survey of the fourth geological district: Albany.

Heezen, B. C., 1956, Corrientes de turbidez del Rio Magdalena: Bol. Soc. Geog. Colombia, v. 51, 52, p. 135–143.

———— 1959, Dynamic processes of abyssal sedimentation—erosion, transportation, and redeposition on the deep-sea floor: Geophys. Jour., Royal Geog. Soc., v. 2, p. 142–163.

———— Tharp, M., and Ewing, M., 1959, The floors of the oceans; Part 1, The North Atlantic: Geol. Soc. America Spec. Paper 65, 122 p.

Hull, J. P. D., Jr., 1957, Petrogenesis of Permian Delaware Mountain sandstone, Texas and New Mexico: Am. Assoc. Petroleum Geologists Bull., v. 41, no. 2, p. 278–307.

Kuenen, Ph. H., 1953, Significant features of graded bedding: Am. Assoc. Petroleum Geologists, v. 37, no. 5, p. 1044–1066.

———— and Carozzi, A., 1953, Turbidity currents and sliding in geosynclinal basins in the Alps: Jour. Geology, v. 61, p. 363–373.

———— and Migliorini, C. I., 1950, Turbidity currents as a cause of graded bedding: Jour. Geology, v. 58, no. 2, p. 91–126.

Lowman, S. W., 1949, Sedimentary facies in Gulf Coast:

Am. Assoc. Petroleum Geologists Bull., v. 33, no. 12, p. 1939–1997.

McBride, E. F., 1950, Martinsburg-Reedsville paleocurrents (abstract): 45th Ann. Mtg. Am. Assoc. Petroleum Geologists and Soc. Econ. Paleontologists and Mineralogists, Atlantic City, program: p. 90–91.

McIver, N. L., 1960, Upper Devonian paleocurrents in the central Appalachian Mountains (abstract): Geol. Soc. America Bull., v. 71, no. 12, p. 1926.

Menard, H. W., 1960, Possible pre-Pleistocene deep-sea fans off central California: Geol. Soc. America Bull., v. 71, no. 8, p. 1271–1278.

Natland, M. L., 1957, Paleocology of west coast Tertiary sediments, *in* Treatise on marine ecology and paleocology, v. 2, edited by H. S. Ladd: Geol. Soc. America Mem. 67, Chap. 19, p. 543–572.

Payne, T. G., 1942, Stratigraphical analysis and environmental reconstruction: Am. Assoc. Petroleum Geologists Bull., v. 26, no. 11, p. 1697–1770.

Phleger, F. B, 1951, Displaced Foraminifera faunas, *in* Turbidity currents and the transportation of coarse sediments to deep water—a symposium: Soc. Econ. Paleontologists and Mineralogists Special Pub. 21, p. 66–75.

Riveroll, D. D., and Jones, B. C., 1954, Varves and Foraminifera of the upper Puente formation (upper Miocene), Puente, California: Jour. Paleontology, v. 28, no. 2, p. 121–131.

Slosson, J. E., 1958, Lithofacies and sedimentary-paleogeographic analysis of the Los Angeles Repetto basin: unpub. Ph.D. dissertation, Univ. Southern Calif., 128 p.

Sullwold, H. H., Jr., 1959, Nomenclature of load deformation in turbidites: Geol. Soc. America Bull., v. 70, no. 9, p. 1247–1248.

———— 1960a, Tarzana fan, deep submarine fan of late Miocene age, Los Angeles County, California: Am. Assoc. Petroleum Geologists Bull., v. 44, no. 4, p. 433–457.

———— 1960b, Load-cast terminology and origin of convolute bedding; further comments: Geol. Soc. America Bull., v. 71, no. 5, p. 635–636.

Van Houten, F. B., 1954, Sedimentary features of Martinsburg slate, northwestern New Jersey: Geol. Soc. America Bull., v. 65, no. 8, p. 813–817.

Wissler, S. G., 1943, Stratigraphic relations of the producing zones of the Los Angeles basin oil fields: Calif. Div. Mines Bull. 118, p. 209–234.

Woodward, A..F., 1958, Sansinena oil field, *in* A guide to the geology and oil fields of the Los Angeles and Ventura regions: Pacific Section, Am. Assoc. Petroleum Geologists, p. 109–118.

SPATIAL DIMENSIONS OF UPPER CRETACEOUS SANDSTONES, ROCKY MOUNTAIN AREA[1]

ROBERT J. WEIMER[2]

Golden, Colorado

ABSTRACT

The Cretaceous of the Rocky Mountain region contains sandstones that were deposited in marine, transitional, and nonmarine environments. Spatial dimensions of sandstones deposited in shallow neritic and transitional environments are regular in character and are easily defined. Only this type of sandstone is here considered, and examples illustrating minimum and maximum geographic distribution are treated.

Minimum size sand bodies are well shown by the Fox Hills sandstone where it is exposed on the northeast flank of the Rock Springs uplift, Wyoming. This formation consists of a series of barrier bar sandstones that change northwestward to lagoonal shales (Lance formation), and southeastward to marine shale (Lewis shale). Detailed surface analysis of one barrier bar shows a thickness of 30 feet and a width of 6–7 miles from the lagoonal shale and sandstone facies to the marine shale and siltstone facies. Each bar is believed to have extended along much of the western margin of the Cretaceous seaway.

The upper part of the Judith River formation of central and eastern Montana exemplifies a transitional and marine sandstone unit having a maximum width. The unit is 140 miles wide and was deposited between lagoonal shale facies to the west and marine shale facies (Pierre shale) to the east. Thickness of the unit ranges from a wedge edge to 100 feet.

The geometric pattern of most of the sand bodies that accumulated along the Cretaceous shoreline is similar in character to the above examples and ranges in size between these extremes.

INTRODUCTION

An understanding of the spatial dimensions of Cretaceous sandstones is becoming increasingly important to petroleum exploration programs in the Rocky Mountains. More and more emphasis is being placed on the search for stratigraphic traps in which accumulation is related to facies change from sandstone to shale. In the last 10 years more than 20 trillion cubic feet of gas reserves have been proved in marine and transitional sandstones that were deposited along the

[1] Read before the Association at Atlantic City, New Jersey, April 28, 1960. Manuscript received, June 1, 1960.

[2] Associate Professor of Geology, Colorado School of Mines. The Colorado School of Mines Foundation, Inc., gave financial aid to defray field expenses and expenses in the final preparation of material for this paper. The close similarity of Cretaceous depositional environments to present depositional environments along the Gulf and Atlantic Coasts was pointed out to the writer by Chester Cassel during discussions in 1954. Mr. Cassel, in unpublished work, determined the close relationship between present shoreline environments and the Cretaceous environments of the San Juan basin. By use of these environmental studies he was able to demonstrate stratigraphic control for the large gas accumulations in that area. His ideas also apply to the areas described herein. To J. D. Haun, Chester Cassel, and Fred E. Moore, the writer extends his gratitude for reviewing the manuscript.

shore of the Cretaceous sea. Although these sandstones may appear to be lenticular (in cross section), in most instances it is possible to determine a depositional pattern that is important in interpreting sandstone trends and predicting areas for future exploration.

During the Cretaceous, sandstones were deposited in nonmarine, transitional, and marine environments in the Rocky Mountain area. Because of their economic importance, this paper is confined to a discussion of the transitional and adjacent marine sandstones which embrace the barrier island, littoral, and shallow neritic environments. These sandstones occur throughout the 10,000–20,000 feet of Cretaceous strata in the Rocky Mountain area. Their distribution and relationship to sediments of other environments have been described in a previous paper (Weimer, 1960).

To explain the geographic distribution of these sandstones, two examples have been selected for discussion—the Fox Hills of Wyoming and the Judith River of Montana. The Fox Hills sandstone of Wyoming is a lithogenetic unit containing many individual sandstone bodies that were deposited as the Cretaceous sea regressed from the Rocky Mountain area. One individual sandstone unit in the Fox Hills exposures on the Rock Springs uplift exemplifies a sandstone having a minimum geographic distribution. The upper part of the Judith River formation of Montana illustrates a sandstone having a maximum geographic distribution. These units were selected because they are easily defined and described, and because they are believed to show characteristics typical of all other Cretaceous marine and transitional sandstones which range in geographic dimensions between these extremes. These formations are not widely known for petroleum production, but both have produced gas and must be regarded as potential petroleum reservoirs over wide areas in Montana and Wyoming.

Properly to define the geographic limits of these examples, it was necessary to establish a time-stratigraphic unit embracing a rock sequence of 100 feet or less. The facies changes within these units, which control the distribution of the sandstones, can be related to environments of deposition, both by fossils and by lithology.

SANDSTONE BODY WITH MINIMUM GEOGRAPHIC DISTRIBUTION

Cretaceous strata exposed on the flanks of the Rock Springs uplift show complex intertonguing of marine and nonmarine sediments. From studies of the lower portion of exposed Cretaceous strata, Hale (1950, 1955) described the intertonguing of nonmarine coal-bearing Mesaverde group with underlying marine Baxter (Mancos) shale and overlying marine Lewis shale. Where they were studied by the writer on the northeast flank of the uplift (Fig. 1), the Lewis, Fox Hills, and Lance formations show similar intertonguing conditions. These formations are the youngest Cretaceous (late Campanian and Maestrichtian) in the area

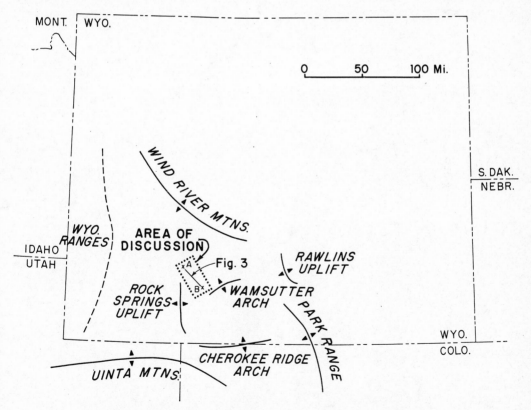

FIG. 1.—Index map showing major structural features of southwest Wyoming, area of discussion, and position (A–B) of restored section (Fig. 3).

and are unconformably overlain by the Tertiary Fort Union formation. Thicknesses and lithologies of these formations, where exposed in T. 21 N., R. 101 W., are shown in Figure 2. The Lewis is gray marine shale overlain by transitional and marine gray, buff, and tan fine-grained sandstone assigned to the Fox Hills. The nonmarine Lance formation consists of gray and tan shale, carbonaceous shale, coal, and tan fine-grained lenticular sandstone. The lithology of each formation reflects the environment in which the sediment was deposited. Environments shifted slowly in time as the shoreline of the Cretaceous sea regressed from west to east across the area.

Figure 3 is a northwest-southeast restored section, along approximately 20 miles of outcrop, showing the stratigraphic relationships of the upper portion of the Mesaverde group (Almond and Ericson), Lewis shale, Fox Hills sandstone, and Lance formation.

The marine Lewis shale was deposited during a widespread transgression of the sea. Marine transgressive sandstones occur at the base of this shale unit and marine regressive sandstones at the top. At point B, where U. S. Highway 30 crosses the east flank of the Rock Springs uplift, the Lewis shale is approximately 850 feet thick. To the northwest the lower part of the Lewis interfingers with the Almond formation and the upper part interfingers with the Fox Hills sandstone, which, in turn, interfingers with the Lance formation. As a result of these facies changes and an unconformity at the base of the Tertiary, the Lewis shale is 300 feet thick near the north end of the uplift.

The Fox Hills sandstone is a lithogenetic unit consisting of a series of individual sand bodies. Because of the facies changes described above, the Fox Hills becomes successively younger to the southeast and east. Surface sections of the Fox Hills sandstone were measured at the intervals indicated on Figure 4 along a low escarpment on

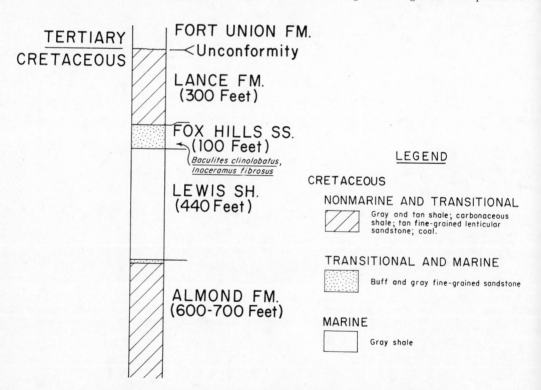

Fig. 2.—Uppermost Cretaceous section exposed near center of T. 21 N., R. 101 W., northeast flank of Rock Springs uplift.

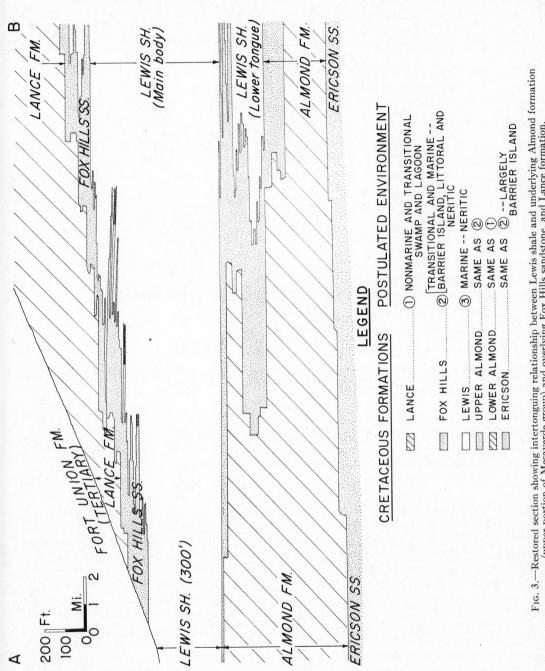

Fig. 3.—Restored section showing intertonguing relationship between Lewis shale and underlying Almond formation (upper portion of Mesaverde group) and overlying Fox Hills sandstone, and Lance formation.

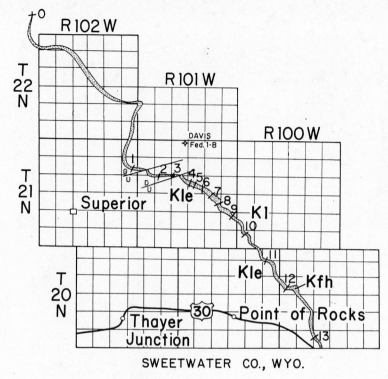

Fig. 4.—Index to outcrop area of Fox Hills sandstone, and position of measured sections on northeast flank of Rock Springs uplift, indicated by numbers 1–13, which correspond with numbers on Fig. 5. Kle=Lewis shale; Kfh=Fox Hills sandstone; Kl=Lance formation.

the northeast flank of the Rock Springs uplift. Cliff exposures permit individual sandstone beds to be traced nearly continuously between the measured sections.

Figure 5 is a restored diagram showing facies changes that occur within one sandstone unit—designated "G" sandstone—of the Fox Hills. The base of "G" sandstone is transitional with the underlying marine shale—a tongue of the Lewis shale; the top of "G" sandstone is sharply defined in relation to the overlying marine shale—another tongue of the Lewis, which is 10–15 feet thick. The base of this shale is used as a marker bed, and is the datum for the section in Figure 5. The "G" sandstone is divisible into upper and lower units. The contact between the upper and lower units between Sections 4 and 8 is sharp and defined by an irregular surface indicated by the dashed line. The lower "G" is finer grained than

the upper "G" along this portion of the outcrop. This irregular, sharp contact may be interpreted in different ways, but the writer believes that it is related to the shifting of the littoral zone and associated environments during regression of the shoreline. At Section 6 the upper 30-foot "G" sandstone is buff, fine grained, well sorted, and porous and permeable. Although sedimentary structures were not studied in detail, between Sections 5 and 6 the sandstone is highly cross-bedded with individual laminae dipping generally to the southeast at 5°–15°. Elsewhere along the outcrop the "G" sandstone appears to be evenly bedded or lacks bedding. To the northwest of Section 6 this sandstone can be traced for 2 miles before terminating by facies change to nonmarine shale and sandstone of the Lance formation. To the southeast the sandstone becomes increasingly silty and changes to marine shale (Lewis) in a

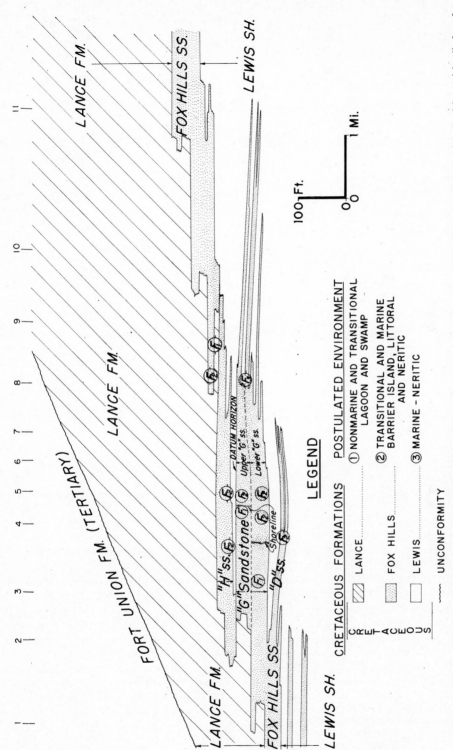

Fig. 5.—Restored section showing relationship of Fox Hills sandstone to underlying Lewis shale and overlying Lance formation. Positions of fossils found in "G" sandstone of Fox Hills are indicated. F_1 = *Ostrea glabra*; F_2 = *Halymenites major*; F_3 = *Baculites clinolobatus* and associated forms. Numbers 1–11 indicate position of measured sections, shown in Fig. 4.

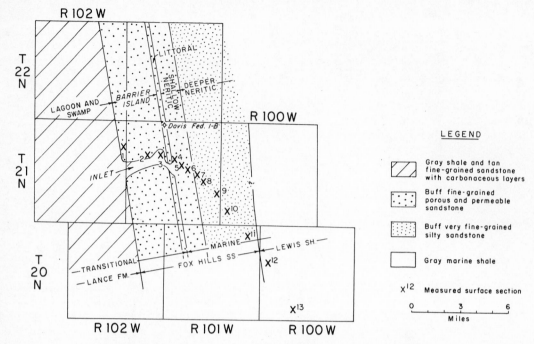

FIG. 6.—Interpretation of environments present during deposition of lower
"G" sandstone. X1, X2, *etc.*, indicate position of measured sections.

distance of 5 miles. Thus, the total observed width of the upper "G" sandstone along the outcrop is approximately 7 miles.

Faunal collections[3] were made from the "G" sandstone and associated beds. At Section 4, the brackish-water oyster *Ostrea glabra* was found throughout the upper "G" sandstone. A few hundred feet to the east the marine fossil *Halymenites major* occurs in the upper portion of the sandstone. A 15-foot bed composed largely of *Ostrea glabra* was found near the base of the lower "G" sandstone at Section 3. At Section 4, *Halymenites major* was found throughout the sandstone. Two miles to the southeast, at Section 8, a marine fauna was collected from a silty sandstone, believed to be correlative with the lower "G" unit, that included the following forms—*Baculites clinolobatus, Inoceramus fibrosus, Discoscaphites* sp., *Pholadomya* sp., *Modiolus* sp.,

[3] The writer is grateful to W. A. Cobban of the U. S. Geological Survey, Denver, Colorado, for identifying fossils collected from the Fox Hills sandstone on the Rock Springs uplift, Wyoming.

Legumen cf. *ellipticum, Nucula* sp., *Halymenites major*, and unidentified specimens of pelecypods. The lower "G" sandstone is silty and contains thin beds of marine shale at this locality.

These fossil data and the lithologies indicate a very close similarity between the environments of deposition present in this area during deposition of the "G" sandstone, and the distribution of sediments and environments along the Gulf Coast today, as described by Shepard and Moore (1955). The oysters (*Ostrea glabra*) at Section 3 appear to have lived in an inlet that cut through a barrier island. Sandstone deposited on this island is terminated by swamp and lagoonal shales near Section 1 (Fig. 6). The generally well-sorted character of the sandstone found at Section 4, containing abundant *Halymenites major*, suggests that this fossil lived in a wave-agitated, neritic environment. The fauna at Section 8 is unquestionably marine and suggests water depths in which wave action was not severe. Numerous specimens of the thin-shelled pelecypod *Legumen* cf. *ellipticum*, with both valves in an open position, were found in the F_3 faunal collection. The silt-stone and shale beds in the sandstone also indicate a quiet, deeper neritic environment.

The north-northwest trend of the environments shown on Figure 6 was established by regional surface and subsurface studies. The line of outcrop examined in this study appears to be oblique to the stratigraphic strike. The units of the Fox Hills sandstone described from the surface exposures are related to the electric log of the Davis

Federal 1-B well in Figure 7. Photographs of the Fox Hills sandstone with the designated subdivisions are shown as Figure 8.

Although the width of "G" sandstone can be determined locally, regional studies of the Fox Hills sandstone in Wyoming and northwest Colorado are necessary to determine its probable length. Regional correlation and distribution of the Fox Hills sandstone and associated formations in eastern, central, and southern Wyoming were

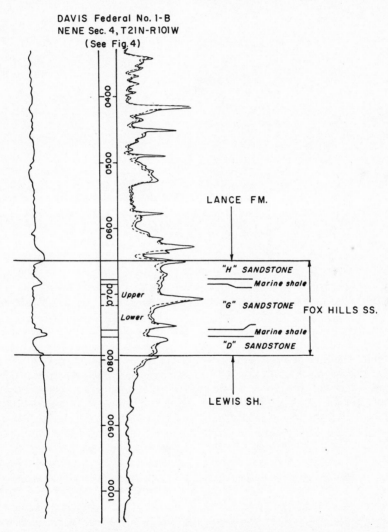

FIG. 7.—Electric log of Davis Federal 1-B well, showing relationship of surface-designated units of Fox Hills sandstone, to subsurface.

FIG. 8.—Outcrops of formations studied on northeast flank of Rock Springs uplift. Compare with Fig. 5. *A*—Units of Fox Hills sandstone at Section 3. *Ostrea glabra* is found in lower "G" sandstone at this locality. *B*—Looking southeast from Section 4. *C*—*Ostrea glabra* in upper "G" sandstone at Section 4. *D*—At Section 5, looking northeast toward Section 4.

described first by Dobbin and Reeside (1930, p. 18). The Fox Hills sandstone varies considerably in age and, therefore, to reconstruct the paleogeography during the Late Cretaceous, it is necessary to use a vertically restricted time-stratigraphic unit. The zone of *Baculites clinolobatus* is thought to be represented by only a few hundred feet of sediments, and this cephalopod has been reported at numerous localities (Cobban, 1958). Using faunal studies by Cobban (1958) and recent stratigraphic studies by Robinson and others (1959, p. 103), Rich (1958, p. 2430), and Weimer (1960, p. 12), sufficient data are available to reconstruct the paleogeography during mid-Maestrichtian.

Besides the occurrence described above in the "G" sandstone (X_1, Fig. 9), *Baculites clinolobatus* has been reported by Cobban (1958, p. 114) from the upper part of the Fox Hills sandstone at

Glenrock, Wyoming (X_2, Fig. 9), the lower part of the Fox Hills west of Newcastle, Wyoming (X_3, Fig. 9), and the upper Pierre shale near Redbird, 35 miles south of Newcastle, Wyoming (X_4, Fig. 9). From studies of the outcrop area along the east flank of the Powder River basin, Robinson and others (1959, p. 103) show the Fox Hills sandstone to become successively younger to the south because of facies change. This same relationship has been observed by the writer in wells along the southwest flank of the Powder River basin between Glenrock and Salt Creek, and on the surface along the east flank of the Red Desert basin between Rawlins and Lost Soldier. Rich (1958, p. 2438) reported *Baculites* cf. *B. clinolobatus* from the upper marine tongue of the Lewis shale in the southeast portion of the Wind River basin, Wyoming (X_6, Fig 9). A few miles west of this locality (Secs. 10 and 15, T. 31 N., R.

92 W.), the marine sandstone and shale change to nonmarine swamp and lagoon sediments. *Inoceramus fibrosus*, a form frequently associated with *Baculites clinolobatus* (Cobban, 1958, p. 114), was reported by Hale (1955, p. 94) from the upper part of the Lewis shale near Rawlins (X_7, Fig. 9). Katich (1959, p. 28) reported an occurrence of *Baculites clinolobatus* from the Lewis shale, 2 miles northeast of Hayden, Colorado (X_5, Fig. 9). West and southwest of this locality, the Lewis shale changes to marine sandstone (Fox Hills) and to the nonmarine Lance formation (Weimer, 1959, p. 13).

Because the exact thickness of the *Baculites*

clinolobatus zone is imperfectly known on a regional basis, the interpretation of paleogeographic and facies trends shown on Figure 9 must be regarded as approximate. Available data appear to be sufficiently accurate, however, to preclude any large deviation from the pattern shown. The data suggest that the width of individual sand units within the Fox Hills becomes greater to the northeast along the shoreline. For convenience, the marine and transitional sandstones are considered as one unit on Figure 9.

Important conclusions from the study may be summarized as follows.

1. The "G" sandstone of the Fox Hills was

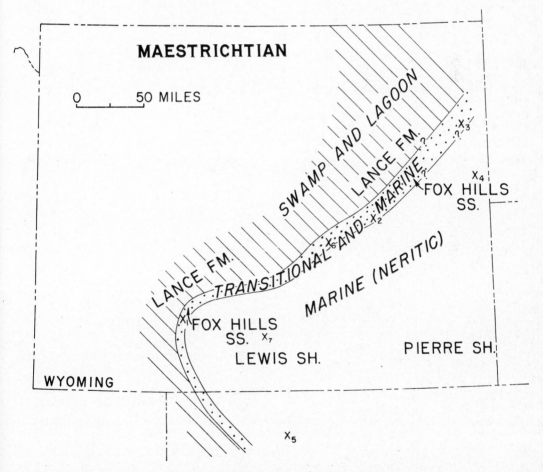

Fig. 9.—Paleogeographic and sediment-distribution map of Wyoming during deposition of upper portions of *Baculites clinolobatus* zone (Maestrichtian). Localities of *Baculites clinolobatus* and associated forms are indicated by X_1, *etc.*

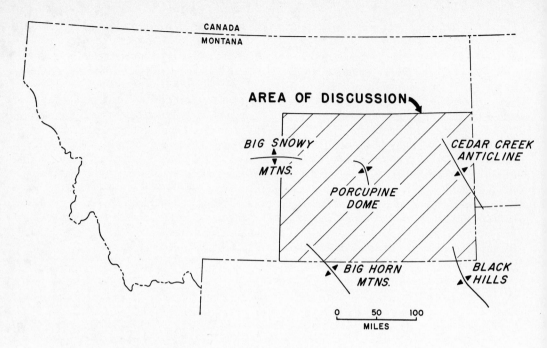

FIG. 10.—Index map of Montana showing area in which Judith River formation was studied.

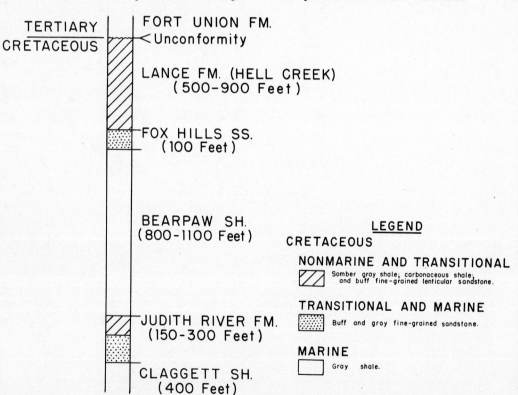

FIG. 11.—Partial stratigraphic section of Cretaceous strata in central and eastern Montana. Upper 100 feet of Judith River formation is nonmarine in central Montana (as shown), and marine in eastern Montana.

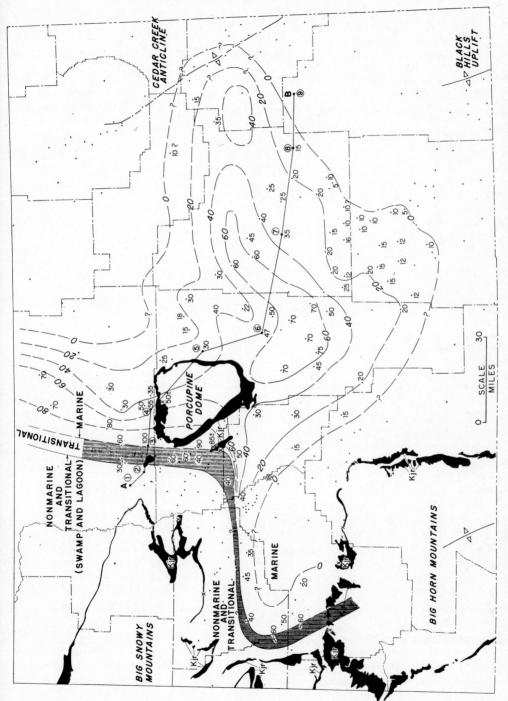

Fig. 12.—Outcrop area of Judith River formation (Kjr) in southeastern Montana, with environments of deposition and isopachs of upper Judith River sandstone (marine); X = location of surface sections; dots are locations of wells, with thicknesses of upper Judith River sandstone. A-B is trace of electric log section shown on Fig. 13.

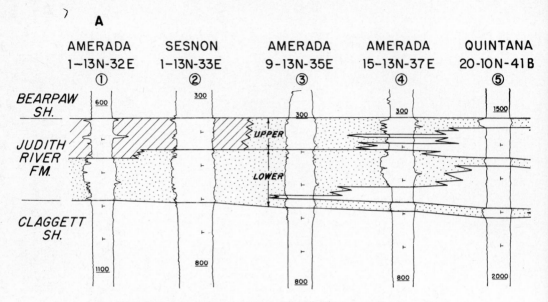

FIG. 13.—Electric-log correlation chart of Judith River formation in southeast
Montana. Trace is shown by line *A–B* in Fig. 12.

deposited in neritic, littoral, and barrier island environments.

2. During its regression across the area, the shoreline of the Cretaceous sea remained stationary long enough to permit deposition of 30 feet of lower "G" sandstone. The upper "G" was deposited during a minor regression ($\frac{1}{2}$ mile). The shoreline then transgressed slightly before resuming the regressive pattern.

3. Regional distribution of the Lance, Fox Hills, and Lewis formations indicates that the trend of the outcrop area studied in the Rock Springs uplift is oblique to the old shoreline trend.

4. Regional lithologic and faunal studies show that the "G" sandstone was deposited along the west margin of a large marine embayment. Its width is between 6 and 7 miles, and paleogeographic studies indicate that the "G" sandstone is part of a sandstone interval that can be traced for hundreds of miles (Fig. 9).

5. The lack of sand supply to that portion of the coast occupying the present area of the Rock Springs uplift and the regional position in a marine embayment may account for the narrow width of the "G" sandstone. It appears to become wider to the northeast along the strike of the shoreline.

6. Because of the narrow width of the sandstones, closely spaced wells are necessary to localize the individual units, especially the more porous parts, in the subsurface. The search for petroleum accumulations in these sandstones is difficult. If they are found, however, the rewards can be great, as is illustrated by gas reserves established in similar units, for example, the Pictured Cliffs sandstone of the San Juan basin.

CRETACEOUS SANDSTONE BODY WITH MAXI-
MUM GEOGRAPHIC DISTRIBUTION

Important facies changes in the Judith River formation of Montana have been studied for more than half a century (Stanton and Hatcher, 1905; Stebinger, 1914; Bowen, 1915). Bowen (1919, p. 15) described the Judith River formation in central Montana as changing eastward from continental shale and sandstone in the area of the Big Snowy anticlinorium, to marine sandstone and shale on the flanks of Porcupine dome (Fig. 10). To gain more precise knowledge of this relationship and the distribution of the marine

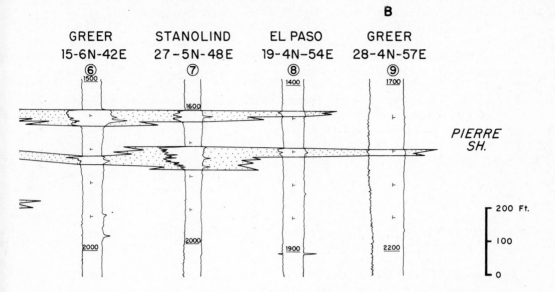

sandstones, surface sections and well logs were studied in central and southeastern Montana (Fig. 10).

The uppermost Cretaceous section in eastern Montana is shown by Figure 11. The Judith River formation is underlain by the marine Claggett shale and overlain by the marine Bearpaw shale, which is the same lithogenetic unit as the Lewis shale in the Rock Springs uplift, Wyoming. The Bearpaw is overlain by the marine Fox Hills sandstone and the nonmarine Lance (Hell Creek) formation. The Judith River crops out extensively in central Montana (Fig. 12), but in eastern Montana the formation is in the subsurface. Marine shale beds of the Pierre shale that are equivalent in age to the Judith River are exposed on the north plunge of the Black Hills anticline in southeast Montana.

The electric log correlation section (Fig. 13) shows the facies changes that occur in central Montana. The location of the section is shown on Figure 12. Although the entire Judith River formation is shown on the section, only the facies changes and distribution of lithologies in the upper 100 feet will be discussed. The important

consideration is the geographic distribution of the marine sandstone in this upper interval.

The upper 100 feet of the Judith River formation in the Sesnon well (Sec. 1, T. 13 N., R. 33 E.) is nonmarine shale that is equivalent to the nonmarine beds described by Bowen (1914, p. 15) along the Musselshell River (Sec. 16, T. 15 N., R. 30 E.). This zone changes to gray fine-grained sandstone in the Amerada wells in Sec. 9, T. 13 N., R. 35 E. and Sec. 15, T. 13 N., R. 37 E. The last well is 6 miles northwest of a surface section (Sec. 8, T. 12 N., R. 38 E.) in which the upper 20 feet of the Judith River is sandstone containing marine shells and *Halymenites* (Bowen, 1919, p. 15). This upper sandstone also contains abundant *Halymenites* where observed by the writer on the northeast flank of Ingomar anticline in T. 9 N., R. 35 E. (also Heald, 1926, p. 12).

Along the west margin of Ingomar anticline (10 miles west of Porcupine dome), thin carbonaceous beds in part of the sandstone suggest the beginning of westward change to swamp and lagoonal conditions. Well data show the sandstone to change completely to swamp and lagoon shales about 10 miles west of Ingomar anticline.

The zone of interfingering is shown on Figure 12 and is designated transitional. This zone includes the barrier island and beach deposits of the upper 100 feet of the Judith River and can be traced regionally as shown on Figure 12. It has a north-south trend between Porcupine dome and the Big Snowy Mountains, but the trend changes abruptly to east-west along the south flank of the Big Snowy Mountains. In the area north of the Big Horn Mountains (Bull Mountain syncline), the trend changes to north-northwest. The position of the zone on the north flank of the Big Horn Mountains was described by Hancock (1919, p. 101) and verified by a study of surface sections by the writer. The marine sandstone facies of the upper Judith River has been penetrated by wells in eastern Montana (Fig. 13). The thickness and distribution of this sandstone are shown by the isopachous map (Fig. 12). The sandstone ranges in thickness from a wedge edge to 100 feet. The sandstone is shown by geographic distribution to be lobe shaped, extending eastward and seaward from the shoreline for a distance of 140 miles. The north-south dimension of the sandstone lobe averages 90 miles. It appears that the eastward tip of the lobe extended across the Cedar Creek anticline. Some of the gas production from the Judith River sandstone on that anticline is probably from the upper sandstone, although most of the production appears to be from lower sandstones of the Judith River.

As shown on Figure 12, the lobe of upper Judith River sandstone was deposited seaward from a point or cape, present along the Cretaceous shoreline, which may have formed at the mouth of a major river. Lobes of sand in shoal water are being deposited in the ocean opposite capes along the Atlantic coast today. It appears that the shoreline processes responsible for the depositional features along the Atlantic coast could be applied to explain the origin and geographic distribution of the upper Judith River sandstone of Montana. Similarly, Silver (1957) has related the sedimentary features along the present Atlantic coast to marine Cretaceous sandstones in the San Juan basin of New Mexico.

The summary of results of the study are as follows.

1. The upper Judith River sandstone is an example of a Cretaceous marine and transitional sandstone with maximum geographic distribution. It has a lobe shape and ranges in thickness from a wedge edge to approximately 100 feet. Sand was deposited seaward for a maximum distance of 140 miles before changing to Pierre shale. The north-south dimension or width of the sandstone lobe is 90 miles.

2. This lobe of sandstone was deposited adjacent to and seaward from a cape along the Cretaceous shoreline, which may have formed at the mouth of a major river. Similar sand deposits are noted along the present Atlantic coast. The conditions responsible for the deposition of these modern sands may also be applied to explain the origin and distribution of the upper Judith River sandstone.

3. The lower sandstone of the Judith River has a distribution similar to that of the upper sandstone. Coastal conditions corresponding to those present during the deposition of these Judith River sandstones may also account for other widespread marine Cretaceous sandstones, such as the Eagle of Montana, the Parkman, Shannon, Sussex, and Frontier of Wyoming, and the Codell of Colorado.

4. Much of the marine Judith River sandstone is impermeable. The problem in the search for petroleum in sandstones of this type is to find shoal areas in the neritic environment where there was sufficient wave or current activity to remove fine detrital material. To be productive, porous and permeable sandstone formed in this manner must have had a subsequent geologic history favoring petroleum accumulation.

REFERENCES

Bowen, C. F., 1915, Possibilities of oil in the Porcupine dome, Rosebud County, Montana: U. S. Geol. Survey Bull. 621, p. 61–70.
—— 1919, Gradations from continental to marine conditions of deposition in central Montana during the Eagle and Judith River epochs: U. S. Geol. Survey Prof. Paper 125, p. 11–23.
Cobban, W. A., 1958, Late Cretaceous fossil zones of the Powder River basin, Wyoming and Montana, *in* Wyoming Geol. Assoc. Guidebook 13th Ann. Field Conf., Powder River basin: p. 114–119.
Dobbin, C. E., and Reeside, J. B., Jr., 1930, The contact of the Fox Hills and the Lance formations: U. S. Geol. Survey Prof. Paper 158-B, p. 9–25.
Hale, L. A., 1950, Stratigraphy of the Upper Cretaceous Montana group in the Rock Springs uplift, Sweet-

water County, Wyoming, *in* Wyoming Geol. Assoc. Guidebook 5th Ann. Field Conf., southwest Wyoming: p. 49–59.

——— 1955, Stratigraphy and facies relationship of the Montana group in south central Wyoming, northeastern Utah, and northwestern Colorado, *in* Wyoming Geol. Assoc. Guidebook 10th Ann. Field Conf., Green River basin: p. 89–94.

Hancock, E. T., 1919, Geology and oil and gas prospects of the Lake Basin field, Montana: U. S. Geol. Survey Bull. 691-D, p. 101–147.

Heald, K. C., 1926, The geology of the Ingomar anticline, Treasure and Rosebud Counties, Montana: U. S. Geol. Survey Bull. 786-A, p. 1–37.

Katich, P. J., Jr., 1959, Late Cretaceous faunal zones, western Colorado, *in* Rocky Mountain Assoc. Geol. Symposium 11th Ann. Field Conf., Cretaceous rocks of Colorado and adjacent areas: p. 26–30.

Rich, E. I., 1958, Stratigraphic relation of latest Cretaceous rocks in parts of Powder River, Wind River, and Big Horn basins, Wyoming: Am. Assoc. Petroleum Geologists Bull., v. 42, no. 10, p. 2424–2443.

Robinson, C. S., Mapel, W. J., and Cobban, W. A., 1959, Pierre shale along western and northern flanks of Black Hills, Wyoming and Montana: Am. Assoc. Petroleum Geologists Bull., v. 43, no. 1, p. 101–123.

Shepard, F. P., and Moore, D. G., 1955, Central Texas coast sedimentation: characteristics of sedimentary environment, recent history and diagenesis: Am. Assoc. Petroleum Geologists Bull., v. 39, no. 8, p. 1463–1593.

Silver, Caswell, 1957, Relation of coastal and submarine topography to Cretaceous stratigraphy, *in* Four Corners Geol. Society Guidebook 2d Ann. Field Conf., southwestern San Juan basin: p. 128–138.

Stanton, T. W., and Hatcher, J. B., 1905, Geology and paleontology of the Judith River beds: U. S. Geol. Survey Bull. 257, 174 p.

Stebinger, Eugene, 1914, The Montana group of northwestern Montana: U. S. Geol. Survey Prof. Paper 90, p. 61–68.

Weimer, R. J., 1959, Upper Cretaceous stratigraphy, Colorado, *in* Rocky Mountain Assoc. Geol. Symposium 11th Ann. Field Conf., Cretaceous rocks of Colorado and adjacent areas: p. 26–30.

——— 1960, Upper Cretaceous stratigraphy, Rocky Mountain area: Am. Assoc. Petroleum Geologists Bull., v. 44, no. 1, p. 1–20.

GEOMETRY OF PRODUCING MESAVERDE SANDSTONES, SAN JUAN BASIN[1]

CHARLES T. HOLLENSHEAD AND ROY L. PRITCHARD[2]

Salt Lake City, Utah, and Farmington, New Mexico

ABSTRACT

Within the San Juan basin the sandstone zones that occur at the top and bottom of the Mesaverde group were not deposited as a continuous blanket sand. In some areas thick, relatively clean sandstone units occur. In other areas thin, poorly sorted sandstone beds are found. These sandstone units exhibit a definite geometric pattern of distribution. Sandstone beds of the Point Lookout formation (lower Mesaverde) were deposited as a shoreline phase of a sea regressing northeastward. Sandstone bodies of the Cliff House formation (upper Mesaverde) represent the shoreline deposits of a sea transgressing southwestward at a later date. The shoreline along which these sands were deposited moved rapidly across some areas. In other areas it remained stationary for relatively long periods of time. The thicker sands correspond to places where the shoreline remained stationary, within a narrow belt, for the longer periods of time.

The successive vertical and lateral positions of the various Cliff House and Point Lookout shorelines have been established and are demonstrated on cross sections and maps. Those positions where the shoreline stabilized for relatively long periods of time are apparent in the form of "steps" that can be traced across the central part of the San Juan basin. The relatively thick, well-sorted sandstone units that correspond to the positions where the shoreline stabilized have been divided into a series of sandstone "benches" of varying widths.

Excellent examples of major "steps" in the Cliff House shoreline can be seen in surface exposures in the southeast and northwest parts of the San Juan basin. Those exposed at the surface in the northwest part of the basin exhibit a similar strand-line trend and in general correlate with the "steps" found in the subsurface.

INTRODUCTION

Within the San Juan basin of northwest New Mexico and southwest Colorado large quantities of gas are presently being produced from sandstones at the top and base of the Mesaverde group. The accumulation of gas in these sandstones is stratigraphic in nature and has no relationship to closed structure. The productive area covers a northwest-southeast belt approximately 70 miles long and 35 miles wide. At the present time there are approximately 1,900 producing Mesaverde gas wells within this belt. The present report is chiefly concerned with this area, an outline of which is shown in Figure 1.

In the San Juan basin the Mesaverde group consists of three formations. The lowest formation, Point Lookout, consists predominantly of fine to very fine grained sandstone beds that cross time lines and climb stratigraphically higher from southwest to northeast. The stratigraphic rise across the area of investigation, in relation to a marker horizon in the Lewis shale, is approximately 350 feet. The middle formation of the Mesaverde group, Menefee, is a nonmarine shale, sandstone, and coal sequence that thins from 860 feet along the southwestern edge of the area to approximately 160 feet along the northeastern edge. The upper formation, Cliff House, consists predominantly of fine to very fine grained sandstone layers that rise stratigraphically as much as 210 feet, in relation to the marker horizon in the Lewis shale. The generalized nomenclature of Upper Cretaceous deposits in the San Juan basin is shown by Figure 2.

The major portion of Mesaverde gas production is found in sandstones of the Point Lookout and Cliff House formations. In some areas gas is produced from sandstones within the Menefee formation. These nonmarine Menefee sands, however, are very erratic in nature and appear to have no distinguishable geometric pattern of distribu-

[1] Read before the Association at Atlantic City, New Jersey, April 25, 1960. Manuscript received January 1, 1960. Publication authorized by El Paso Natural Gas Company.

[2] El Paso Natural Gas Company. The authors wish to express their appreciation to Warren L. Taylor, Robert G. Young, and Chester C. Cassel for their critical analysis of and the helpful suggestions for, this paper. The writers acknowledge the petrographic work contributed by El Paso Natural Gas Company petrographers, W. J. Barrett and W. G. Park. Thanks are extended to G. N. Jackson for drafting the illustrations.

tion. For this reason they are not included in this study.

The accumulation of gas in the Cliff House and Point Lookout formations is controlled largely by the distribution of individual sandstone "benches," and by their internal porosity and permeability characteristics. It was observed that the sandstones of these formations are quite variable, being almost entirely absent or very silty and clayey in some areas, but quite thick and relatively clean and permeable in other areas. The original study undertaken in 1953 was for the purpose of determining, if possible, some regularity of pattern for this unequal distribution of sandstone.

Evidence has accumulated since that time to suggest internal natural fracturing as an important element in determining the productivity of certain areas. The present paper deals chiefly, however, with the geometric pattern of distribution of the sandstone units and their lithologic characteristics.

Many papers pertaining to the stratigraphy of the Upper Cretaceous in the San Juan basin area

have been published. The broad theoretical concepts advanced by the earlier workers are in remarkable agreement, and constituted the point of departure for the study. The information presented in these earlier papers, as well as more recent ones, has been drawn on freely for the present paper.

The words *step* and *bench* are used throughout this paper. Herein, *step* is used to imply an abrupt change in the stratigraphic position of the Point Lookout-Menefee or Cliff House-Menefee contact (strand-line contact). The word *bench* pertains to the unusually thick sandstone bodies that are related to major *steps* in the strand line.

BASIS FOR STUDY

This paper is an elaboration of ideas and techniques presented in an unpublished report submitted by Chester Cassel, consulting geologist, Golden, Colorado, to El Paso Natural Gas Company in March 1954, which was prepared with the assistance of C. T. Hollenshead. That report, entitled "Distribution of Mesaverde Sands in the San Juan Basin," was based on a detailed sub-

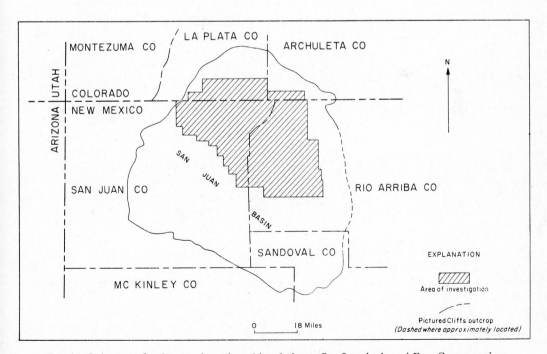

FIG. 1.—Index map showing area investigated in relation to San Juan basin and Four Corners region.

PERIOD	EPOCH	GROUP	LITHOLOGIC UNITS SAN JUAN BASIN
CRETACEOUS	MONTANAN		Mc Dermott (cgl.)
			Kirtland (sh)
			Fruitland (ss, sh, coal)
			Pictured Cliffs (ss)
			Lewis (sh.)
		MESAVERDE	Cliff House (ss)　　　☼
			Menefee (ss, sh, coal)
			Point Lookout (ss)　　　☼
	COLORADOAN		Mancos (sh.)
	LOWER	DAKOTA	Dakota (ss, sh., coal)

Fig. 2.—Nomenclature of Upper Cretaceous deposits in the San Juan basin area.

surface study which had been undertaken by Cassel at the request of the Company in 1953. The original study was achieved essentially through the use of electric and gamma ray-neutron logs. The present study revises and expands the original work to include the use of descriptions of well samples, thin section analysis, additional electric logs, sample logs, and core analysis.

TRANSGRESSIVE AND REGRESSIVE UPPER CRETACEOUS SHORELINES

The broad depositional concepts that are accepted by the authors and form the foundation for this study, were reviewed by Sears, Hunt, and Hendricks (1941) in their paper, "Transgressive and Regressive Cretaceous Deposits of Southern San Juan Basin." These concepts suggest that the Mesaverde group was deposited in a broad, shallow sea that extended generally north-south for several thousand miles and had an average width of approximately 1,000 miles. The western shoreline of this sea extended across the San Juan basin in a northwest-southeast direction. During Late Cretaceous time numerous fluctuations occurred in the position of the shoreline and at times this sea encroached southwestward over the gentle slope of the adjoining land. At other times the sea gradually retreated northeastward toward the deeper part of the basin. Many such fluctuations in the position of the shoreline took place during Late Cretaceous time.

These authors suggested that both transgressive and regressive sediments of the Mesaverde group were deposited during continuous sinking of the trough, and that both transgressive and regressive deposits were controlled by the rate of sinking in relation to the supply of material being brought in. Thus, at any given time one of three sets of conditions was possible (Pike, 1947)—(1) The rate of sedimentation predominated over subsidence, causing regression of the shoreline. (2) The rate of subsidence predominated over sedimentation, resulting in transgression of the shoreline. (3) The rates of sedimentation and subsidence were in equilibrium, causing the shoreline to remain in one place for a longer period of time and resulting in deposition of a relatively thick shoreline and nearshore sand section.

On any given depositional time plane, marine mud and silt were being deposited contemporaneously with shoreline sand. In a landward direction coal bearing swamp and flood-plain deposits were forming contemporaneously with shoreline sand. Therefore, during any given Mesaverde time there existed four environmental zones. The facies relationship of these four zones is illustrated by Figure 3.

It has been widely accepted by many geologists that the lowermost Mesaverde sands (Point Lookout formation) were deposited as a shoreline phase of a sea that was retreating northeastward. The upper sands (Cliff House formation) were deposited along the shoreline of a sea transgressing southwestward, at a later date. Thus, in the southern part of the San Juan basin the upper part of the Mancos shale was deposited contemporaneously with the lower part of the Mesaverde group; whereas the lower part of the Lewis shale is the time equivalent of the upper part of the Mesaverde group. Figure 4, a diagrammatic southwest-northeast cross section of the Mesaverde group through the San Juan basin, illustrates these relationships.

STEP-LIKE CHARACTER OF SUCCESSIVE SHORELINE POSITIONS

This study indicates that the regressive Point Lookout and transgressive Cliff House shorelines did not move uniformly, depositing a blanket sand of constant thickness. Instead, they moved very rapidly across some areas, whereas in other areas they remained stationary, within a narrow belt, for relatively long periods of time. The distance that the shoreline moved during a given period of time depended on the rate of subsidence in relation to sedimentation (or possibly to slight eustatic changes in sea level). In those areas where the shoreline moved rapidly, thin, poorly sorted sandstones occur. In the areas where the shoreline remained more or less stationary for long periods of time (subsidence in equilibrium with sedimentation), thick, relatively well-sorted sandstone bodies are present. Figures 5 and 6 present in diagrammatic form the conditions that are believed to have existed along this irregularly moving shoreline. Figure 5 demonstrates four hypothetical stages of deposition along the regressing Point Lookout shoreline. Figure 6 shows three stages of deposition along the transgressing Cliff House shoreline. Successive positions of the Point Lookout and Cliff House shorelines can be seen on these diagrams. Those positions where the shoreline stabilized for relatively long periods are apparent in the form of thick sandstone development, which results in steps in the strandline contact between shoreline sand of the Cliff House or Point Lookout, and the underlying or overlying nonmarine, coal-bearing sediments.

From the wealth of information compiled by various authors (Sears, Hunt, and Hendricks, 1941; Pike, 1947; Cassel, 1954; Silver, 1957), it can be concluded that Mesaverde sediments were derived from a land mass that existed somewhere to the west and southwest. The limited amount of petrographic thin-section work completed by El Paso Natural Gas Company petrographers indicates that the source terrane included both igneous and sedimentary rocks.

METHOD OF ANALYSIS

One of the fundamental points of departure in the original study made by Cassel and Hollenshead was the establishment of an easily recognizable marker that can be used as a datum horizon from which to measure successive positions of the strand line and to correlate accurately sandstone benches of the Point Lookout and Cliff House formations.

A marker that possesses these requirements is found in the lower part of the Lewis shale. This has been designated the "Green Marker Horizon" on the electric-log cross sections (Figs. 8 and 9). The marker is characterized by a persistent

(Text continued on page 104)

C. T. HOLLENSHEAD AND R. L. PRITCHARD

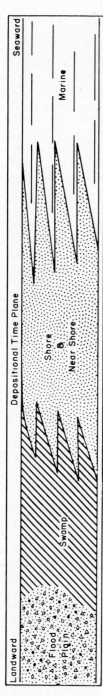

Fig. 3.—Generalized cross section illustrating environmental zones of deposition that existed during any given Mesaverde time.

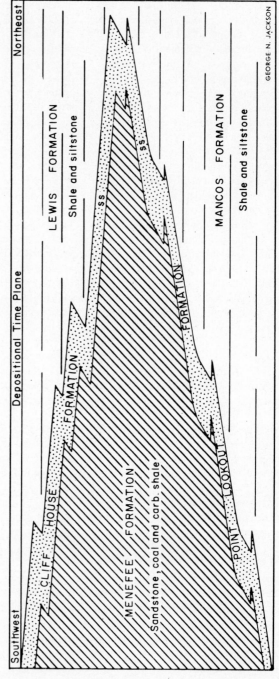

GEORGE N. JACKSON

Fig. 4.—Diagrammatical southwest-northeast cross section of the Mesaverde group through the San Juan basin, showing time relationship.

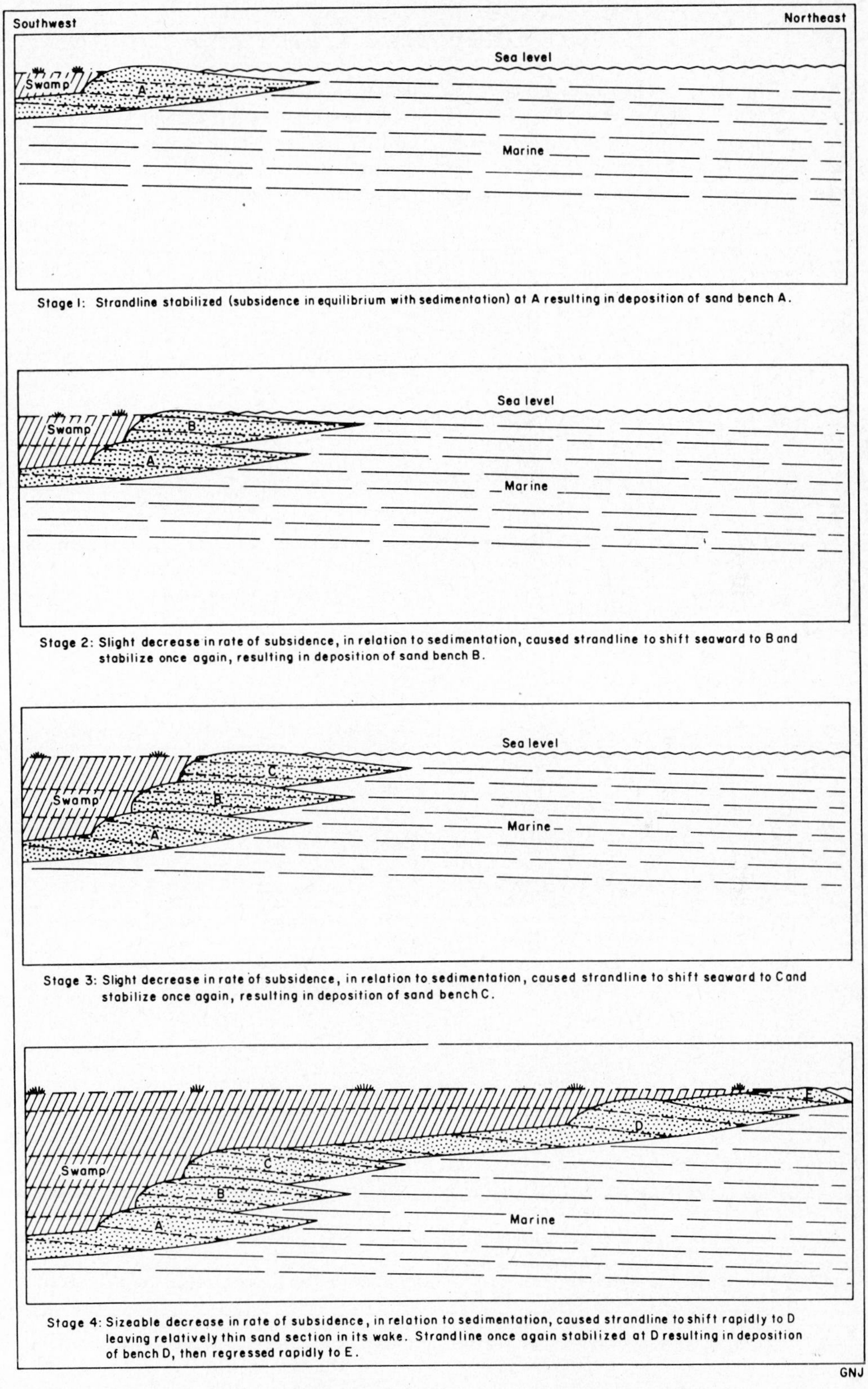

Southwest   Northeast

Sea level

Swamp   A   Marine

Stage 1: Strandline stabilized (subsidence in equilibrium with sedimentation) at A resulting in deposition of sand bench A.

Sea level

Swamp   B

A   Marine

Stage 2: Slight decrease in rate of subsidence, in relation to sedimentation, caused strandline to shift seaward to B and
        stabilize once again, resulting in deposition of sand bench B.

Sea level

Swamp   C

B

A   Marine

Stage 3: Slight decrease in rate of subsidence, in relation to sedimentation, caused strandline to shift seaward to C and
        stabilize once again, resulting in deposition of sand bench C.

D   E

Swamp

C

B

A   Marine

Stage 4: Sizeable decrease in rate of subsidence, in relation to sedimentation, caused strandline to shift rapidly to D
        leaving relatively thin sand section in its wake. Strandline once again stabilized at D resulting in deposition
        of bench D, then regressed rapidly to E.

GNJ

FIG. 5.—Diagrammatical cross sections illustrating irregularity of sand deposition
along regressive Point Lookout shoreline.

resistivity "low" that can be correlated over the area of investigation with a reasonable degree of reliability. Along the extreme northeast and southwest edges of the area of investigation this marker loses its character somewhat. However, with the help of additional higher markers it is possible to correlate the "Green Marker Horizon" into these fringe areas without difficulty. A part of three typical electric logs is shown (Fig. 7) to illustrate the resistivity characteristics of the "Green Marker Horizon."

Borehole cuttings of the lower Lewis shale from

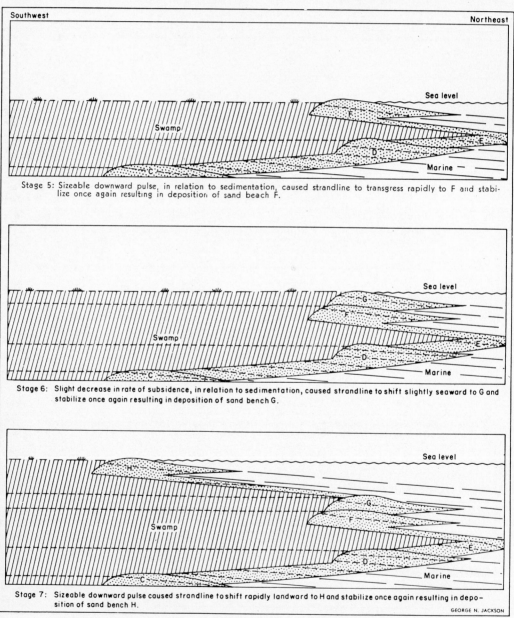

Stage 5: Sizeable downward pulse, in relation to sedimentation, caused strandline to transgress rapidly to F and stabilize once again resulting in deposition of sand beach F.

Stage 6: Slight decrease in rate of subsidence, in relation to sedimentation, caused strandline to shift slightly seaward to G and stabilize once again resulting in deposition of sand bench G.

Stage 7: Sizeable downward pulse caused strandline to shift rapidly landward to H and stabilize once again resulting in deposition of sand bench H.

GEORGE N. JACKSON

Fig. 6.—Diagrammatical cross sections illustrating irregularity of sand deposition along transgressive Cliff House shoreline.

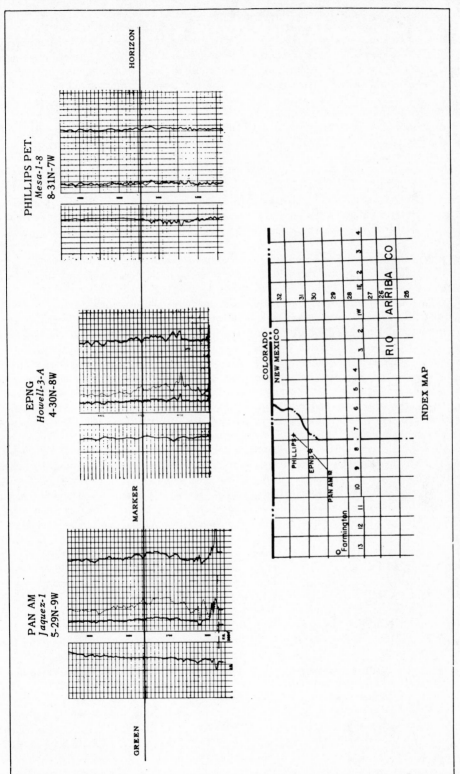

FIG. 7.—Electric logs illustrating resistivity characteristics of "Green Marker Horizon."

wells scattered throughout the area of investigation were analyzed to determine, if possible, the lithologic nature of the marker. The examination of cuttings demonstrated that the "Green Marker Horizon" lies within a somewhat bentonitic zone, but did not conclusively prove that the marker is actually representative of a bentonite bed. Its reliability is reinforced by its remarkable parallelism to other similar resistivity "lows" that can be correlated over more limited areas. It is believed to represent approximate contemporaneity and therefore can be used to delineate accurately major vertical steps in the regressive Point Lookout and transgressive Cliff House strand lines.

The majority of the Mesaverde wells within the area of investigation were drilled through the Mesaverde group using natural gas as a circulating medium. For this reason relatively few borehole cuttings are available. Where available, cuttings were examined for the purpose of determining, as exactly as possible, the contact between shoreline sandstones and the underlying or overlying coal-bearing deposits (strand-line contact) of the Menefee formation. After comparing numerous electric logs with sample descriptions, it became apparent that in the majority of cases the strand-line contact can be recognized by distinctive electric-log characteristics of the coal-bearing Menefee formation. Thus, in the many instances where borehole cuttings were not available, strand-line contacts were determined from the electric logs. In some areas very little, or no sandstone is present at the strand-line contact. The change from marine shale and silt (Mancos or Lewis) to coal-bearing sediments is, nevertheless, generally recognizable.

The two cross sections (Figs. 8 and 9) illustrate the method of analysis. In these cross sections the positions of the upper and lower Menefee contacts have been established in relation to the "Green Marker Horizon." In this way it is possible to delineate clearly the successive positions and major steps of the shifting shorelines. Distribution of major sandstone benches, particularly in the Cliff House formation, is directly related to the location of major steps in the strand line. The cross sections show that these sandstone benches terminate abruptly in a landward direction against swamp deposits of the Menefee formation. In a seaward direction the sandstone benches grade into silt and eventually into marine shale of either the Lewis or Mancos formation. It also may be noted on the cross sections that abrupt termination of sandstone benches against Menefee swamp deposits in all instances takes place on the southwest side of the sandstone bench. A structure map drawn on the "Green Marker Horizon" (Fig. 10) shows the regional dip to be to the northeast over the greater part of the area. Thus, shoreline sandstone zones terminate abruptly up dip against relatively impervious swamp or lagoonal deposits. In the extreme northeast part of the area the dip is generally south. Here the Mesaverde wells are producing from sands that grade up dip into marine shale and silt. It therefore seems reasonable to believe that either of the aforementioned stratigraphic relationships represents the barrier that keeps the gas in place, depending on the direction of dip.

By studying a series of northeast-southwest cross sections through the area it became apparent that the major sandstone benches continue for many miles in a northwest-southeast direction. It was found that these benches could be traced across the basin by the use of isopach maps representing the interval between the "Green Marker Horizon" and the Cliff House-Menefee or Point Lookout-Menefee strand-line contacts. Figure 11 represents this interval for the Cliff House-Menefee contact, which was established on all available electric logs, with the help of borehole cuttings, and plotted on the map. In those areas where major steps in the transgressing strand line exist, there appears a crowding of the isopach lines. These steps correspond to the areas where the shoreline was stable, within a narrow belt, for relatively long periods of time. The sandstone benches occur immediately northeast and along the trace of the crowding of the isopach lines. It became apparent that by the use of these isopach maps the trend of the successive shorelines could be determined. Once the trend of major sandstone benches has been thus established it becomes a much easier task to project them into relatively unexplored areas with a minimum of wildcat control. The approximate limits of three major Cliff House sandstone

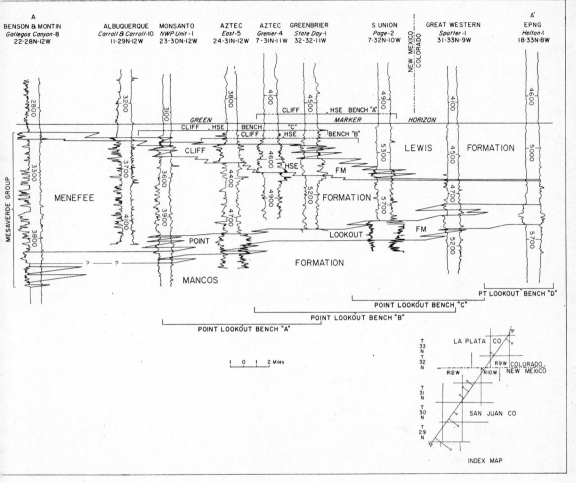

FIG. 8.—Southwest-northeast cross section *A-A'* through the central part of the San Juan basin, showing stratigraphic relations of various Mesaverde sandstone units. Trace of section is line *A-A'*, Fig. 11.

benches have been established and superimposed on the isopach map (Fig. 11).

Figure 12 is an isopach map representing the interval between the "Green Marker Horizon" and the Point Lookout-Menefee strand-line contact. Four major Point Lookout sandstone benches have been established and superimposed on this isopach map (Fig. 12). In the case of the Point Lookout, the steps in the regressing strand line are of lesser magnitude than those of the transgressive Cliff House strand line. This is explained by the belief that pulses of subsidence that took place during Point Lookout time were

of lesser magnitude and were more evenly spaced than those that took place during Cliff House time.

GENERALIZED DISCUSSION OF MAJOR
SANDSTONE BENCHES

Cliff House sandstone benches.—The various sandstone benches corresponding to successive steps in the transgressive Cliff House shoreline have been designated *A*, *B*, and *C* on the isopach map pertaining to the Cliff House formation (Fig. 11) and on the cross sections (Figs. 8 and 9). The southwest edge of each bench terminates

(*Text continued on page 112*)

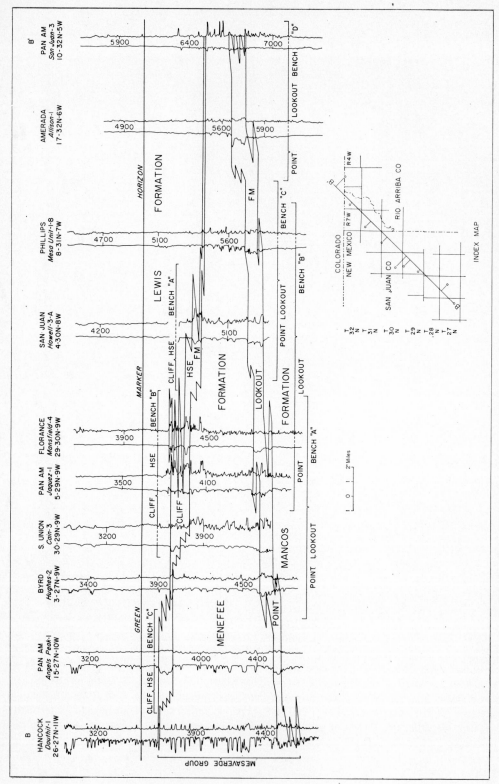

FIG. 9.—Southwest-northeast cross section *B-B'* through the northwestern part of the San Juan basin, showing stratigraphic relations of various Mesaverde sandstone units. Trace of section is line *B-B'*, Fig. 11.

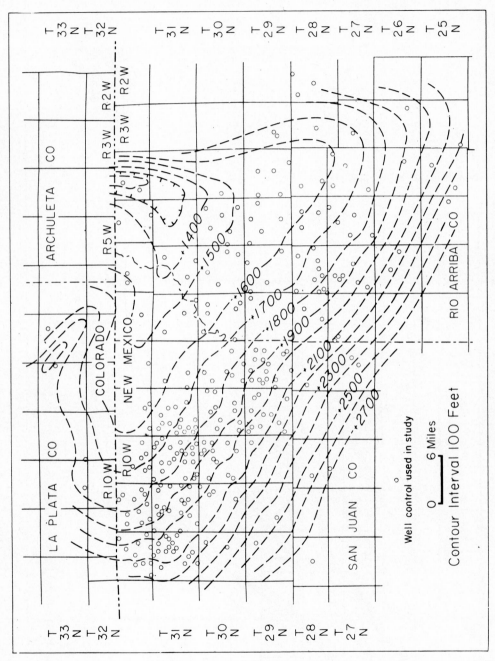

FIG. 10.—Structure map drawn on "Green Marker Horizon."

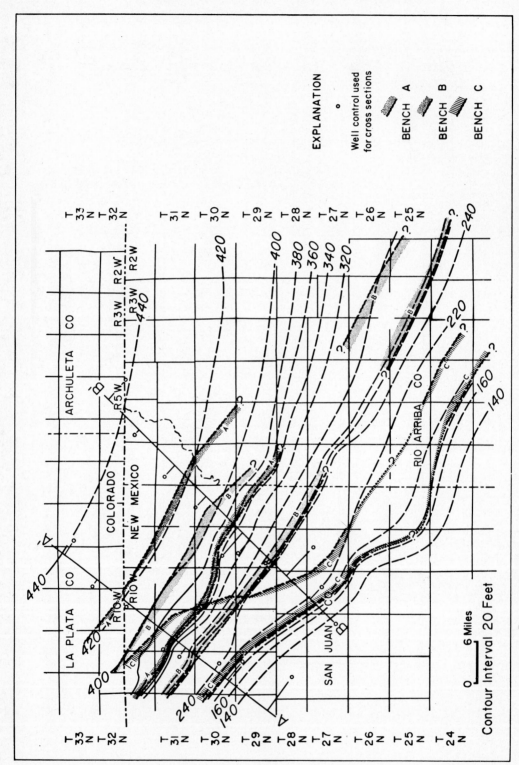

FIG. 11.—Map showing isopach lines representing interval between "Green Marker" in Lewis shale and top of Menefee coal-bearing deposits. Distribution of principal Cliff House benches superimposed. Central San Juan basin, New Mexico. *A-A'* and *B-B'* indicate trace of sections shown in Figs. 8 and 9, respectively.

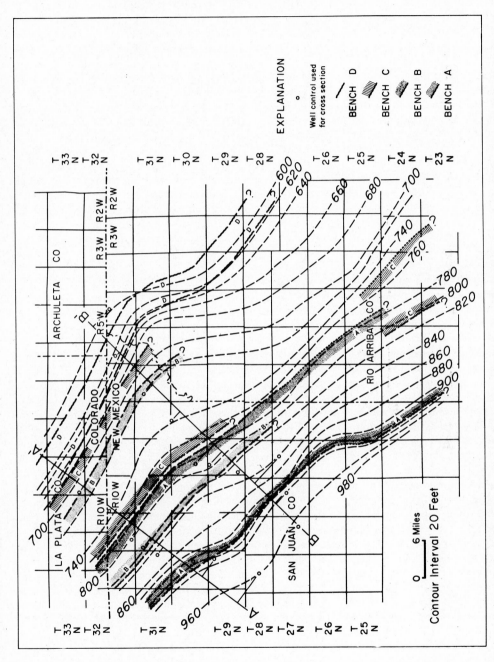

Fig. 12.—Map showing isopach lines representing interval between "Green Marker" in Lewis shale and base of Menefee coal-bearing deposits. Distribution of principal Point Lookout sandstone benches superimposed. Central San Juan basin, New Mexico. *A-A'* and *B-B'* indicate trace of sections shown in Figs. 8 and 9, respectively.

abruptly against coastal swamp deposits and can easily be recognized and traced. Northeastward, however, these sandstone benches gradually grade into silt and marine shale. For this reason the northeast limits of these benches, as shown in Figure 11, are approximate.

This study indicates that all three Cliff House sandstone benches converge in the northwest part of the area to form what appears to be one thick sandstone unit. It is also in this area that the sandstone benches attain their maximum thickness. Southeast of this area the three Cliff House sandstone benches diverge into distinct, separate sandstone units. It therefore seems reasonable to believe that the transgressive Cliff House strand line remained more or less stationary in this northwest area while it continued to transgress in the southeast area. A reasonable explanation is that subsidence was taking place more slowly in the northwest area, and that sedimentation in this area was approximately in balance with subsidence. This caused the shoreline to remain in one place for a longer period of time. Southeastward subsidence was taking place somewhat faster, in pulses, causing transgression.

It should be pointed out that not all electric log and sample control fits smoothly into the picture. In the extreme northwest part of the area, along the Colorado-New Mexico State boundary, Cliff House sands seem to lie directly upon Menefee sands. This creates a problem, as the true Cliff House-Menefee strand-line contact cannot be located from electric logs or from borehole cuttings. Thus, only an estimate as to the location of the strand-line contact can be made in this limited area.

Point Lookout sandstone benches.—Relatively few electric logs have been run through the Point Lookout part of the section. For this reason the isopach map (Fig. 12) pertaining to the Point Lookout formation is much more generalized than that pertaining to the Cliff House (Fig. 11). The four major sandstone benches corresponding to successive steps in the regressive Point Lookout shoreline have been designated *A*, *B*, *C*, and *D* in Figure 12 and on the cross sections (Figs. 8 and 9).

In a very general way these four benches converge in the northwest part of the area studied. They do not, however, converge to the same extent as the Cliff House benches. Generally speaking, steps in the Point Lookout strand line are not as sharp as those in the Cliff House. Moderate thicknesses of Point Lookout sandstone are present over the entire area, although the thickness varies from place to place. The two most prominent steps in the Point Lookout strand line are those that controlled deposition of sandstone benches *A* and *D*. The two steps that controlled deposition of sandstone benches *B* and *C* are not well defined and may actually be a combination of several smaller steps.

All four Point Lookout benches have their thickest development in the northwest part of the area studied. Southeast of this area, steps in the Point Lookout strand line become somewhat vague and their related sandstone benches become thin. For this reason, these benches cannot be traced continuously from the northwest to the southeast part of the area.

SURFACE EXPOSURES OF BENCHES

No attempt has been made to trace the various sandstone benches from the subsurface to the surface exposures on the northwest and southeast flanks of the basin. The exact lithologic nature of the electric log "Green Marker Horizon" is not known and cannot be established in surface exposures. Thus, benches found in surface exposures are difficult to correlate exactly with the subsurface benches. The actual presence of such benches and their trends have been determined in surface exposures, however, by various workers, particularly in the Cliff House formation. They are illustrated by Wanek's (1954) cross sections. Figure 13 is a redrafting of these and the index map showing their locations. These stratigraphic sections were constructed by Wanek from measured surface sections taken approximately perpendicular to the strand line. Trends of Wanek's Cliff House benches have been determined from his sections and are shown on the index map of Figure 13 and on Figure 14. Trends of surface benches have a similar direction to those of the subsurface and appear to be closely related to them. The surface bench labeled "Barker Dome Tongue" by Wanek could very possibly correlate with Cliff House subsurface bench *C*. Surface bench labeled "Lower Tongue" by Wanek appears to be a combination of Cliff House subsurface benches *A* and *B*. This seems reasonable because

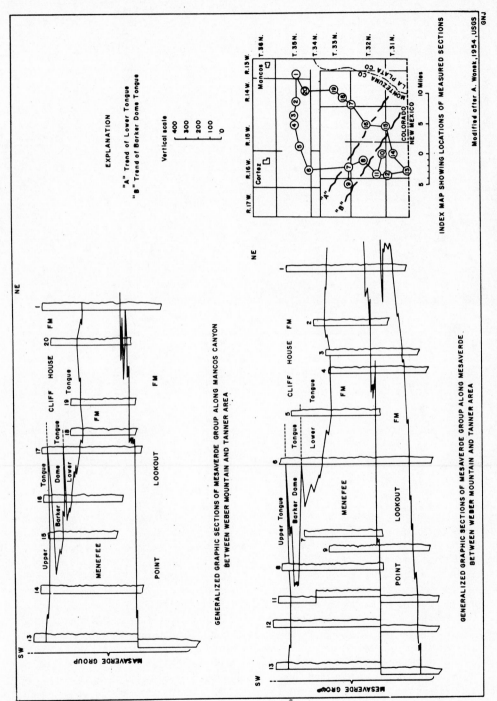

FIG. 13.—Cross sections illustrating surface exposures of major Cliff House benches (tongues) northwest of area investigated. Modified after Wanek, 1954.

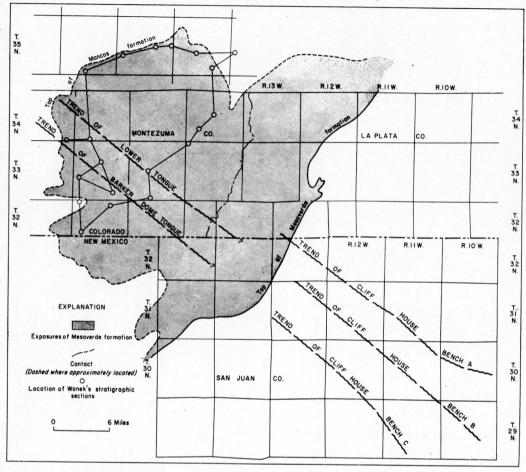

Fig. 14.—Map showing trends of benches mapped in the subsurface in relation to trends of benches (tongues) mapped in surface exposures by Wanek, 1954.

bench *B* partially overlies bench *A* in the subsurface, and convergence of the two benches in a northwest direction is indicated. These surface-to-subsurface bench correlations are purely conjectural as there is no actual proof that the suggested corresponding benches lie at the same stratigraphic position. It is important, however, to know that benches can be recognized at the outcrop, and that their trends closely parallel those of the subsurface.

Point Lookout steps shown on cross sections by Wanek (1954) are much more gentle than those mapped in the subsurface. If the sharp subsurface step controlling bench *A* were projected northwestward at its present trend, it would crop out along the southwest edge of the two measured sections. No such step is indicated by the cross sections. The Point Lookout portion of Wanek's measured Sections 11, 12, and 13 are offset from the rest of the sections. These offsets indicate that the sections are composites. It may be that this major Point Lookout step was somehow missed, owing to the use of composite sections. On the other hand, it is possible that the trend of this step could change from a northwesterly direction and bend sharply to the southwest. The step would then lie southwest of the measured sections. Only additional measuring of sections can determine this point.

A major Cliff House sandstone bench is exposed in the southeast part of the basin, approximately 25 miles south, and slightly east of the area investigated. This bench ("La Ventana" sand) is shown by Dane (1936, p. 90) in a generalized cross section; the accompanying geologic map shows the extent of the surface exposure. Correlation of this bench with subsurface control indicates that the bench has a northwest-southeast trend. Thus, the surface exposure is approximately prependicular to the strand line. Surface-to-subsurface correlation of this bench also indicates that it is younger, and lies at a higher stratigraphic position, than Cliff House benches *A*, *B*, or *C*. Figure 15 shows the surface exposure and a generalized cross section of this bench approximately normal to the strand line. This sandstone attains a maximum thickness of approximately 900 feet. To the southwest, in a landward direction, the entire 900 feet of sandstone grades rapidly into nonmarine, coal-bearing sediments. In a northeast, or seaward direction, the upper 700 feet of the sandstone bench grades into marine shale of the Lewis formation. These rapid changes can be seen on both the cross section and the geologic map in Figure 15. The shoreline was evidently stable, within a narrow belt, in this general area for a very long period of time.

MINERALOGICAL, PHYSICAL, AND RESERVOIR
CHARACTERISTICS OF MESAVERDE
SANDSTONES

Cliff House sandstone.—A typical binocular microscope description of Cliff House sandstone indicates that it is light to medium gray, very fine grained, well cemented, and laminated with light to dark gray carbonaceous shales. Thin sections prepared of Cliff House sands from seven

wells scattered throughout the area investigated verified this as a generalized description.

It was originally intended to undertake a petrographic study of cores and cuttings from the individual benches that make up the Cliff House formation. A petrographic study was started with the idea that sands of the different Cliff House benches should possess at least minor differences in mineralogical and physical characteristics. It soon became apparent that lack of core control and the poor quality of borehole cuttings made this approach impractical. However, the 19 petrographic thin sections studied offer information from which general observations can be made. This petrographic work indicates that the median grain size of sand from all three Cliff House benches ranges from .08 to .22 millimeters and in almost all cases varies from angular to subangular. The quartz content ranges from 50 to 75 per cent, whereas the feldspar content ranges from a trace to 15 per cent. Chert is also found in these sands, ranging from a trace to 40 per cent. Argillaceous material was found in all Cliff House slides, ranging from 5 to 15 per cent. Calcareous cementing material is present and ranges from a trace to 15 per cent. Table I presents the petrographic characteristics of the average Cliff House sands as determined from the 19 analyses. Only those sands within the lateral limits of the three Cliff House benches were considered in determining the average analysis shown in Table I.

Point Lookout sandstone.—A typical binocular microscope description of Point Lookout sandstone indicates that it is light to medium gray, fine to very fine grained, well cemented, angular to subangular, and laminated with gray and carbonaceous shale. Petrographic study of thin sec-

TABLE I. PETROGRAPHIC CHARACTERISTICS OF AVERAGE SANDS FROM CLIFF HOUSE FORMATION
(Determined from 19 samples)

Cement (per cent)		Quartz (per cent)	Feldspar (per cent)	Rock Fragments (per cent)	Median Grain Size (mm)
Argillaceous	Calcareous				
10	15	60	10	5	0.10

Range of Grain Size	Roundness	Sorting	Source	Average Texture	Rock Name
Clay to 0.24 mm	Angular to subangular	Poor to fair	Igneous and sedimentary	Uniform	Quartzose sand

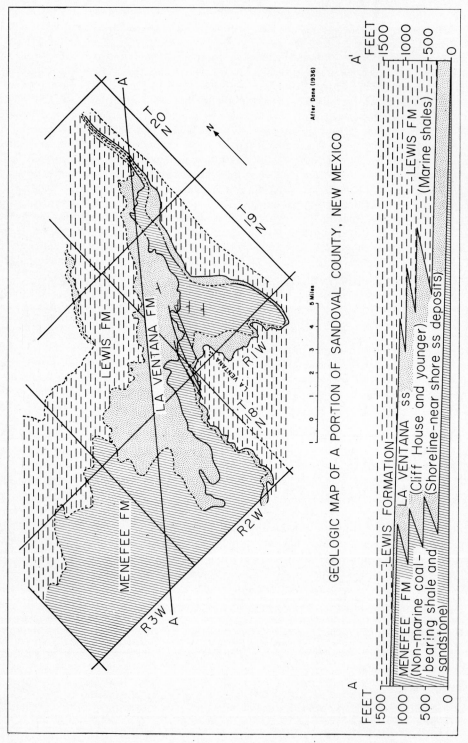

GEOLOGIC MAP OF A PORTION OF SANDOVAL COUNTY, NEW MEXICO

Fɪɢ. 15.—Geologic map and cross section through a portion of Sandoval County, New Mexico, illustrating surface exposure of major Cliff House bench. After Dane, 1936.

tions prepared from Point Lookout cores and cuttings verified this as a generalized description.

The 38 thin sections studied offer information from which general observations can be made. This petrographic work indicates that the median grain size of sand from all four Point Lookout benches ranges from 0.08 to 0.22 millimeters and in almost all cases the grains range from angular to subangular. The quartz content ranges from 30 to 60 per cent and the feldspar content ranges between a trace and 35 per cent. Chert is found in these sands, ranging from a trace to 15 per cent. Argillaceous cementing material was found in all Point Lookout slides, ranging from 5 to 30 per cent. Calcareous cementing material is present and ranges from a trace to 15 per cent. A petrographic analysis of what is considered to be an average Point Lookout sand is shown in Table II. Only the sands within the lateral limits of the four Point Lookout benches were considered in determining the average analysis shown in Table II. In many cases thin sections of sands from the most favorable part of the benches could not be made because of lack of core or sample control.

GENERAL

It must be stated that the petrographic description of an average Cliff House and Point Lookout sandstone (Tables I and II) does not fit the physical and mineralogical characteristics of sands found on many present-day beaches. In general, all Mesaverde sand is not as well sorted, is more argillaceous, and has sand grains more angular than those of many present-day beaches and bars. Nevertheless, a binocular microscope examination of Mesaverde sandstone cuttings from numerous wells indicates that the best

sorted and cleanest sand lies along the extreme southwest edge of each bench, and that the proportion of silty and shaly material increases in a seaward direction. Not enough core control is available from any given sand beach to verify or disprove this statement by rigorous petrographic analysis. It is quite possible that sedimentation during Mesaverde time was more rapid than sedimentation taking place along many of our present-day shorelines. It seems reasonable to believe that if sedimentation were relatively rapid the sands would not have had time to be washed clean and to develop rounding of the grains.

Allen (1955) indicated that sands of the Cliff House and Point Lookout formations contain up to 30 per cent montmorillonite and that the pores of the sands are lined with as much as 75 per cent montmorillonite. This being the case, the argillaceous fraction indicated in Tables I and II probably consists predominantly of montmorillonite. The actual presence of swelling clays could not be recognized by use of the petrographic microscope. Their presence in the sands does seem reasonable, however, as abundant swelling-type clays were observed in both the Lewis and Menefee formations. Surface water entering at the outcrops of the various Point Lookout and Cliff House sandstone benches may have caused the clay to swell, thus closing the pores, and preventing escape of gas.

Most Cliff House and Point Lookout cores examined exhibit varying degrees of fracturing. The greatest amount of fracturing seems to be present in the more lucrative gas producing areas. For this reason it is believed that the amount of fracturing is an important factor in productivity,

TABLE II. PETROGRAPHIC CHARACTERISTICS OF AVERAGE POINT LOOKOUT SAND
(Determined from 38 samples)

Cement (per cent)			Quartz (per cent)	Chert (per cent)	Feldspar (per cent)	Rock Fragments (per cent)
Argillaceous	Calcareous	Quartz				
15	Trace	10	55	Trace	15	5

Range of Grain Size	Median Grain Size	Roundness	Sorting	Source	Average Texture	Rock Name
Clay to 0.26 mm	0.12 mm	Angular	Poor to fair	Igneous and sedimentary	Uniform	Graywacke

in addition to such other factors as the character and distribution of the sand bodies.

Hydrodynamic factors have undoubtedly played some part in forming the tremendous accumulations of gas that are present in the structurally low parts of the basin. The discussion of such factors, however, is beyond the scope of the present paper.

CONCLUSION

It may be concluded that the sandstone zones of the Mesaverde group, within the San Juan basin, possess a definable geometric pattern of distribution. By establishing this pattern it is possible to project with a reasonable degree of accuracy, known producing sandstone benches into relatively unexplored areas. This pattern of distribution, the varying lithologic characteristics of the sand benches, the degree of fracturing, and possibly certain hydrodynamic factors, control gas accumulation and production.

The results of this study fit the broad theoretical concepts now accepted by the majority of workers in the San Juan basin area. One problem that needs further study should be noted—clean, well-sorted sands, containing well-rounded grains, such as are found on many present-day beaches, appear to be absent within the Mesaverde group. The reason for this is not completely understood and cannot be adequately explained by the authors. Perhaps future petrographic work in conjunction with detailed studies of surface exposures of the various benches will explain the absence of such sand or may yet reveal its presence in relatively limited parts of the sand benches. It must be remembered, in this connection, that a large part of any given sand bench was probably deposited in the off-shore water directly adjacent to the beach, where cleaning and sorting would not be complete.

It is believed that the method of analysis used in this subsurface study can be applied to the study of Upper Cretaceous sediments in other structural basins within the Rocky Mountain region, and that some of the techniques here outlined can be used to predict sandstone development and project known producing benches into relatively unexplored areas, with a minimum of wildcat control.

REFERENCES

Allen, R. W., Jr., 1955, Stratigraphic gas development in the Blanco-Mesaverde pool of the San Juan basin, *in* Four Corners Geol. Soc. Guidebook Field Conf. No. 1, Parts of Paradox, Black Mesa, and San Juan basin: p. 40–43.

Beaumont, E. C., Dane, C. H., and Sears, J. D., 1956, Revised nomenclature of Mesaverde sands in San Juan basin, New Mexico: Am. Assoc. Petroleum Geologists Bull., v. 40, no. 9, p. 2149–2162.

Cassel, Chester, 1954, Distribution of Mesaverde sands in the San Juan basin: unpub. report submitted to El Paso Natural Gas Co., March 15, 1954.

Dane, C. H., 1936, The La Ventana-Chacra Mesa coal field, Pt. 3 *of* Geology and fuel resources of the southern part of the San Juan basin, New Mexico: U. S. Geol. Survey Bull. 860-C.

Elias, G. K., 1957, Nomenclature chart of the Four Corners area, *in* Four Corners Geol. Soc. Guidebook 2d Field Conf., Southwestern San Juan basin: p. 10.

Pike, W. S., Jr., 1947, Intertonguing marine and non-marine Upper Cretaceous deposits of New Mexico, Arizona, and southwestern Colorado: Geol. Soc. America Mem. 24.

Reeside, J. B., Jr., 1944, Maps showing thickness and general character of the Cretaceous deposits in the interior of the United States: U. S. Geol. Survey Oil and Gas Inv. Prelim. Map 10.

Reneau, W. E., Jr., and Harris, James D., Jr., 1957, Reservoir characteristics of Cretaceous sands of the San Juan basin, *in* Four Corners Geol. Soc. Guidebook 2d Field Conf., Southwestern San Juan basin: p. 40–43.

Sears, J. D., Hunt, C. B., and Hendricks, T. A., 1941, Transgressive and regressive Cretaceous deposits in southern San Juan basin, New Mexico: U. S. Geol. Survey Prof. Paper 193-F.

Silver, Caswell, 1957, Relation of coastal and submarine topography to Cretaceous statigraphy, *in* Four Corners Geol. Soc. Guidebook 2d Field Conf., Southwestern San Juan basin: p. 128–137.

Wanek, A. A., 1954, Geologic map of the Mesa Verde area, Montezuma County, Colorado: U. S. Geol. Survey Oil and Gas Inv. Map OM-152.

Young, R. G., 1955, Sedimentary facies and intertonguing in the Upper Cretaceous of the Book Cliffs, Utah-Colorado: Geol. Soc. America Bull., v. 41, no. 8, p. 177–201.

———— 1957, Late Cretaceous cyclic deposits, Book Cliffs, eastern Utah: Am. Assoc. Petroleum Geologists Bull., v. 41, no. 8, p. 1760–1774.

SAND TRENDS AND PALEOSLOPE IN ILLINOIS BASIN AND MISSISSIPPI EMBAYMENT[1]

WAYNE ARTHUR PRYOR[2]

Pittsburgh, Pennsylvania

ABSTRACT

Relationships between major sand body trends and facies distributions of the Cretaceous Gulfian Series in the Mississippi embayment and the Mississippian Chesterian Series in the Illinois basin have been investigated. This study indicates that trends of major sand bodies in these two depositional basins are intrinsically related to their paleoslopes, depositional strikes, and basin axes. Major sand bodies in the Gulfian and Chesterian Series have southwesterly trends that parallel the respective paleoslopes and basin axes, and that are normal to depositional strikes. Studies of directional properties enhance the predictability of these trends.

An impressive similarity exists between the sediments in the Gulfian Series of the Mississippi embayment and the Chesterian Series of the Illinois basin. Both basins were open-ended to the south and sediments were introduced longitudinally at the northeastern end; the paleoslopes were to the southwest and parallel with the basin axes; the depositional strikes were east-west, normal to the basin axes; sediment transport directions were to the southwest; and the depositional patterns are those of deltaic deposition in the north, becoming increasingly marine to the south.

Based on the parallelism exhibited by these features, a depositional model has been developed for this type of sedimentation in an intracratonic basin. Within the model, trends of major sand bodies are oriented parallel to the basin axis, paleoslope, and sediment transport direction, are normal to the depositional strike, and are the result of a deltaic pattern of sedimentation.

INTRODUCTION

It has long been known that the distribution pattern of linear sand bodies in depositional basins is organized and not random. It would be economically advantageous if the exploration geologist could predict correctly the distributive pattern of linear sand bodies within a depositional basin, with a limited amount of geological information.

The purpose of this paper is to relate various aspects of sediment deposition in the Chesterian Series of the Illinois basin and in the Gulfian Series of the Mississippi embayment to the established trends of sand bodies. It is the purpose also to compare and contrast the findings in the two basins. From this comparison a unified concept relating sand trends and facies is developed for the Chesterian Illinois basin and the Gulfian Mississippi embayment. This conceptual framework then serves as the basis of a depositional model for predicting various trends in these basins and in other similar basins.

[1] Read before the Association at Atlantic City, New Jersey, April 25, 1960. Manuscript received, April 26, 1960.

[2] Gulf Research and Development Company.

GENERAL GEOLOGY

The Illinois basin and the Mississippi embayment are on the buried south-central flank of the Canadian shield (Fig. 1). They are bordered on the north and east by two broad regional uplifts—the Kankakee arch and the Cincinnati arch-Nashville dome, and on the southwest by the Ozark dome. The southern extremes of the Illinois basin are overlapped by the Mississippi embayment in southern Illinois. Cratonic sedimentation on a slowly subsiding shelf is typical of the early Paleozoic Era throughout the area and resulted in a thick ($\pm 10,000$ feet) sequence of mature marine clastics, derived chiefly from the Canadian shield, and widespread marine carbonates.

Major carbonate deposition in the Illinois basin ended with the introduction of large quantities of immature clastics at the beginning of mid-Mississippian time. During this time a known maximum thickness of more than 1,300 feet of shales, sandstones, and carbonates was deposited in deltaic and shallow marine-shelf environments. There are many features indicative of shallow-water deposition in Chesterian sediments, including many thin and discontinuous coal beds. The shales are gener-

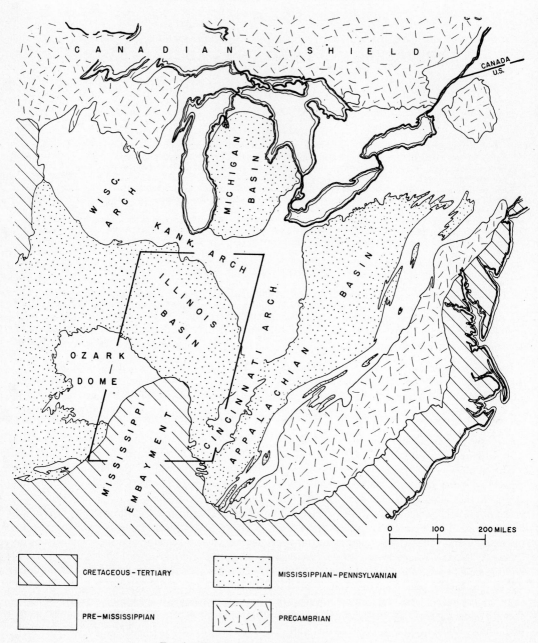

FIG. 1.—Eastern North America and study area.

ally silty and nonfossiliferous. Many of the limestones are thin and laterally extensive.

There are thirteen major intervals of sandstone accumulation in the Chesterian Series (Fig. 2). The distribution patterns of sandstone bodies within these intervals are widely variable; several sands may be well developed at any one point. Maximum sand development is associated commonly with channeling. Channel-phase sandstones are generally 30–70 feet thick and range up to 150 feet, but the laterally equivalent sheet-phase sandstones generally are less than 30 feet thick. Chesterian sandstones are the major petroleum reservoirs in the Illinois basin. Petrographically, the Chesterian Series sandstones are fine- to very fine-grained protoquartzites. The coarsest and best sorted sandstones occur in the channel phases. Plants are the most common fossils in the sandstones, although marine fossils have been observed. Swann (1951, p. 2576), and Siever (1953, p. 215) have suggested a marine-shelf strand-line origin for the Chesterian sandstones; however, indications of recent investigations by Potter and others (1958, p. 1041), are that fluviatile and deltaic environments were dominant over shallow marine-shelf conditions.

The original extent of Chesterian sedimentation is not known definitely, but it is thought (Potter and others, 1958, p. 1018) to have extended eastward across the Cincinnati arch to the Appalachian basin. Undoubtedly, it also extended farther north and farther south than the present erosional edge. Unlike most of the lower Paleozoic sediments in the Illinois basin, Chesterian clastics were derived chiefly from the northern Appalachian geosyncline and the eastern Canadian shield (Potter and others, 1958; and Potter and Pryor, in preparation).

Following Chesterian sedimentation, the Mississippian and earlier Paleozoic sediments were truncated by erosion; and a surface of low relief, bearing a well developed stream channel system, was produced (Siever, 1951, p. 561). This erosional surface was buried later by Pennsylvanian sediments. There is no evidence that the Illinois basin was a depositional site during the Permian, Triassic, or Jurassic Period. It was probably a site of mild uplift and erosion during this time span. The locus of cratonic deposition shifted southward (Potter and Pryor, in preparation), and in Late Cretaceous time the Mississippi embayment was formed (Pryor, 1959, 1960). The initial Gulfian deposits in the basin are residual gravels and clays derived from adjacent Paleozoic rocks. As the Gulfian seas transgressed northward into the embayment (Stearns, 1958; and Pryor, 1959, 1960), more than 1,200 feet of marine-shelf carbonates and intercalated immature deltaic sands and clays were deposited (Fig. 2). The carbonate sediments are best developed and most widespread in the lower half of the Gulfian Series. These sediments range from relatively pure chalks in the south to extremely argillaceous chalks in the north. Marine clays form only a small percentage of the sediments and are laterally and vertically transitional with the chalks and the sands. These transitional clays are calcareous, glauconitic, and fossiliferous.

Sands form more than half of the Gulfian Series in the Mississippi embayment. They are interbedded with lignitic silts and clays in the northern part of the area, and with calcareous clays and chalks in the southern part. Lack of closely spaced well records in the area prohibits detailed knowledge of the shape and orientation of individual sand bodies; however, the gross aspects can be determined. Petrographically, the Gulfian sands are fine- to very fine-grained protoquartzites (Pryor, 1959, 1960). Stephenson (1914) suggested that these sands are shallow-water, littoral deposits. More recently, Stearns (1958, p. 1089) suggested a shallow-water beach environment. The present writer (1959, 1960) supports a deltaic-fluviatile origin as the dominant depositional environment for the sands of the Gulfian Series.

Late Cretaceous Gulfian sediments are preserved essentially in their original extent. The present Ozark escarpment was the approximate western limit of deposition; the Cincinnati arch-Nashville dome was the approximate eastern limit. Facies studies (Stearns and Armstrong, 1955; Stearns, 1958; and Pryor, 1959, 1960) are suggestive of a northern limit of Gulfian sedimentation in the Mississippi embayment, not more than a few miles north of the present outcrop in the southern tip of Illinois. The clastics of the Gulfian Series were derived in large part from crystalline and metamorphic terrain of the Blue

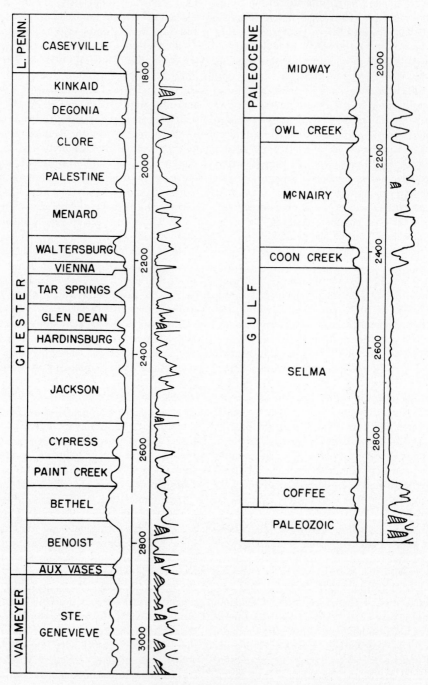

Fig. 2.—Generalized stratigraphic sections for the Illinois basin Chesterian
Series and the Mississippi embayment Gulfian Series.

Ridge and Piedmont Plateau of the southern Appalachian Mountains (Pryor, 1959, 1960). A period of emergence followed deposition of the Gulfian Series and preceded the subsidence of the embayment and subsequent deposition of the widespread, fine-grained marine clastics of the Paleocene Midway Series. The locus of cratonic sedimentation again shifted southward and the coarse-grained, dominantly nonmarine, Eocene sediments were deposited.

FACIES TRENDS

CHESTERIAN SERIES

Basin-wide facies relations are modifications of those presented by Swann and Bell (1958). In order to show these relations for a nearly complete section, over as wide an area as possible, the interval between the base of the Chesterian Series (base of Aux Vases sandstones) and the top of the Waltersburg unit (base of Palestine sandstone) was selected. The truncated stratigraphic section is omitted from the mapping. A general thickening of the Chesterian Series to the southwest is shown by the isopachous lines (Fig. 3). The thickness ranges from less than 600 feet in the north, to more than 1,200 feet in the southwest. The southwest-trending axis of the depositional basin is delineated by the increased thickness of the section toward the central part of the area.

Clastic ratios (Fig. 3) are greater than 4:1 in the north, and decrease to less than 2:1 in the south. There is a transition in the patterns of

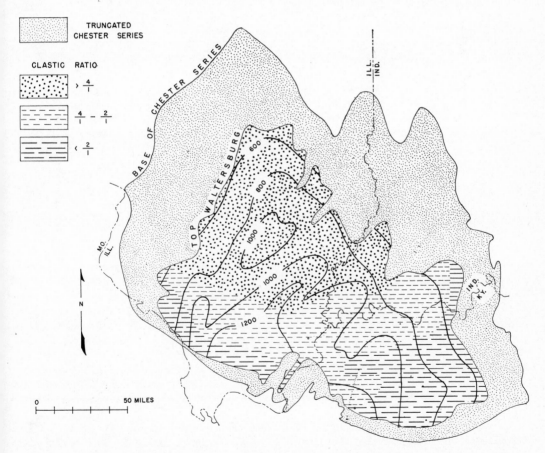

FIG. 3.—Thickness and clastic ratio of Chesterian Series in interval from base of Aux Vases sandstone to top of Waltersburg interval (base of Palestine sandstone), in Illinois basin. Modified from Swann and Bell, 1958.

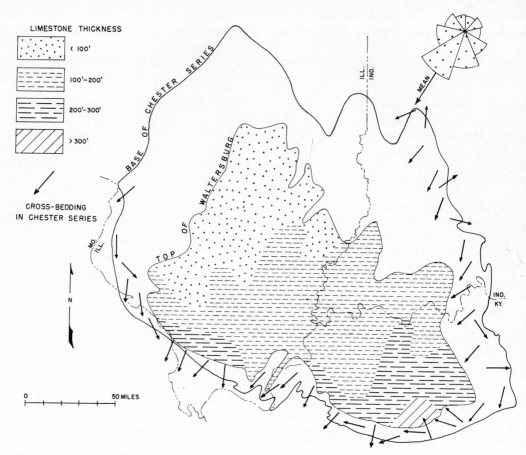

Fig. 4.—Directions of cross-stratification in sandstones of Chesterian Series (modified from Potter and others' 1958) and thickness of limestone in interval from base of Aux Vases sandstone to top of Waltersburg interval, in Illinois basin (modified from Swann and Bell, 1958).

clastic ratios from north to slightly southwest. The strike of the patterns is east-west. Total Chesterian limestone thickness increases to the south and southwest (Fig. 4), reaching a maximum thickness of more than 300 feet in the southern-most part of the Illinois basin. The strike of this pattern is east-west. Studies of directional properties of Chesterian Series sandstones (Potter and others, 1958) are summarized in Figure 4 and suggest that major paleocurrent directions were to the southwest.

The major Chesterian facies grade to the south and southwest and strike east-west. The plunge of the axis of the depositional basin is to the south-west and the trend of the paleocurrent system is to

the south and southwest. These combined features are suggestive of a southwest-trending paleoslope and an east-west depositional strike for the Chesterian Series in the Illinois basin. The *paleoslope* is the inferred slope or gravity gradient, down which ancient sediments have been transported. The *depositional strike* is the trend of isopleths on a paleoslope, which can be used to define energy gradients or shorelines. Partly on the basis that the sandstone bodies of the Chesterian Series appear to be regional slope (paleoslope) rather than depositional strike deposits, Potter and others (1958) concluded that they were fluvial and shallow marine-shelf deposits. Mixed fluvial and subordinate shallow marine conditions on a low lying coastal plain and marine shelf are strongly suggestive of a deltaic environment of deposition for the Chesterian Series of the Illinois basin.

GULFIAN SERIES

The Gulfian Series is thinnest in the north, thickens to the south, and thins rapidly to the west. The thickness (Fig. 5) ranges from less than 200 feet in the north to more than 1,000 feet in the southern part of Tennessee. Although the isopach lines are truncated in the eastern part of this area, immediately to the south, in Mississippi, they recurve southward. Stearns (1958, p. 1089) shows the closure of the lines in an elongate area in northwestern Mississippi, adjacent to the Mississippi River. In addition to this, there is a marked, eastward stratigraphic thinning of the Gulfian units within the broad truncated area. A projection of this thinning suggests a wedging out of the section just west of the Nashville dome. There is a general thickening of the stratigraphic section toward the central part of the Mississippi embayment, delineating the northeast-southwest depositional axis, parallel to the present course of the Mississippi River and the structural axis (Stearns and Armstrong, 1955) of the Mississippi embayment.

Sand-clay ratios (Fig. 5) decrease southward. The ratios range from greater than 2:1 in the north to less than 1:2 in the southern part of the area. The fine clastics, in the Gulfian Series, are increasingly calcareous to the southwest and grade into more marine sediments to the south. The percentage, by thickness, of marine beds (as opposed to clearly nonmarine beds) in the Gulfian Series (Pryor, 1959, 1960) shows a significant pattern of distribution (Fig. 6). Marine sediments increase to the south and southwest, reaching a maximum of 100 per cent in southwestern Tennessee. There is an area of predominantly nonmarine sediments (less than 25 per cent marine beds) in the northeastern part of the embayment

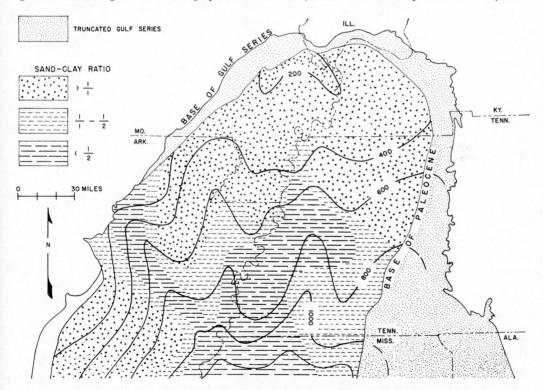

FIG. 5.—Thickness and sand-clay ratios of Gulfian Series in interval from base of Gulfian Series to base of Paleocene Clayton formation in Mississippi embayment. Modified from Pryor, 1959, 1960.

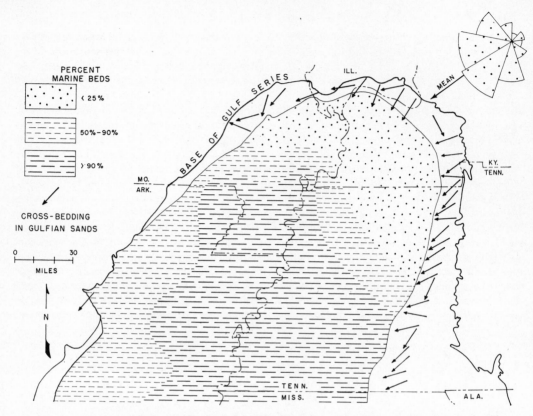

FIG. 6.—Directions of cross-stratification in McNairy formation sands and percentage of marine beds in Gulfian Series, in Mississippi embayment. Modified from Pryor 1959, 1960.

The strike of this facies gradient is northwest-southeast. The principal direction of Gulfian paleocurrents, as interpreted from cross-bedding, in the Mississippi embayment was to the southwest, parallel to the axial trace of the depositional basin (Fig. 6).

The major facies in the Gulfian Mississippi embayment grade to the south and southwest and strike northwest-southeast. The axial plunge of the depositional basin is to the southwest, and the paleocurrent system trend is to the southwest. The facies distribution and paleocurrent pattern are suggestive of a southwest-trending paleoslope and a northwest-southeast depositional strike for the Gulfian Series of the Mississippi embayment. The distribution of major facies, the depositional pattern, and paleontological evidences led the writer (Pryor, 1959, 1960) to conclude that the Gulfian Series in the Mississippi embayment was

the result of deltaic deposition on a shallow-marine shelf.

SAND TRENDS

Linear sand bodies in the Chesterian Series of the Illinois basin (Swann, 1951; Pryor and others, 1957; Swann and Bell, 1958; and Potter and others, 1958) are distributed throughout the thirteen intervals of sand deposition. Axes of trends of 15 known elongate sand accumulations (Fig. 7) are aligned to the southwest and south, though a few are aligned to the southeast. In the Gulfian Series Mississippi embayment, axes of four major sand bodies are discernible (Fig. 7). The two southernmost axes define trends of sand bodies in the lower part of the Gulfian Series; the northern two are in the upper part. These trends are also aligned to the southwest.

Studies of directional properties in the Illinois

basin (Potter and others, 1958) and in the Mississippi embayment (Pryor, 1959, 1960) are indicative of a good regional correlation between the direction of cross-stratification along basinal margins, and major sand trends within the basins. The mean directions of Chesterian and Gulfian cross-stratification are to the southwest (Fig. 7), directly parallel with the major sand trends. Sand

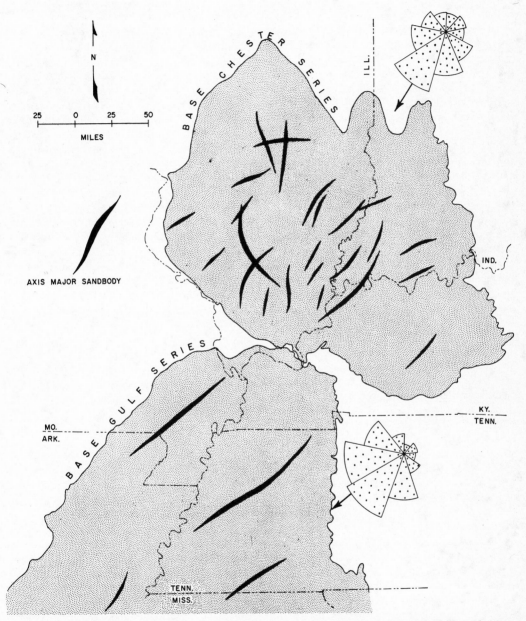

Fig. 7.—Axial trends of major sand bodies and cross-stratification summaries in Illinois basin (modified from Swann, 1951; Pryor and others, 1957; Swann and Bell, 1958; and Potter and others, 1958) and in Mississippi embayment (modified from Stearns and Armstrong, 1955; Stearns, 1958; and Pryor, 1959, 1960).

trends in these two depositional basins are highly predictable from directional data taken along the margins of the basins.

Sand trends in the Chesterian Series of the Illinois basin are related to major basinal features as follows (1) the trends are parallel with the axis of the depositional basin, the sediment transport direction, and the paleoslope; and (2) they are generally normal to the lines of equal thickness, the strike of the lithofacies patterns, the lines of equal limestone thickness, and hence are normal to the depositional strike. The sand trends of the Gulfian Series in the Mississippi embayment are parallel to the axis of the depositional basin, the sediment transport system, and the paleoslope; and they are normal to the lithofacies patterns and the per cent marine-beds pattern; they are normal to the depositional strike. Sand bodies that are peripheral to the distal margins of most modern deltas do not appear to be prominent in either of these two basins. The absence of these depositional strike sand bodies suggests that burial of the deltaic sediments proceeded rapidly enough to preserve them from attack by waves and redistribution of the sands into new patterns by currents.

BASINAL SIMILARITIES

Parallel relations between the Chesterian Series and the Gulfian Series are impressive. There are over-all similarities in the architecture of the two depositional basins: both are oblong with southward plunging axes, both are open-ended to the south, and both received sediments longitudinally into the closed northeastern end. Particularly striking are the similarities between facies distribution, paleoslope, transport direction, depositional strike, and spatial distribution of marine and nonmarine sediments. Deltaic sedimentation on a shallow marine shelf is the deduced dominant depositional mode in both basins. Sand trends are directly related to this mode. The linear sand bodies, in the Chesterian and Gulfian Series, are deltaic-fluviatile in origin.

The main differences between the sediments of the two basins are in age, degree of consolidation, scale, and degree of preservation. Of these, only scale and degree of preservation are pertinent. The Gulfian Series, as mapped here, extends a

distance of approximately 200 miles from southern Illinois to the northern part of Mississippi (Fig. 8). In this distance there are facies as diverse as fluvial, delta, and shelf. The embayment Gulfian Series continues southward into central Mississippi, where it enters the east-west trending Gulf Coast miogeosyncline. The Mississippian sequence of the Illinois basin is also approximately 200 miles in length. The Chesterian is thought to be a deltaic sequence, and the dominantly calcareous Valmeyer Series is thought to be mainly a marine-shelf sequence. The Mississippian System of the Illinois basin represents only a small part of a larger depositional system that was similar to the Cretaceous Mississippi embayment. Only this small part is preserved because of subsequent structural development and truncation. However, northward in the Michigan basin, the lower Mississippian sequence becomes more clastic than its Illinois basin equivalent; and the Chesterian Series is absent. To the south, in central Kentucky, central Tennessee, northern Mississippi, and in northern Arkansas, the Chesterian Series is composed chiefly of carbonates and fine clastics; and sandstones are not abundant.

It is suggested here that a depositional, intracratonic basin, analogous to the Cretaceous Mississippi embayment, existed on the south flank of the Canadian shield during the Mississippian Period. It is believed to have extended from at least as far north as the Michigan basin southward into Arkansas and Mississippi, where it entered the marginal miogeosyncline.

AVAILABILITY OF DATA

At this point it is pertinent to bring out the factor of available data from both basins. Wells penetrating the Chesterian Series in the Illinois basin number in the tens of thousands. There are excellent geophysical and lithologic records, and they are widespread and well spaced. Thousands of these well records were used to obtain the preceding regional picture of the Chesterian Series. In contrast, less than 100 subsurface records are available for the Gulfian Series in the northern Mississippi embayment. These records are chiefly drillers' logs and well sample descriptions, and only a few geophysical records. Approximately 50 subsurface records, of sufficient

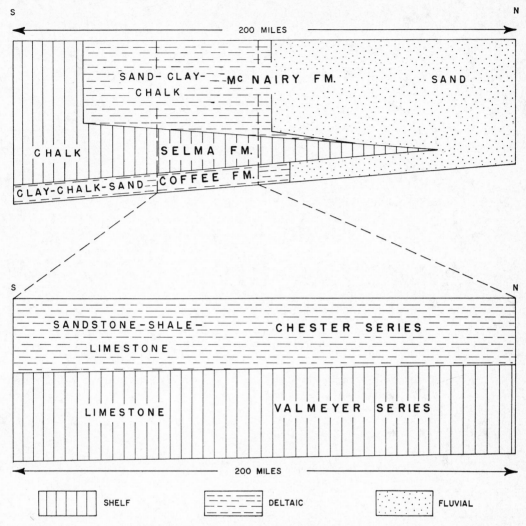

FIG. 8.—Lateral scalar relationships between Gulfian Series of the Mississippi embayment and Mississippian sequence of the Illinois basin, in north-south diagrammatic cross sections.

quality, were used to obtain the preceding regional picture of the Gulfian Mississippi embayment. In both basins outcrops are neither abundant, nor widespread. However, outcrops of Chesterian sediments are qualitatively and numerically superior to those of the Gulfian Series.

The qualitative and numerical superiority of the data available for the Chesterian Series of the Illinois basin, as compared to that available for the Gulfian Series of the Mississippi embayment,

is readily apparent in view of the detailed knowledge of the Chesterian stratigraphy and disposition of sandstone bodies. However, a very satisfactory regional description of the Gulfian Mississippi embayment, comparable to that presented for the Chesterian Illinois basin, has been obtained on the basis of rather meager data. It is suggested here that a limited number of properly spaced exploration wells, accompanied by a limited number of properly spaced outcrop descriptions, will yield sufficient data to outline a satisfactory regional picture. Use of this regional description, within the framework of the following conceptual depositional model, can aid in exploration and enhance predictions of economic sand trends within depositional basins of this type.

DEPOSITIONAL MODEL

In recent years a concept has been held that there are relatively few types of sedimentary basins and that the vast majority of sedimentary rocks belong to a relatively small number of recurring patterns of sedimentation (Potter, 1959). It has been suggested (Potter, 1959, and Pryor, 1960) that a systematic study of a relatively few, carefully selected basins would lead to the elucidation of the different depositional patterns.

The Illinois basin and Mississippi embayment have been studied in sufficient detail to serve as a basis for one such conceptual model (Fig. 9). In this depositional model the basin is oblong and the axis plunges toward the open end. The depositional pattern is interpreted as a delta in the closed end of the basin, grading down the paleoslope into a region of marine-shelf sedimentation. The facies gradient is parallel to the depositional axis. The paleoslope and sediment transport directions are parallel to the basin axis and the facies gradient. The depositional strike is normal to the basin axis, the facies gradient, the paleoslope, and the sediment transport direction. The trends of major sand bodies, in this depositional model, are parallel to the basin axis, facies gradient, paleoslope, and transport direction; and are normal to the depositional strike.

This conceptual model of deposition can be a guide for exploration in an intracratonic basin in which available subsurface information is meager, and yet sufficient for the construction of a suitable regional picture. There are indications that the subsequent Tertiary sedimentation pattern in the Mississippi embayment is the same as that of the underlying Gulfian Series. The present Mississippi River delta complex is a continuation of that pattern. If this is the case, then the above model can be used as a guide to the exploration of the Tertiary sediments along and adjacent to the axial trace of the Mississippi embayment and its southward projection.

In order to contrast this model with that of another type, a model for sedimentation in a linear basin can be tentatively offered. This model is based on the regional investigations of the facies, paleocurrents, and sand trends in the upper Paleozoic sediments of the Appalachian miogeosyncline, in Maryland, Pennsylvania, and New York, by Pelletier (1958) and Yeakel (1958). In this conceptual model (Fig. 10) the facies trend, paleoslope, and sediment transport direction are parallel with each other, but are normal to the basin axis. The depositional strike is parallel to the basin axis. The trends of major linear sand bodies are normal to the depositional strike in the intracratonic basin model (Fig. 9), but here (Fig. 10) they are parallel with the depositional strike. With the development of major deltaic sedimentation at any place along the margins of this linear basin, the model could be altered to include a subbasin of another type, such as the intracratonic basin model.

SUMMARY AND CONCLUSIONS

The relations between trends of major sand bodies and regional characteristics in the Chesterian Series of the Illinois basin and in the Gulfian Series of the Mississippi embayment have been investigated. Evidence from regional facies and thickness distributions, and sediment transport direction is used to establish the depositional basin architecture, paleoslope, depositional strike, and the depositional pattern for each of the basins. From these interrelations the following conclusions are drawn.

1. Trends of major linear sand bodies in both basins are internally consistent and well oriented. They trend to the southwest.

2. The sediment pattern of deposition of both basins is indicative of deltaic conditions in the northern end, and a gradation into shallow marine conditions to the south. The linear sand bodies are fluviatile-deltaic in origin.

3. The trend of paleoslopes and basinal axes is northeast-southwest in both basins; the trend of depositional strikes is nearly east-west.

4. The trends of major sand bodies are related intrinsically to these regional features in both basins, being parallel to the paleoslope and normal to the depositional strike. Cross-stratification

studies increase the accuracy of predicting the trends of linear sand bodies.

5. A limited amount of properly selected surface and subsurface data is sufficient to yield an adequate regional picture of major basinal trends.

Similarities between these two depositional basins lead to the development of a conceptual model of deposition in an intracratonic basin. The model is an oblong, open-ended basin, receiving sediments longitudinally at the closed end. The

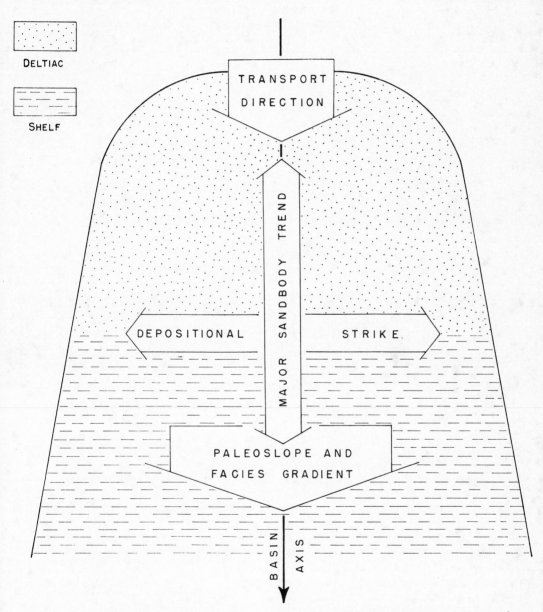

DELTIAC

SHELF

Fig. 9.—Dragrammatic sedimentation model of an open ended, oblong, intracratonic basin. Conceptual model based on Chesterian Illinois basin and Gulfian Mississippi embayment.

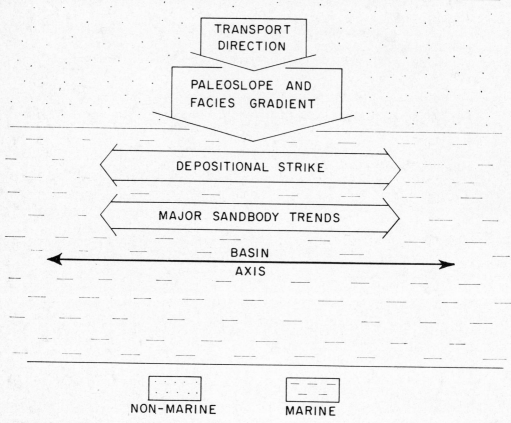

Fɪɢ. 10.—Preliminary sedimentation model of an elongate intercratonic miogeosynclinal basin; based on the Ordovician, Silurian, Devonian, and Mississippian sequence of Pennsylvania, Maryland, and New York (Pelletier, 1958; and Yeakel, 1958).

axis of the basin plunges toward the open end. It is deduced from the depositional patterns that the mode of deposition was deltaic and that the site of deposition was a shallow marine shelf. The facies gradient, paleoslope, and sediment transport directions are parallel to the basin axis and are normal to the depositional strike. Major sand body trends are parallel to the facies gradient, paleoslope, sediment transport direction, and basin axis, and are normal to the depositional strike. Development of conceptual models of this type and of other diverse types of depositional basins can facilitate exploration and enhance predictions of trends of economic importance.

REFERENCES

Pelletier, B. R., 1958, Pocono paleocurrents in Pennsylvania and Maryland: Geol. Soc. America Bull., v. 69, no. 8, p. 1033–1064.
Potter, P. E., 1959, Facies model conference: Science, v. 129, no. 3358, p. 1292–1294.
—— Nosow, Edmund, and others, 1958, Chester cross-bedding and sandstone trends in Illinois basin: Am. Assoc. Petroleum Geologists Bull., v. 42, no. 5, p. 1013–1046.
—— and Pryor, W. A., 1961, Dispersal centers of Paleozoic and later clastics of the upper Mississippi Valley and adjacent areas: Geol. Soc. America Bull., v. 72, no. 8.
Pryor, W. A., 1959, Cretaceous geology and petrology of the upper Mississippi embayment: unpub. Ph.D. dissertation, Rutgers Univ., New Brunswick, N. J.
—— 1960, Cretaceous sedimentation in upper Mis-

sissippi embayment: Am. Assoc. Petroleum Geologists Bull., v. 44, no. 9, p. 1473–1504; correction, v. 44, no. 12, p. 1939.

—— Maxey, G. B., and Parizek, R. R., 1957, Sources of groundwater for waterflooding in Illinois, *in* Symposium on waterflooding: Illinois Geol. Survey Bull. 80, p. 51–76.

Siever, Raymond, 1951, The Mississippian-Pennsylvanian unconformity in southern Illinois: Am. Assoc. Petroleum Geologists Bull., v. 35, no. 3, p. 542–581; Illinois Geol. Survey Rept. Inv. 152.

—— 1953, Petrology and sedimentation of upper Chester sandstones: Jour. Sed. Petrology, v. 23, no. 4, p. 207–219; Illinois Geol. Survey Rept. Inv. 170.

Stearns, R. G., 1957, Cretaceous, Paleocene, and lower Eocene geologic history of the northern Mississippi embayment: Geol. Soc. America Bull., v. 68, no. 9, p. 1077–1100.

—— and Armstrong, C. A., 1955, Post-Paleozoic stratigraphy of western Tennessee and adjacent portions of the upper Mississippi embayment: Tennessee Div. Geology Rept. Inv. 2, p. 1–29.

Stephenson, L. W., 1914, Cretaceous deposits of the eastern Gulf region and species of *Exogyra* from the eastern Gulf regions and the Carolinas: U. S. Geol. Survey Prof. Paper 81.

Swann, D. H., 1951, Waltersburg sandstone oil pools of lower Wabash area, Illinois and Indiana: Am. Assoc. Petroleum Geologists Bull., v. 35, no. 12, p. 2561–2581.

—— and Bell, A. H., 1958, Habitat of oil in the Illinois basin, *in* Habitat of oil, a symposium: Am. Assoc. Petroleum Geologists, p. 447–472.

Yeakel, L. S., 1958, Early Silurian and late Ordovician paleocurrents in the central Appalachians (abst.): Geol. Soc. America Bull., v. 69, no. 12, p. 1667–1668.

PROPERTIES AND GENESIS OF "JACKPILE" SANDSTONE, LAGUNA, NEW MEXICO[1]

J. S. SCHLEE[2] AND R. H. MOENCH[3]
Athens, Georgia, and Denver, Colorado

ABSTRACT

The "Jackpile" sandstone, a term of local usage, is exposed near Laguna, New Mexico. It is the uppermost unit in the Morrison formation, of Jurassic age. The petrography, sedimentary structures, and shape of the unit, its relation to tectonic structures, and analogies to similar ancient and modern sandstones suggest that it was deposited by a northeast-flowing stream system that was largely confined by contemporaneous structural depression. Continued downwarping after deposition, followed by erosional truncation, emphasized the structural localization of the unit.

The sandstone is fine to medium grained, friable, and moderately well sorted; coarser grained beds are more abundant near the base of the unit. The composition ranges from a calcite-cemented subarkose near the base to kaolinite-indurated quartz sandstone near the top. This compositional variation probably is a result of weathering prior to deposition of the Dakota sandstone. Terrestrial plant remains are locally abundant.

The "Jackpile" sandstone is a northeast-trending tabular body as much as 13 miles wide, at least 33 miles long, and locally more than 200 feet thick. It splits into distributary-like fingers to the northeast, and cross-beds in the sandstone dip mostly northeast. The unit wedges to the northwest and southeast along an angular unconformity bounded by the overlying Dakota sandstone, and broad folds in the strata below this unconformity parallel the southeastern limit of the "Jackpile" sandstone.

Other stratigraphic units in the Morrison formation tend to thicken in the area of the "Jackpile" sandstone. This suggests that structural downwarping was active in the area before, as well as during and after, deposition of the unit.

INTRODUCTION

The discovery of the large Jackpile uranium deposit by the Anaconda Company stimulated considerable economic and scientific interest in the area near Laguna, New Mexico (Fig. 1). Subsequent exploration by Anaconda, the Saint Anthony Uranium Corporation, and other companies, plus mapping by the writers and their co-workers of the U. S. Geological Survey, delineated the major host sandstone. It was found to be confined to a northeast-trending belt, and as much as 13 miles wide and at least 33 miles long. Local

[1] Read before the Association at Atlantic City, New Jersey, April 25, 1960. Publication authorized by the Director, U. S. Geological Survey. Manuscript received April 26, 1960.

[2] U. S. Geological Survey and University of Georgia.

[3] U. S. Geological Survey. The authors wish to acknowledge drill hole data supplied by the Anaconda Company and by the Saint Anthony Uranium Corporation. Permission to study the area was granted by the Laguna Indian Tribal Council and the writers were ably assisted in the field by W. P. Puffett, Frank Hensley, and W. B. Bryan, Jr. In particular, the writers are greatly indebted to L. C. Craig and R. A. Cadigan of the U. S. Geological Survey for many helpful suggestions and valuable discussions. The work was done on behalf of the Division of Raw Materials of the U. S. Atomic Energy Commission.

workers have called this unit the "Jackpile" sandstone, after the Jackpile mine, and have recognized it as the uppermost unit in the Morrison formation, of Jurassic age.

The subject of this paper is the paleostructural control and petrology of the "Jackpile" sandstone. The shape of the unit, its sedimentary structures, textures, and composition, will be described and related to the origin of the deposit. Also, the effect of contemporaneous tectonic structures on the geometry of the sandstone body will be discussed.

The "Jackpile" sandstone is exposed in a broad belt of outcrops that extends northeastward across the area (Fig. 1). These exposures revealed the limits, thickness variations, and other geologic relations of the southeastern half and northeastern part of the unit. Northwest of the outcrop belt, however, Cretaceous strata bury the "Jackpile" sandstone. Here, data furnished by Anaconda and the Saint Anthony Uranium Corporation from more than 600 drill holes revealed the limits, thickness variations, and other properties of the central and northwestern part of the unit. More than half of these holes were concentrated within about 5 miles of the Jackpile mine (Fig.

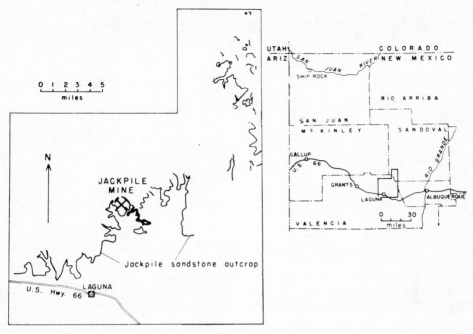

FIG. 1.—Index map showing outline of Laguna area, New Mexico, and outcrops of "Jackpile" sandstone.

1). The remaining holes, however, were adequately distributed to determine the isopachs shown in Figure 3. The solid lines cannot be shifted more than a few hundred feet. The dashed lines may be shifted a mile or more, but not enough to change the shape of the unit significantly.

REGIONAL STRATIGRAPHY

The sedimentary rocks exposed in the Laguna district include strata that range in age from Triassic through Cretaceous. In ascending order these include the Chinle formation, of Triassic age; the Entrada sandstone, Todilto limestone, Summerville formation, Bluff sandstone, and the Morrison formation, of Jurassic age; and the Dakota sandstone and overlying strata, of Cretaceous age (Fig. 2). An angular unconformity separates the strata of Jurassic and Cretaceous age, and southward from the Laguna area this unconformity truncates successively older beds. Jurassic rocks total more than 1,300 feet in thickness, and contain all the uranium deposits in the Laguna area and most of the deposits in the

southern San Juan basin mineral belt (Hilpert and Moench, 1958, 1960). The terminology of Jurassic strata used here is consistent with that used by Freeman and Hilpert (1956, p. 312, Fig. 59), Hilpert and Freeman (1956, p. 300), and Craig and others (1955, p. 132–134).

This report is concerned with the Morrison formation. Craig and others (1955, Figs. 22, 28, 29) define a threefold subdivision of the Morrison formation in much of northwestern New Mexico. In ascending order these members are the Recapture, Westwater Canyon, and Brushy Basin. The Recapture member is composed of interstratified sandstone, siltstone, and mudstone; the overlying Westwater Canyon member is largely arkose and subarkose; and the Brushy Basin member is largely bentonitic mudstone, with some thin beds of arkosic sandstone. In their study of the stratigraphy and uranium deposits of northwestern New Mexico, Freeman and Hilpert (1956, p. 312, 313, Fig. 59) and Hilpert and Freeman (1956, p. 300) retain this classification, and in the area north of Laguna they add a fourth subdivision—the "Jackpile" sandstone—at the top of the Morrison

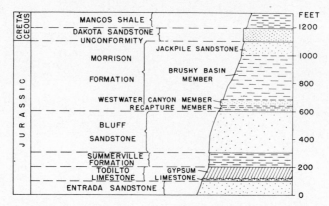

FIG. 2. Partial stratigraphic section for Laguna area, New Mexico.

formation; but they use this term in an informal sense. Freeman and Hilpert (1956, Fig. 61) recognized that the Westwater Canyon member and the "Jackpile" sandstone—the two major host rocks for uranium deposits in the region of Grants and Laguna—are different units that are separated by a thick section of Brushy Basin which is largely mudstone. In accord with these authors, the term "Jackpile" sandstone is used here in an informal sense.

PETROLOGY OF THE "JACKPILE" SANDSTONE

By analogy with certain ancient and modern sandstone deposits, the salient features indicate that the "Jackpile" sandstone was deposited by a system of anastomosing, northeastward-flowing streams. Its excessive thickness, however, suggests that subsidence influenced the deposition of the sandstone. The textures and the compositional variations of the unit suggest that it was weathered before it was buried beneath strata of Cretaceous age.

Shape.—The "Jackpile" sandstone is confined to a belt as much as 13 miles wide, and at least 33 miles long, which extends northeasterly across the Laguna district (Figs. 3 and 4). To the northeast the unit broadens and splits into at least two smaller trough-shaped fingers. According to Krynine's classification (1948, p. 146, and Fig. 9) of the geometry of sandstone bodies, the "Jackpile" sandstone is a tabular body, with a thickness-to-width ratio of about 1:300. Because the deposit is truncated at its top by an angular

unconformity, its present dimensions are smaller than its original dimensions. Conceivably the "Jackpile" sandstone may have extended as a thin sheet over a much wider area. We believe, however, that the original dimensions of the main trough-shaped body of sandstone were not greatly different from the present dimensions. This belief is supported by the fact that the "Jackpile" sandstone thins by loss of beds at the base of the unit (see Fig. 10) as well as by wedging beneath the unconformity.

Two additional factors affect the shape of the unit, as shown in Figure 3, but do not bear on the conclusions. First, because the "Jackpile" sandstone intertongues with the Brushy Basin member, it is not everywhere possible to choose unequivocally the base of the "Jackpile" sandstone. This means that some contours may be shifted somewhat. Second, the Dakota sandstone channels as much as 20 feet into the "Jackpile" sandstone. Such deep scours, however, are rare; and this factor is probably important only locally.

General lithology.—In outcrops the "Jackpile" sandstone has a characteristic chalky white cast in the upper part of the unit, which reflects its kaolin content. This color, actually ranging from yellowish gray to nearly white, is pervasive, and is characteristic of drill cores as well as surface exposures. The sandstone is generally fine to medium grained, poorly to moderately well sorted, and is mostly friable. It is composed of quartz, and minor amounts of feldspar, clay galls, chert and igneous rock fragments; clay, silica, or

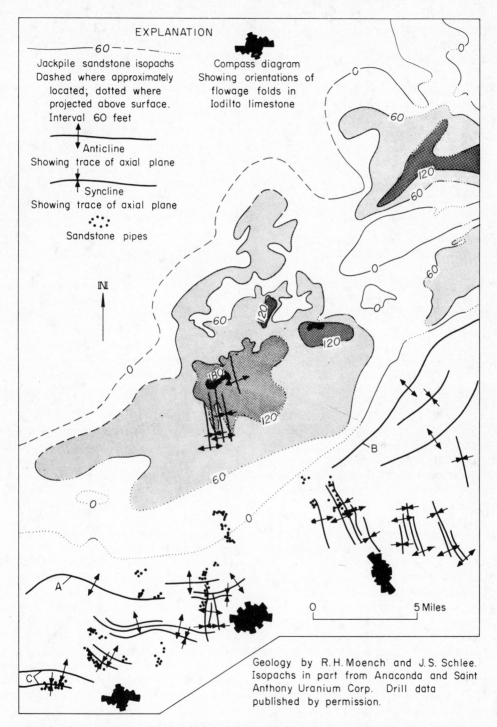

EXPLANATION

—— 60 — — — ....
Jackpile sandstone isopachs
Dashed where approximately
located; dotted where
projected above surface.
Interval 60 feet

Compass diagram
Showing orientations of
flowage folds in
Iodilto limestone

Anticline
Showing trace of axial plane

Syncline
Showing trace of axial plane

Sandstone pipes

5 Miles

Geology by R.H. Moench and J.S. Schlee.
Isopachs in part from Anaconda and Saint
Anthony Uranium Corp. Drill data
published by permission.

Fig. 3.—Generalized map showing thickness of "Jackpile" sandstone, and elements of pre-Dakota structures in Laguna area.

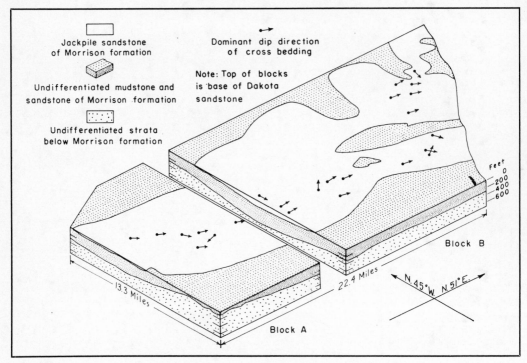

Fig. 4.—Generalized isometric block diagram, showing relations of "Jackpile" sandstone to broad pre-Dakota depression; vertical exaggeration is about 15 times.

calcite, or any mixture of these, compose the cement. According to the classification of McKee and Weir (1953), the unit tends to be thick to thin bedded, and massive, but festoon cross-bedding is well developed in sets as much as 4 feet thick. Beds, or internal sedimentary units, are indistinct, and where they can be distinguished they can be traced a few hundred feet, at most. A few discontinuous beds of greenish gray bentonitic mudstone occur in most exposures.

Organic remains are not abundant in the "Jackpile" sandstone, but local concentrations provide ample evidence of terrestrial origin. Silicified logs are locally abundant in the sandstone, and in some places seem to have formed log jams. Logs as large as 3 feet in diameter and 60 feet in length have been found; they do not have branches, suggesting that they have been transported and rolled some distance from their place of origin. A small concentration of coalified plant remains was found in a collapse structure in the Jackpile mine. As this

structure is buried by additional sandstone, these plant remains were undoubtedly buried during "Jackpile" sedimentation. A large bone fragment —probably from a dinosaur—was found in another collapse structure. Silicified logs were also found in many exposures of sandstone that are stratigraphically well below the "Jackpile" sandstone, and indicate a terrestrial origin for the entire Morrison formation.

Cross-bedding.—Cross-bedding planes dip mostly northeastward, indicating that sediments were transported northeastward, parallel to the length of the unit. Two hundred and ninety-one measurements of cross-bedding attitudes were made at 27 localities. For each locality the dip directions were plotted on compass diagrams, and coded units were used in computation of the arithmetic mean of the directions. The mean dip direction for each of 24 localities is shown on Figure 4, where they are plotted in accord with isometric projection. With few exceptions, they are nearly parallel to the known limits and to the axis of the "Jackpile" sandstone body.

Grain size.—In contrast with the cross-bedding analysis, we were unable to detect a systematic areal change of modal or maximum grain size. Modal grain size was determined at 68 localities that are distributed from one end of the unit to the other. Thirty determinations were made on outcrops, and the material was hand sieved in the field. The remaining 38 determinations were made by Anaconda geologists from diamond drill cores. Maximum grain size was determined at 18 localities. The largest material found in most exposures was in the 2–4 mm size range, but coarse pebbles (32–64 mm) of quartz and chert were found locally at the base of some thick exposures.

In order to determine vertical gradations in grain size, stratigraphic sections through the "Jackpile" sandstone were subdivided into two or three parts, depending on the height of the section. All sections over 90 feet thick were subdivided into lower, middle, and upper parts; those sections between 40 and 90 feet thick were subdivided into two parts—upper and middle. These subdivisions are arbitrary, and from one outcrop to another they are not stratigraphic equivalents, because the thickness of the "Jackpile" sandstone is controlled both by an angular unconformity at the top and by addition of beds at the base. For gross vertical changes in grain size, however, the subdivisions are adequate. Modal size values for each part were then averaged; approximately 3 to 4 values per subdivision for each section were used to obtain the means. Of 68 stratigraphic sections 43 show an upward decrease in average modal grain size.

Maximum grain size was determined and averaged in the same manner, and a smaller tendency for upward decrease is shown. Of 18 sections only 10 show an upward decrease in the average maximum size; the remainder show no trend, or a reverse trend.

In order to visualize the vertical size change, modal grain-size values from 30 stratigraphic sections were averaged (arithmetic mean) for each 10-foot interval and plotted against depth below the Dakota sandstone (Fig. 5). By plotting the values in this manner some error is probably introduced, because there is no way of estimating the thickness of "Jackpile" eroded and whether more has been removed in one place than in another. In spite of these uncertainties, the maximum and to a less degree modal grain size show a tendency to decrease toward the top of the unit. The grain-size change is not gradational as in a graded bed, for coarse-grained sandstone layers

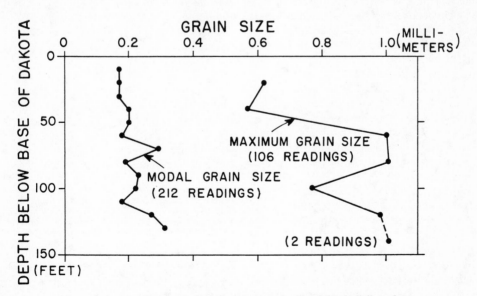

FIG. 5.—Graphs showing vertical changes in grain size of "Jackpile" sandstone.

occur locally in the upper part of the "Jackpile" sandstone. The grain-size relations show only a tendency for the coarser grained beds to be in the lower part of the "Jackpile" sandstone.

Composition and texture.—The composition of the "Jackpile" sandstone is variable, and changes vertically. Using Pettijohn's classification (1957, p. 291) many samples from the lower part of the sandstone are composed of arkose or subarkose, and many from the upper part are composed of subarkose and orthoquartzite. Other samples, comprising nearly half of the 46 thin sections studied, contain clay as the dominant cement, and if the same classification is used, these clay-rich rocks are graywackes. Because the clay-indurated sandstones lack other properties normally associated with graywackes—dark color, good induration, association with basic volcanic rocks or thinly laminated shales—we call these rocks clayey sandstones.

The main detrital constituents are quartz, feldspar, and a variety of rock fragments. Subangular to subrounded quartz grains comprise 80 to 95 per cent of the detrital fraction. Both strained and unstrained varieties are present, and grains are clear or inclusion filled. In most of the sections, the quartz grains are bounded by sharp discontinuous overgrowths which are in optical continuity with the detrital grains. The outline of some quartz grains has been affected by grain interpenetration and by etching due to reaction with the cement or matrix.

Detrital feldspar is a minor constituent (1–19 per cent, average 5 per cent), but has much the same size as quartz. It is more angular than quartz and has an equant to rectangular habit (Fig. 6-A). Most of the feldspar is orthoclase, though some plagioclase and perthite are present also. Grains display all degrees of alteration; some are so greatly altered that only the relict outline of the grain remains, but other grains in the same slide may be completely unaltered. Most feldspar is altered to some extent, as indicated by a dusty appearance in thin section or by alteration to clay along the cleavage traces (Fig. 6-A). Some of the feldspar is extensively embayed or almost entirely replaced by calcite.

Though rock fragments are a minor constituent their variety is large, including volcanic debris, metaquartzite, chert and claystone fragments. The amount of volcanic material may be greatly underestimated because it is commonly altered. Unless a relict texture or shard structure is preserved, its true volcanic identity may be overlooked; such may be the case for many of the claystone fragments and much of the finer interstitial debris. A few isolated grains retain the relict-texture of greatly altered feldspar laths set in a cryptocrystalline groundmass (Fig. 6-B). Metaquartzite fragments have a ragged outline, and the quartz aggregates exhibit sutured boundaries. Chert grains are well rounded, and like feldspar, show all degrees of alteration. In hand specimen claystone fragments are pale greenish gray; in thin section, they are microcrystalline aggregates of clay plus fragments of quartz and feldspar. Other claystone fragments are composed of light brown chloritic material.

The dominant heavy minerals are zircon and tourmaline; lesser amounts of leucoxene, magnetite, rutile, garnet, and sillimanite are also present.

The "Jackpile" sandstone is dominantly calcite cemented near its base, and upward the unit becomes increasingly clay cemented. The rock is friable and porous in most exposures, but near the top of the unit the grain interstices tend to be completely filled with white clay. In typical thick exposures calcite "sand crystals" as much as 10 millimeters across are prevalent near the base of the unit, and impart a mottled luster to the rock. Upward, the sand crystals and finer grained calcite decrease in abundance and small, sparsely disseminated spots of white clay appear. The white clay increases in abundance, and near the top of the unit it thoroughly cements the sandstone. As determined by X-ray analysis the white clay is dominantly kaolinite.[4] Quartz overgrowths on quartz grains are present throughout the unit.

[4] Complete mechanical and X-ray clay analyses were run by John C. Hathaway on 6 samples from the Jackpile mine. Kaolinite was found to predominate greatly over mixed-layered mica-montmorillonite in the clay fractions of four samples of fine- to medium-grained sandstone, which contain abundant white clay. Two samples of finer grained rocks, with little visible white clay, contain dominant mixed-layered mica-montmorillonite, and subordinate kaolinite. Hand picked white clay gives a good kaolinite X-ray powder pattern, determined by Moench.

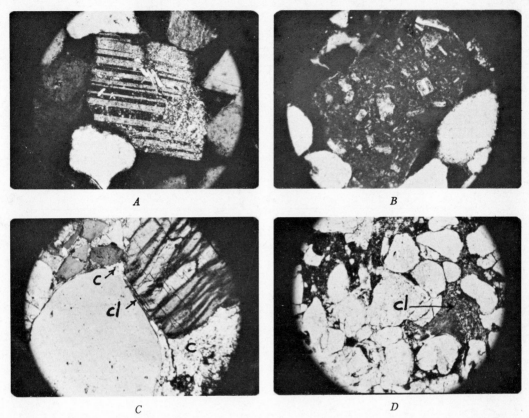

FIG. 6.—Photomicrographs showing typical features of "Jackpile" sandstone. *A*—Partly altered plagioclase grain; crossed nicols; × 84. *B*—Volcanic rock fragments; crossed nicols; × 84. *C*—Relations of clay and calcite between detrital grains; *cl*=clay, *c*=calcite; crossed nicols; × 32. *D*—Typical occurrence of clay matrix; *cl*=clay, probably kaolinite; uncrossed nicols; × 32.

The overgrowths commonly have euhedral crystal faces, and they locally coalesce and bind several adjoining grains. Where clay and mineral cement are present in the same rock, the mineral cement, at least the calcite, appears to have formed later than the clay. In Figure 6-*C*, for example, clay occupies the boundary between two detrital grains, and calcite appears to "invade" the clay from either side.

As seen in thin section the clay ranges in occurrence from extremely fine grained indeterminate aggregates to clots that contain well-crystallized booklets, probably kaolinite (Fig. 6-*D*). In places the clay aggregates completely fill interstices, and in places clay only coats sand grains in a single layer of plates that are oriented normal to the sand grains. Elsewhere only isolated clots of clay

are visible in thin section; they correspond to the spotted occurrence of white clay seen in hand specimens, and may represent thoroughly altered feldspar grains or volcanic debris. All these occurrences of clay may be observed in a single thin section.

The vertical changes in rock classification reflect corresponding mineralogic variations (Fig. 7). In order to determine these changes, stratigraphic sections from which samples were obtained were classified in the manner used for modal and maximum grain size—upper, middle, and lower third, for exposures more than 90 feet thick, and upper and middle categories for exposures 40 to 90 feet thick. The upper and middle categories for the relatively thick and thin exposures are grouped because depth below the

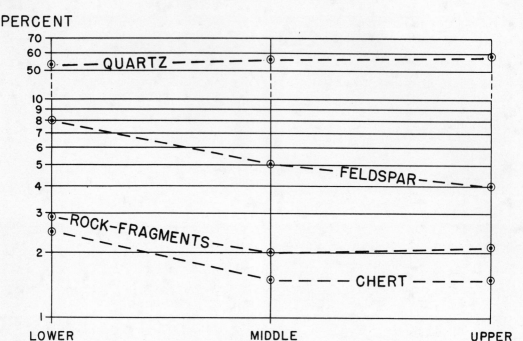

Fɪɢ. 7.—Graph showing vertical changes in mineralogy of "Jackpile" sandstone.

Dakota sandstone seems to be a determining factor of mineralogic variation. We are not, however, comparing stratigraphic equivalents. The detrital composition of each thin section was determined by use of the Folk visual estimate chart (Folk, 1951, p. 32–33), and many thin sections were analyzed by the point-count method, which confirmed the visual estimates. The results were averaged for each position category, and plotted on Figure 7. Upward, the stable constituent—quartz—is enriched relative to the unstable constituents—chert, feldspar, and rock fragments.

When these data are combined with the observations on vertical changes in cementing materials, we conclude that the clay content—mainly kaolinite—is nearly inversely proportional to the feldspar and rock fragment content. This suggests that the clay formed at the expense of the relatively unstable constituents, and the textural relations support this conclusion.

Alteration.—The "Jackpile" sandstone has an excess of interstitial clay compared to ordinary river sand. Lane (1938, p. 505) points out that in spite of the large amount of silt and clay carried by the Mississippi River, the channel sands are "clean"—devoid of fine interstitial detritus. The channel sandstone deposits of the Berea sandstone (Pepper and others, 1954, p. 91) are composed of detrital quartz and feldspar cemented by calcite. Sand 19*B*, a buried Oligocene sand of deltaic-plain origin (Nanz, 1954, p. 112, 117), has a far greater variety of detrital constituents but the rock is cemented by calcite; fine detritus composes only 5.5 per cent of the rock. Both the Berea sandstone and sand 19*B* probably had an "openwork" texture initially, and the voids were later filled by calcite.

The excess of clay in the "Jackpile" sandstone, particularly near the top of the unit, is best explained by weathering prior to the deposition of the Dakota sandstone. The contact between the "Jackpile" and the Dakota marks the hiatus between Upper Jurassic and Cretaceous. During this hiatus the Morrison and underlying formations in the Laguna area were gently folded and beveled by erosion. A regional study of this hiatus by Leopold (1943) disclosed the presence of kaolin and kaolin-cemented sandstones at the top of the Morrison formation in northeast Arizona and northwest New Mexico; he postulated that the kaolin is a product of weathering prior to deposition of Dakota sandstone. In the Laguna district and to the south, the angular unconformity truncates successively older Jurassic and Triassic strata. Where sandstone beds in the Morrison formation and underlying strata converge with the unconformity, they, as well as the "Jackpile" sandstone, are kaolin bearing— which supports Leopold's conclusion. The mineralogic changes are consistent with weathering of relatively unstable detrital constituents. The decomposition of the relatively unstable constituents could give rise to kaolinite, and smaller quantities of other clay minerals, and this decomposition would also result in the observed relative enrichment of quartz and impoverishment of feldspar and rock fragments.

Some decomposition, or weathering, may have taken place during, as well as after, sedimentation. In places the clay fills all interstices of the rock instead of occurring in isolated clots after detrital feldspar or rock fragments. This suggests that in places clay and sand were deposited simultaneously. In addition, some layers near the top of the "Jackpile" sandstone are completely devoid of clay and the labile constituents, and are composed wholly of quartz grains with some overgrowths. This suggests that "Jackpile" sediments were reworked locally by the streams that deposited them and that the weathering products were removed.

Free silica given up during the breakdown of feldspar and volcanic rock fragments may have contributed to silica cementation and to silicification of logs in the "Jackpile" sandstone.

Mode of deposition.—The locally abundant terrestrial plant remains in the "Jackpile" sandstone and other sandstone beds of the Morrison formation indicate a terrestrial origin. The facts that the "Jackpile" sandstone is elongate, trough-shaped, and broadens and branches in the inferred down-current direction provide additional clues to its mode of deposition.

That the "Jackpile" sandstone was deposited in a fluvial milieu is compatible with conclusions reached by other workers for the Morrison forma-

tion in northwest New Mexico and Arizona. McKee and others (1956, Figs. 4 and 8, Pl. 9) suggest that the rocks deposited in the last part of the Jurassic were laid down under subaerial conditions, perhaps as an alluvial fan or floodplain deposit. Similar conclusions were reached by Craig and others (1955, p. 157), who state— "Structures and textures in the Westwater Canyon member and in the sandstones of the Brushy Basin member indicate that they were deposited in a fluvial environment." Harshbarger and others (1957, p. 55) concluded from a study of the Morrison formation west of the Laguna area that it ". . . was deposited by a system of braided streams on a generally flat surface. . . . The sediments are primarily fluvial, consisting of alternating flood plain and channel deposits."

The cross-beds indicate a northeast direction of sediment transport, parallel to the length of the "Jackpile" sandstone. This pattern is consistent with the Jurassic paleogeography of the region as outlined by Harshbarger and others (1957, p. 55) from a study in the Navajo country to the west. Rubey and Bass (1925) measured crossbeds in the Rocktown channel sandstone member of the Dakota sandstone, and found that the dominant dip direction is parallel to the trend of the channel (Fig. 9-*D*), indicating the direction of stream flow. Other studies have relied on the gross stratigraphic relations of the region to determine upstream and downstream directions (see Table I and Fig. 9).

The vertical grain-size change appears to be characteristic of a fluvial environment. LeBlanc and Nanz (Nanz, 1954, p. 110–111) have demonstrated an upward size decrease in point-bar deposits of the Rio Grande, and Nanz was able to show a similar upward change in modal and maximum grain size for sand 19*B*, a buried sand of Oligocene age in the central Rio Grande embayment. Apparently, the upward size decrease has been noticed in other deposits of this type, though detailed studies have not been made. Rittenhouse (Pepper and others, 1954, p. 76) mentioned an upward grain-size change in the Berea sandstone as based on a log from a well drilled in West Virginia. The vertical grain-size change in the "Jackpile" sandstone is not as pronounced as in sand 19*B*. This lack of a pronounced trend suggests that the "Jackpile" was deposited in several channel systems at different levels within the unit rather than in one channel system. The complete lack of systematic areal variation of any of the properties other than cross-bedding, and the difficulty in tracing and correlating units within the "Jackpile" sandstone would suggest some re-working at different levels and different times, as one might expect in an anastomosing, aggrading system of river channels.

The shape of the "Jackpile" sandstone com-pares favorably with modern and ancient channel sand deposits, and seems to be similar to sands deposited by distributary stream systems in deltas or deltaic plains. For example, the sand deposits of the Rio Grande deltaic plain (Nanz, 1954, Fig. 7) are similar in areal configuration to the "Jackpile" sandstone, in that they broaden and branch in a down-current direction (Fig. 8). Deltas, however, are not the only areas where down-current branching patterns can originate.

As shown by Fisk (1952, p. 99–101, Fig. 27), the course of the ancestral Mississippi River has been diverted several times, and as much as 240 miles upstream from the delta. The diversions took place well within the alluvial valley, and each was accompanied by the formation of a new set of meander belt deposits. Patterns formed by such channel breakthroughs branch downstream and are confined to gradually widening valleys..

A similar analogy to distributary channel sand deposits appears when we compare the "Jackpile" sandstone with some ancient deltaic deposits. Four examples of channel sand deposits—with similar and contrasting relations to the "Jackpile" sand-stone—are shown in Figure 9. Sand 19B (Fig. 9-A) of Oligocene age is interpreted to have been deposited under conditions much like those of today in the Rio Grande delta (Nanz, 1954, Fig. 6, and p. 117). This sand is remarkably similar in areal configuration to the "Jackpile" sandstone, and both broaden and branch in the inferred down-current direction. The Pennsyl-vanian "Booch sandstone" (Fig. 9-B) of eastern Oklahoma forms a "generalized deltaic distribu-tary system of channel sands which diverge in a basinward direction . . ." (Busch, 1959, Fig. 12 and p. 2840; also see Busch, 1954). In contrast,

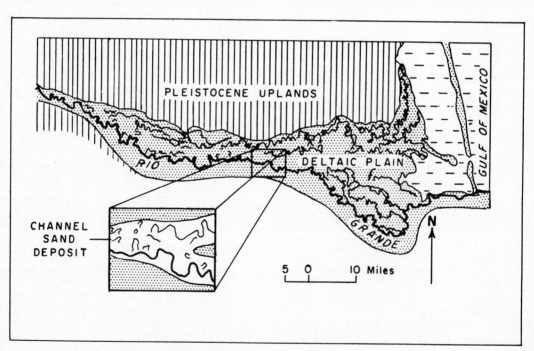

FIG. 8.—Modern fluvial channel sand body. Modified after Nanz, 1954, Fig. 7.

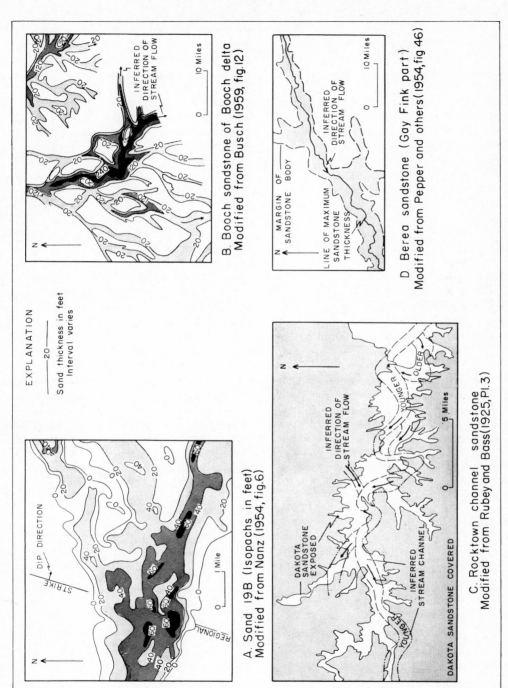

Fig. 9 —Ancient fluvial channel sand bodies.

the Rocktown channel sandstone (Fig. 9-C) of Cretaceous age in Kansas does not branch in a downstream direction; instead, the channel pattern is a meandering one (Rubey and Bass, 1925, p. 57–62). In West Virginia the Berea sandstone (Fig. 9-D) of Mississippian age is concentrated as channel deposits far enough upstream so that tributary channel sands join the main one, and the trunk sand narrows and branches in the upstream direction (Pepper and others, 1954, p. 78).

The foregoing comparisons indicate that the "Jackpile" sandstone was deposited by a stream system that branches downstream. This distributary system may have been part of a delta, or possibly part of a broad alluvial plain that was far removed from any delta. Craig and others (1955, p. 157) suggest that the Westwater Canyon member of the Morrison formation "formed as a broad fan-shaped alluvial plain," and that "it was formed by an alluviating distributary system of braided channels." They further suggest that the Westwater Canyon member reflects "a rejuvenation of the source area, in west-central New Mexico." The "Jackpile" sandstone may represent a repetition of the same type of sedimentation and may reflect a second major rejuvenation of the same source area. If so, the original "Jackpile" sediments should have spread over a far greater area than we are now aware of. This is not unlikely, because we have no way of knowing how much of the original unit was removed by pre-Dakota erosion. If, on the other hand, the "Jackpile" sandstone is a deltaic plain deposit, the

"Jackpile" stream system flowed northeastward into a body of water. Marine or lacustrine deposits that might be time equivalents of the "Jackpile" sandstone have not been recognized in the region to the northeast of the Laguna area, but such deposits may have been removed by pre-Dakota erosion.

Although the shape of the "Jackpile" sandstone closely resembles that of some ancient and modern fluvial channel sand bodies, its thickness compares only with those deposits in which sedimentation was probably accompanied by subsidence or regional tilting (Table I). Among the ancient and modern sand deposits listed in Table I, those that exceed 200 feet in maximum thickness are interpreted as having been deposited contemporaneously with subsidence or tilting (Busch, 1954; Pepper and others, 1954). As the "Jackpile" sandstone locally exceeds 200 feet in thickness, this comparison provides evidence that subsidence influenced its deposition. In short, it appears unlikely that river channeling could cut a trough at least 200 feet deep during a single phase of channel scour and deposition. We have found little evidence of scouring at the base of the unit, and the fact that it intertongues with the Brushy Basin member is strong evidence against large-scale cut and fill.

In summary, the "Jackpile" sandstone was probably deposited by a distributary system of anastomosing streams, much as illustrated in Figure 10. From its excessive thickness for this type of deposit, we infer that the "Jackpile"

TABLE I. CHARACTERISTICS OF "JACKPILE" SANDSTONE AND SOME ANCIENT AND MODERN FLUVIAL CHANNEL DEPOSITS

Locality	Reference	Known Length (miles)	Approx. Maximum Width (miles)	Maximum Thickness (feet)	Vertical Grain-Size Diminution	Cross-bedding Dip Directions	Tilting or Subsidence Involved
Rio Grande delta	Nanz (1954)	—	—	—	Yes	—	—
Sand 19B	Nanz (1954)	> 7.5	6	60	Yes	—	—
Booch sand	Busch (1954)	>30	4	240	—	—	Yes
Berea sandstone	Pepper and others (1954)	>60	3	235	Yes	—	Yes
Rocktown channel sandstone member	Rubey and Bass (1925)	>28	1.5	100	—	Parallel to channel axis	—
"Jackpile" sandstone		>33	13	200	Yes	Parallel to trough	Yes

Notations: > =greater than figure given; —=not mentioned in reference cited.

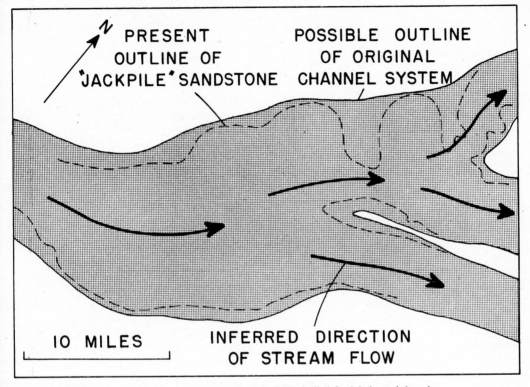

PRESENT
OUTLINE OF
"JACKPILE" SANDSTONE

POSSIBLE OUTLINE
OF ORIGINAL
CHANNEL SYSTEM

10 MILES

INFERRED DIRECTION
OF STREAM FLOW

Fig. 10.—Schematic diagram of original "Jackpile" fluvial channel deposit.

channel sands accumulated on a gradually widening and gently subsiding flood plain. The fact that the "Jackpile" sandstone intertongues with the Brushy Basin member supports this interpretation, because it indicates that the process was mostly depositional, with a minimum of cut and fill.

What, then, localized the stream system that deposited the "Jackpile" sandstone? This question leads to the consideration of structural history.

STRUCTURAL GEOLOGY

Although the strata of the Laguna district are nearly flat lying, three periods of deformation have affected the rocks. The first deformation took place during and after deposition of stratigraphic units within the Jurassic System but prior to the erosional truncation that preceded deposition of the Dakota sandstone of Cretaceous age. This was mainly a broad and gentle warping on the northern flank of the Jurassic highland that extended east-west through central New Mexico (McKee and others, 1956, Pl. 8, Figs. 5–8). In latest Cretaceous and early Tertiary time the strata were warped again, accounting for the present form of such major structures as the Zuni uplift, southwest of Grants, New Mexico, and the San Juan basin. In middle Tertiary to Recent time they were intensely fractured, essentially contemporaneously with the formation of the north-trending Rio Grande depression that lies a short distance east of the Laguna district. Here we are concerned only with the first period of deformation and the many features that suggest that "Jackpile" sedimentation was strongly influenced by this deformation.

Two sets of broad pre-Dakota anticlines, synclines, and monoclines are shown in Figure 3, one trending sinuously east to northeast, and the other slightly west of north. Although the two sets are nearly normal to one another, they probably formed contemporaneously. The east-trending folds define the major pre-Dakota structural element of the region, and we suspect that the largest structures are several miles wide, and several hundred feet high. Fold C, the most pronounced east-trending fold in the southern part of Figure 3, has 200 feet of relief in a horizontal distance of 1 mile from the synclinal to anticlinal axes. The folds labeled A and B (Fig. 3) possibly reflect the southern boundary of a depression many miles wide. Although later erosion prevents them from being joined, these folds may be part of a single set of structures that mark the boundary between the gentle northward dip into the depression, and a broad rolling structural terrace to the south that contains many smaller pre-Dakota folds.

The second set of folds trends slightly west of north, normal to the trend of the first set and the trend of the "Jackpile" sandstone. Folds of the second set are locally pronounced—as much as 100 feet of relief in a distance of less than half a mile—but they are definitely smaller than the largest folds of the first set. Whereas, the folds of the first set are simple anticlines and synclines, most of the folds of the second set are structural depressions, bounded by opposing monoclines. Strata on either side of a typical north-northwest-trending depression are essentially horizontal, but within the depression they dip inwardly as much as 10°.

Both sets of folds are truncated by the unconformity at the base of the Dakota sandstone. In good exposures, sandstone beds in the Morrison formation, and well defined formational boundaries such as the top of the Bluff sandstone and the base of the Todilto limestone, may be seen to converge and diverge with the base of the Dakota sandstone. These stratigraphic horizons are good structure markers, and their exposure in broad areas greatly aids the mapping of the pre-Dakota folds. The simplicity of the post-Dakota structures makes it possible to trace such folds by means of opposing attitudes in the Jurassic rocks.

These relations clearly indicate a pre-Dakota—post-"Jackpile" age for the folds. That folding also took place throughout much of Jurassic sedimentation, however, is indicated by a variety of intraformational structures in the Jurassic

strata. Intraformational folds in the Todilto limestone parallel both sets of pre-Dakota folds (Fig. 3). From the dominantly plastic characteristics of the intraformational folds and the fact that the limestone thickens in the pre-Dakota synclines and thins on the anticlines, we infer that poorly consolidated calcareous mud flowed down the limbs of the folds. This implies that folding was active shortly after, and possibly during, Todilto deposition. Sandstone pipes, which are cylindrical collapse structures attaining a few hundred feet in height and 150 feet in diameter, are abundantly exposed in the Summerville, Bluff, and Morrison formations in the Laguna district. The pipes are buried by the upper parts of the units that contain them, indicating that they formed during sedimentation of the Jurassic strata (Hilpert and Moench, 1958, Fig. 6; and 1960, Fig. 8). The concentration of most pipes in belts that parallel the pre-Dakota folds (Fig. 3) suggests that the two features are genetically related, and is further evidence that folding was active during Jurassic sedimentation. Schlee (1959, p. 1669) gives a general discussion of the origin of the sandstone pipes. Finally, thickening of stratigraphic units in the pre-Dakota synclines provides definite evidence of contemporaneous folding and sedimentation. At one locality the lower part of the Bluff sandstone (Fig. 2) is about 100 feet thicker in a syncline than it is on either side, indicating that this syncline formed during Bluff sedimentation. As shown in Figures 4 and 11, similar thickening was observed in the Morrison formation.

As shown in Figure 3, the southern boundary of the "Jackpile" sandstone is parallel to broad east- to northeast-trending pre-Dakota folds. Exposures in the southern part of the Laguna district show that a pre-Dakota erosion surface bevels these folds, and that the "Jackpile" sandstone is cut out on its southeast side by this unconformity. Drilling data indicate similar relations on the northwest side of the unit. These relations are shown in Figure 4 in which the post-Dakota structure has been removed, and it may be concluded that the "Jackpile" sandstone is preserved in a broad pre-Dakota syncline.

Three features, however, suggest that this broad structure formed before and possibly during, as well as after, "Jackpile" deposition. First, as seen in Figures 4 and 11, the part of the Morrison formation that underlies the "Jackpile" sandstone thickens markedly toward the center of the belt of "Jackpile" sandstone. Near the margins of the "Jackpile" sandstone the underlying part of the Morrison formation is 300–350 feet thick, but is about 450 feet thick near the center of the belt of "Jackpile" sandstone. That is, the Morrison formation thickens about 100 feet more than is accountable to thickening of the "Jackpile" sandstone. Second, as pointed out previously the "Jackpile" sandstone thins by loss of sandstone layers at the base of the unit; that is, it intertongues with the Brushy Basin member. Such intertonguing is too detailed for illustration in Figure 4, but by further vertical exaggeration this relation is shown diagrammatically in Figure 11, which is about equivalent to the southwest face of block B, Figure 4. As the "Jackpile" sandstone thins by subtraction of sandstone beds at its base as well as by wedging beneath the angular unconformity, we infer that a slight downwarp first localized a stream that deposited lowermost "Jackpile" sediments. Subsequent "Jackpile" sediments may have filled the downwarp during a

period of quiescence, gradually forming a wider flood plain. On the other hand, subsidence and "Jackpile" sedimentation may have been contemporaneous, in which case the rate of sedimentation must have exceeded the rate of subsidence. Otherwise the stream system would have been confined to the axis of the downwarp. Third, the present shape of the "Jackpile" sandstone is governed in part by the angular unconformity that bounds the northwest and southeast sides of the unit. Some downwarping, therefore, followed sedimentation and was followed in turn by erosional truncation. Because the sediments were probably transported parallel to the length of the sandstone body, and not at some angle to this direction, it seems likely that the post-depositional downwarp represents a reactivation or continuation of the downwarping that localized "Jackpile" sedimentation.

From these data it appears that the "Jackpile" sandstone was deposited during a tectonically active period. The unit was probably deposited in a broad structural depression that formed before, during, and after "Jackpile" sedimentation, and the streams that deposited the unit flowed in this depression.

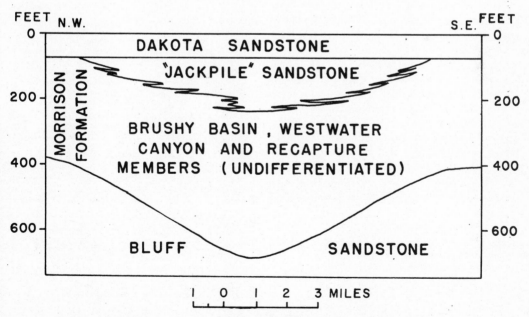

FIG. 11.—Exaggerated section across "Jackpile" sandstone. Vertical exaggeration is 53 times.

CONCLUSIONS

The geometry of the "Jackpile" sandstone body appears to have been controlled by fluvial-channel sedimentation combined with structural downwarping and erosional truncation. The "Jackpile" sandstone was deposited by an anastomosing stream system that flowed northeastward across the Laguna district with distributaries to the northeast. This distributary channel sand deposit may reflect deposition on a deltaic plain by a stream system that flowed into a body of water. On the other hand, it may reflect deposition on a broad fan-shaped alluvial plain that was far removed from any delta. The sediments were transported northeastward, possibly from the same general source area—west-central New Mexico—that Craig and others (1955, p. 157) propose for the sediments of the Westwater Canyon member. Similarly, the "Jackpile" sandstone may reflect a second major rejuvenation of that source area.

A broad, gentle, east- to northeast-trending downwarp apparently contained the stream system, and localized sedimentation. This downwarp probably formed before, during, and after sedimentation, and restricted the area of channel-sand deposition to a northeast-trending belt. Downwarping during sedimentation probably accounts for the abnormal thickness for this type of deposit. Continued folding and erosional truncation that followed "Jackpile" sedimentation modified, but did not completely alter, the shape of the channel-sand body.

The "Jackpile" sandstone was partly weathered during deposition but was more thoroughly weathered during and following erosional truncation. In the upper part of the unit the relatively unstable constituents were weathered to kaolinite and minor amounts of other clay minerals, giving rise to a quartz-rich, clay-indurated sandstone.

REFERENCES

Busch, D. A., 1954, Deltas significant in subsurface exploration: World Oil, v. 139, no. 7, p. 95–98.
———— 1959, Prospecting for stratigraphic traps: Am. Assoc. Petroleum Geologists Bull., v. 43, no. 12, p. 2829–2843. See also this volume.

Craig, L. C., and others, 1955, Stratigraphy of the Morrison and related formations, Colorado Plateau region, a preliminary report: U. S. Geol. Survey Bull. 1009-E, p. 125–168.
Fisk, H. N., 1952, Geological investigation of the Atchafalaya basin and the problem of Mississippi River diversion, v. 1: U. S. Corps of Engineers, Waterways Expt. Sta., Vicksburg, Miss.
Folk, R. L., 1951, A comparison chart for visual percentage estimation: Jour. Sed. Petrology, v. 21, no. 1, p. 32–33.
Freeman, V. L., and Hilpert, L. S., 1956, Stratigraphy of the Morrison formation in part of northwestern New Mexico: U. S. Geol. Survey Bull. 1030-J, p. 309–334.
Harshbarger, J. W., Repenning, C. A., and Irwin, J. H., 1957, Stratigraphy of the uppermost Triassic and the Jurassic rocks of the Navajo country: U. S. Geol. Survey Prof. Paper 291.
Hilpert, L. S., and Freeman, V. L., 1956, Guides to uranium deposits in the Morrison formation, Gallup-Laguna area, New Mexico, in Page, L. R., Contributions to the geology of uranium and thorium: U. S. Geol. Survey Prof. Paper 300, p. 299–302.
———— and Moench, R. H., 1958, Uranium deposits of the southern margin of the San Juan basin, New Mexico, in 2nd U. N. Internat. Conf. Peaceful Uses Atomic Energy, Geneva, Proc.: v. 2, p. 527–538.
———— and ————, 1960, Uranium deposits of the southern margin of the San Juan basin, New Mexico: Econ. Geology, v. 55, no. 3, p. 429–464.
Krynine, P. D., 1948, The megascopic study and field classification of sedimentary rocks: Jour. Geology, v. 56, no. 12, p. 130–165.
Lane, E. W., 1938, Notes on the formation of sand: Am. Geophys. Union Trans., 19th Ann. Mtg., p. 505–508.
Leopold, L. B., 1943, Climatic character of the interval between the Jurassic and Cretaceous in New Mexico and Arizona: Jour. Geology, v. 51, no. 1, p. 56–62.
McKee, E. D., and Weir, G. W., 1953: Terminology for stratification and cross-stratification in sedimentary rocks: Geol. Soc. America Bull., v. 64, no. 4, p. 381–390.
———— and others, 1956, Paleotectonic maps of the Jurassic System: U. S. Geol. Survey Misc. Geol. Inv. Map I-175.
Nanz, R. H., Jr., 1954, Genesis of Oligocene sandstone reservoir, Seeligson field, Jim Wells and Kleberg Counties, Texas: Am. Assoc. Petroleum Geologists Bull., v. 38, no. 1, p. 96–117.
Pepper, J. F., de Witt, Wallace, Jr., and Demarest, D. F., 1954, Geology of the Bedford shale and Berea sandstone in the Appalachian basin: U. S. Geol. Survey Prof. Paper 259 [1955].
Pettijohn, F. J., 1957, Sedimentary rocks, 2d ed.: New York, Harper and Brothers.
Rubey, W. W., and Bass, N. W., 1925, The geology of Russell County, Kansas, with special reference to oil and gas resources: Kansas Geol. Survey Bull. 10, p. 1–86.
Schlee, J. S., 1959, The origin of sandstone pipes, Laguna district, New Mexico (abstract): Geol. Soc. America Bull., v. 70, no. 12, p. 1669.

FLUVIAL AND EOLIAN SANDSTONE BODIES IN COLORADO PLATEAU[1]

WM. LEE STOKES[2]

Salt Lake City, Utah

ABSTRACT

The Colorado Plateau has been the site of accumulation and preservation of nonmarine sediments since late Paleozoic time. The climatic conditions have been desert-like for long periods, and wind-blown sand is a common sedimentary type. Much of the alluvial material was carried only relatively short distances and can be related to nearby source areas. The deep and intricate erosion of the region permits excellent three-dimensional views of the sedimentary bodies.

Extensive eolian deposits occur in the Permian, Triassic, and Jurassic Systems. These are mainly interpreted as superposed dune fields. In many instances the edges of the formations are abrupt, and comparison with modern sharply defined dune areas is obvious. Tangential cross-bedding with occasional contorted masses characterize these deposits. Chief interest attaches to the determination of wind directions; apparently the source of most of the sand lay to the north and northwest.

Fluvial deposits are common above the Pennsylvanian. These offer excellent opportunity to study sedimentary variations resulting from differences in climate, weathering, distance of transport, provenance, and energy relations of stream systems. The common occurrence of uranium deposits in the fluvial sandstones has stimulated geologic investigation. The petroleum possibilities of these beds are also receiving increased attention.

Practically every type of deposit seen in process of formation in modern rivers can be detected in the consolidated rocks. The overbank or flood-plain deposits are of less variety and interest than the channel deposits. All types of bars and channel-fill deposits are present, but those formed during the building of alluvial plains are most common. Apparently, the final composition of a typical fluvial formation depends on the gradient of the streams, the total amount of sediment supplied, and the relative amounts of fine and coarse material.

Internal structures of channel sandstones show great variety and can be related to stream volume and velocity. Ripple mark, festoon cross-bedding, rib and furrow, and lineation are the most common.

INTRODUCTION

The Colorado Plateau physiographic province displays the geologic features of sedimentary rocks in textbook style. Intricate erosion and absence of cover have laid bare three-dimensional exposures of many types of deposits so that not only minor textures and structures, but also complete large scale facies relationships may be seen and examined in their natural settings. The exposures of continental sediments are especially outstanding and varied.

TECTONIC SETTING

The Colorado Plateau is a unique structural feature of North America. It has been little

[1] Read before the Association at Atlantic City, New Jersey, April 25, 1960. Manuscript received, January 1, 1960.

[2] Department of Geology, University of Utah. The following paper is a summary of observations of many individual geologists who have taken part in the intensified study of the Colorado Plateau during recent years. Only by drawing freely upon the work of others is it possible to present a fair and comprehensive summary of what is known about the continental sandstone bodies of this region.

affected by the intense deformation and igneous action of surrounding areas, and has the appearance of having been strong and rigid enough to withstand the tectonic forces that operated in its general vicinity (Fig. 1). It has, however, been uplifted as a unit from near sea level to an altitude of 5,000–10,000 feet. This unusual tectonic behavior has had a pronounced effect upon sedimentation in the area and provides a reasonable explanation for the high proportion of continental sediments in the area (Stokes, 1958).

For a variety of reasons, the area of the Colorado Plateau has been more or less surrounded by high-standing topographic features since middle Paleozoic time (Fig. 2). These elements have tended to interfere with the transportation of sediment into, across, or out of the region so that relatively large volumes were permanently trapped near the source areas and did not escape to the margins of the continent. The chief tectonic elements that have acted as barriers and sediment sources are as follows.

Transcontinental arch.—This broad and poorly defined feature sometimes called the "backbone of North America" includes most of the Colorado

Plateau but is more pronounced in the southern part. This feature was in evidence during the Paleozoic and Mesozoic and generally stood high enough to separate Pacific seas from those of the continental interior; only very rarely did what is now the southern part of the Colorado Plateau receive marine sediments. The area was, instead, a site of shifting sand dunes and playa lakes for long intervals.

Ancestral Rockies.—Elements of the Ancestral

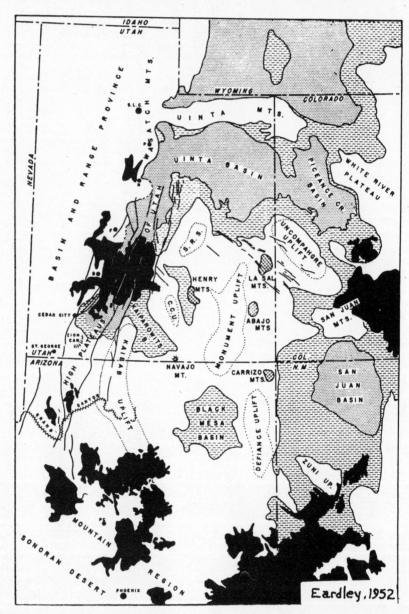

Fig. 1.—Geologic features of the Colorado Plateau and adjacent regions. Dark areas represent volcanic rocks, stippled areas are Tertiary, and dashed areas are Cretaceous. C.C.U. = Circle Cliffs uplift; S.R.S. = San Rafael swell. From Eardley, 1952.

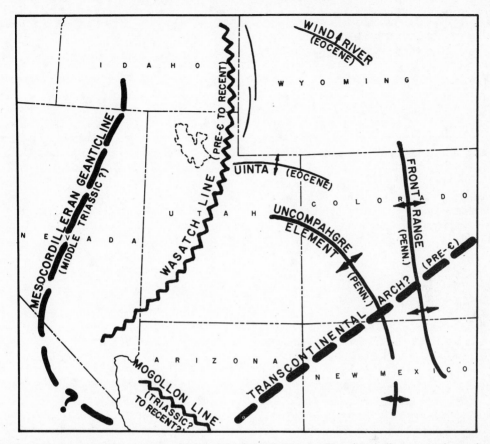

Fig. 2.—Major tectonic features in the vicinity of the Colorado Plateau. Notations indicate approximate time of disturbance and uplift. Note how the area of the plateau became increasingly isolated with successive orogenies.

Rockies rose in a curving arch around the eastern and northeastern margins of what was to be the Colorado Plateau during Pennsylvanian time. The Uncompahgre element was a wide and lofty mountain range that not only supplied much sediment during the Permian and Triassic, but also effectively blocked eastward drainage out of the area. The complementary downwarp, the Paradox basin, received much sediment from the nearby range.

Mesocordilleran highland.—An elongate barrier referred to by Schuchert as the "Mesocordilleran geanticline" came into existence along the approximate axis of the Cordilleran geosyncline in Middle Triassic time. This became a permanent barrier to Pacific waters so that western Utah and eastern Nevada never again received marine sedi-

ments. The uplift supplied detritus eastward during the Late Triassic, Jurassic, and Cretaceous, and prevented westward escape of drainage during the same period. The eastward margin lay at the Wasatch line; the westward margin is less clearly defined.

Mogollon Rim or highland.—The prominent mountain rim which separates the Plateau and Basin-Range provinces of Arizona is an ancient feature that dates at least to the early Mesozoic. It may be a continuation or branch of the Mesocordilleran highland. In any event it too was a sediment source and barrier during most of the Mesozoic.

In summary, it may be said that the area of the Colorado Plateau was low and surrounded by structural barriers on the south, southeast, east, northeast, and west, during most of the Mesozoic. During intervals of general flooding such as the Late Jurassic, the seas could enter only from the north. Later, after the general submergence of the Late Cretaceous, when the surface expressions of the Transcontinental arch and the Ancestral Rockies were somewhat subdued, the Colorado Plateau became even more isolated by the creation of Laramide structures and the rejuvenation of older ones. The Uinta Range on the north completed an essentially high rim around the entire region. The Colorado River which drains and crosses the area, enters on the northeast and leaves on the southwest corner through what are essentially gaps in the structures that ring the area.

SEDIMENT SOURCES

The various uplifts which ringed the Colorado Plateau were sources of abundant clastic material. The Precambrian basement rocks that were exposed at various times in the Transcontinental arch, the Ancestral Rockies, and the Laramide ranges were mainly of crystalline and granitic composition and supplied great volumes of sand, silt, and clay, rich in mica, feldspar, and quartz. The Mesocordilleran highland was apparently composed predominantly of sedimentary rocks and supplied relatively more chert, and on the whole, somewhat finer detritus. At various times abundant volcanic debris was carried in by wind or water action from the west.

The source of the eolian sandstones is not entirely clear. The Mesozoic paleogeography of the area north and west of the present Colorado Plateau is not well understood and the exact parent rocks cannot yet be identified. Ignoring details, it is obvious that the sediments supplied to the area during the late Paleozoic and Mesozoic were unusually rich in coarse fragmental constituents that could be sorted and distributed by currents of wind and water according to prevailing conditions.

Disintegrated fragments from the Ancestral Rockies may be found resting directly upon the parent rock, or hundreds of miles from it. Sediments from this source can generally be detected without difficulty. By contrast, sediments from the Mesocordilleran highland travelled an un-

known but certainly much greater distance, and are difficult to relate to specific sources.

CLIMATOLOGICAL INFLUENCES

The climate of the Colorado Plateau is mostly arid or semi-arid at present, and this seems to have been the case for long intervals in the past. All geologic evidence, both biologic and lithologic, suggests desert-like environments in the late Pennsylvanian, Permian, Triassic, Jurassic, and Early Cretaceous. Evidence includes abundant evaporites, red beds, wind-blown sand, playa lakes, fossils of desert-like vegetation, and general absence of organic remains where they might otherwise be expected.

Several factors have obviously contributed to produce low precipitation in this region. At present the Sierra Nevada creates an effective rain shadow, and in the past a similar effect may have been due to elevated portions of the Mesocordilleran highland. The height and configuration of this feature are unknown. More important is the position of the Colorado Plateau in relation to the continental margin and the Pacific Ocean. This creates a climate under the influence of the warm and dry descending air of the horse latitudes. Important also is the presence, off the west coast, of cool ocean currents that are capable of supplying only limited amounts of moisture to the interior. The paleoclimate of this region seems to have a direct bearing on the problem of continental drift and the permanence of ocean basins, but not enough is known to permit meaningful conclusions.

The sedimentary processes of arid regions that can be observed in operation at present give important clues to ancient sedimentation and erosion. Although precipitation may be low, there are frequent torrential floods capable of great erosive and depositional effects. Under such conditions large quantities of loose material are moved relatively short distances, sorting is poor, mineral grains are unweathered, and individual bodies of sediment can be traced only short distances. Geologically, the chief effect is to pile up relatively thick accumulations of detrital material not far from the source areas.

If the area of low rainfall is tectonically active, undrained interior basins will be created. This is in strong contrast to the effects in humid areas. In arid climates water and sediment cannot fill the depressions created by tectonic activity; in humid areas, with the same tectonic effects, there is enough water, if not sediment, to fill all basins, integrate drainage, and accelerate the wearing down of the landscape. Playa lakes and evaporites record ponding effects, as well as high evaporation, in arid environments.

The combined influences of source areas, low rainfall, and the tectonic obstructions operated to produce great thicknesses of coarse detritus which accumulated under nonmarine influences and was preserved until the great denudation of the Colorado Plateau began in Tertiary time.

EOLIAN SANDSTONES
GENERAL STATEMENT

When the intricately cross-bedded sandstones of the Colorado Plateau were first observed by the geologist Newberry in 1859 they presented a type of sedimentary structure entirely foreign to his experience. Newberry considered them to be chemical precipitates perhaps "deposited from water, at times very much agitated" (Newberry, 1876, p. 92). The concept of eolian deposition came later but did not gain immediate universal favor. H. E. Gregory, pioneer student of the Colorado Plateau, was a champion of the eolian theory. The idea of large scale wind deposition is now generally accepted. The long period of wind deposition began in the Permian and ended in the Jurassic. The center of maximum activity was in southern Utah and northern Arizona where thick cross-bedded sandstones of Permian, Triassic, and Jurassic age are found. Figure 3 shows the nonmarine sedimentary section, including the eolian sandstones, of the Four Corners area.

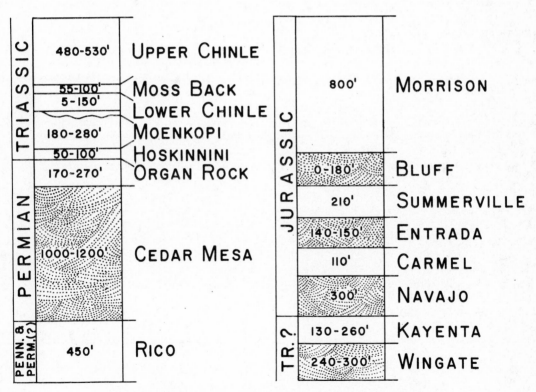

Fig. 3.—Typical section of nonmarine rocks as exposed in the Four Corners area. Eolian deposits are indicated by cross-bed symbol.

PERMIAN SANDSTONE FORMATIONS AND MEMBERS

Coconino sandstone (Leonard age).—The Coconino sandstone is well known from its many exposures in north-central Arizona, especially those in the Grand Canyon. Its correlations beyond these exposures are not entirely clear, but it is fairly well established that it interfingers with the Toroweap formation and is equivalent to only a portion of the so-called "Coconino" of the San Rafael swell. The type Coconino is about 400 feet thick, whereas the composite "Coconino" may reach over 2,000 feet. The Coconino originally covered an area of at least 45,000 square miles.

Cedar Mesa sandstone member of the Cutler (Wolfcamp age).—The Cedar Mesa sandstone is exposed chiefly in Grand and San Juan Counties, Utah, where it has been carved into the famous natural bridges. It ranges from 1,000 to 1,500 feet in thickness, and is considered to be correlative, in part, with the Esplanade sandstone member of the Supai in the Grand Canyon, and with the Queantoweap sandstone of northwestern Arizona (Heylmun, 1958). Northwestward, it merges with the White Rim sandstone and in the San Rafael swell makes up part of the undifferentiated "Coconino." The original extent may have been about 10,000 square miles.

White Rim sandstone member of the Cutler (Leonard age).—The White Rim sandstone is exposed chiefly in south-central Utah, in the vicinity of the junction of the Green and Colorado Rivers. It appears to be the continental equivalent of the marine Toroweap and of the upper part of the "Coconino" of the San Rafael swell. It reaches a thickness of approximately 600 feet and has an areal extent of about 7,000 square miles.

De Chelly sandstone member of the Cutler (Leonard age?).—The De Chelly member of the Cutler formation has a maximum thickness of 800 feet at Canyon De Chelly, Arizona, but thins northward by interfingering into undifferentiated Cutler, and disappears in the vicinity of Dove Creek, Colorado. To the northwest it probably passes into undifferentiated "Coconino." Its correlation is uncertain but it appears to be closely related to the Coconino of the Grand Canyon. The original extent was about 20,000 square miles.

GLEN CANYON GROUP

The best known and most extensive of the Colorado Plateau eolian sandstones are included in the Glen Canyon group (Fig. 4). The Wingate at the base and the Navajo at the top display unmistakable dune structure but the middle formations, the Kayenta and Moenave, are chiefly fluvial. The age of these rocks has been difficult to determine; at first the entire group was regarded as Jurassic but recent fossil discoveries have placed much of it in the Triassic. Details need not concern us here. For an excellent treatment of the age problem see Harshbarger, Repenning, and Irwin (1957).

The Wingate has complex facies relationships with underlying and adjacent formations. It appears to grade laterally into red silty sediments deposited by water, that have usually been mapped as Chinle units. The complexity of crossbedding increases with increase in sand content, suggesting reworking of fluvial sediments by wind action, and vice versa.

The Navajo formation occupies a much larger area than the other Glen Canyon formations. It is known to extend beyond the Colorado Plateau into Wyoming, Idaho, and Nevada, and may have covered an area of 200,000 square miles. It is composed of medium to fine grained quartz grains and is intricately dune bedded throughout. Although it is known to interfinger with the upper part of the Kayenta, its margins and contacts are much more easily defined than those of the other Glen Canyon units.

The upper contact of the Navajo is an unconformity of regional extent and serves as one of the most useful horizons for correlation in the Colorado Plateau (Fig. 4). The time lapse between the deposition of the Navajo and succeeding formations may have been a long one, during which considerable induration and erosion of the Navajo occurred.

SAN RAFAEL GROUP AND MORRISON FORMATION

During Late Jurassic time eolian activity was practically continuous in the vicinity of the Four Corners. Eolian sandstone units within the Carmel formation of southwestern Utah inter-

FIG. 4.—Eolian sandstones exposed along the Colorado River about 4 miles upstream from the mouth of Rock Creek. The Navajo sandstone forms first cliff and bench above river level, the undifferentiated San Rafael group makes up lower massive part of the mesa, and the Morrison formation appears in the ledgy upper part. *Courtesy Upper Colorado River Basin Archeological Salvage Project, University of Utah.*

finger northward with typical marine deposits. The succeeding Entrada sandstone is very widespread and, like the Navajo, has equivalents far beyond the Colorado Plateau, in eastern New Mexico, eastern Colorado, Wyoming, and Idaho. The interfingering of water- and wind-laid facies within the Entrada is extremely complex; in general the formation is predominantly water laid in the western part of its range and eolian to the east. Dune bedding is interrupted and truncated by horizontal beds of aqueous origin in almost every exposure, and nowhere does the cross-bedding approach the grand style of the Navajo.

Several other Late Jurassic formations pass into eolian facies as they are traced into southern Utah, northern Arizona, and northwestern New Mexico. The Summerville formation and the Bluff and Recapture members of the Morrison merge gradually into a massive unit—the Cow Springs sandstone, which reaches a maximum thickness of about 360 feet on the north slope of Black Mesa, Arizona, 4 miles east of Cow Springs.

This mass of sandstone has been referred to as "the Great Sand Pile," for it seems to have been in process of formation during most of San Rafael and Morrison time. The original thickness must have been greater, for the summit is truncated by an erosion surface of regional extent (Harshbarger and others, 1957).

A probable equivalent of the Cow Springs sandstone in Utah is the Winsor formation (Fig. 5), which also appears to grade into the Summerville and lower Morrison. Eolian sandstone is the dominant rock type in the San Rafael group and the lower Morrison formation, in New Mexico.

EXTERNAL AND INTERNAL FEATURES OF EOLIAN SANDSTONE BODIES

The eolian sandstone bodies consist of numerous sets of cross-beds, each set generally representing what is preserved of an individual fossil dune. Sets show great variety in total volume and shape, and also in the thickness, inclination, and curvature of the constituent cross-beds or cross-laminations. According to the classification of

Fig. 5.—Massive, light-colored Winsor sandstone overlain by conglomerate of Lower Cretaceous age on Paria Creek, Kane County, Utah.

hard layers and thick, soft ones in the Navajo formation near Kanab, Utah. This regularity is made evident chiefly by the thin, hard layers which protrude from the surface. Other exposures show similar regular divisions into thick and thin units, but the thin layers may be softer or of a contrasting color. The meaning of the recurrent subdivisions is not fully understood, but it probably represents periodic avalanching on over-steepened lee faces of advancing dunes. The regularity seems to depend on sand of very uniform grain size and undeviating winds over considerable periods of time.

A number of detailed studies of cross-bedding and inferred wind directions have been published. The pioneer study is that of Reiche (1938) on the Coconino of northern Arizona. Kiersch (1950) studied minor structures of the Navajo of the San Rafael swell, and Stewart, Poole, and Wilson (1957) summarized work on several formations in the Colorado Plateau. It is evident from these papers that most of the eolian sands of southern Utah and northern Arizona were deposited chiefly by winds blowing from the north (Figs. 7–9). Much could be done in the way of regional studies of the cross-bedding of these and other eolian sandstones in relation to wind direction, polar wandering, and continental drift.

Local patches of sandstone, confined to individual sets, may show highly convoluted, contorted or "gnarly" bedding. This is especially notable in the Navajo sandstone (Kiersch, 1950). As individual thin laminations do not lose their identity in these contorted masses, it seems likely that the sand at the time of disturbance must have been water saturated so as to remain highly cohesive during sliding. Although it has been suggested that the contorted masses require a subaqueous origin, it seems possible that local seepage and saturation by ground water may be sufficient.

Ripple marks are common on bedding planes in eolian sandstone. The ripples are of the asymmetrical type, with long wave length and low amplitude.

Among the very minor but significant features of eolian sandstones are animal tracks. These have been observed in most eolian formations of the Colorado Plateau. Best known are those of

McKee and Wier (1953), most eolian bedding is large scale, high angle, and of the trough type. In most cross sections the internal structure of an eolian sandstone may appear superficially to be totally random and confusing. There are, however, certain features with considerable regularity and consistency. Thus, in any one sand body the cross-beds incline predominantly in one direction. Cliff faces eroded so as to be parallel with this direction show set upon set with similar dip and configuration. There may even be a high degree of regularity in the thickness of the cross-beds or cross-laminations in certain sets. Figure 6 shows an uncommonly regular cyclic alternation of thin,

FIG. 6.—Evenly spaced cross-bedding in the Navajo sandstone on Kanab Creek, Kane County, Utah.

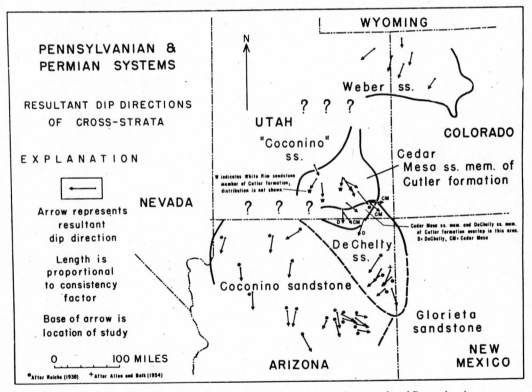

FIG. 7.—Map of resultant dip directions of cross-strata in sandstone units of Pennsylvanian and Permian age. From Stewart, Poole, and Wilson, 1957.

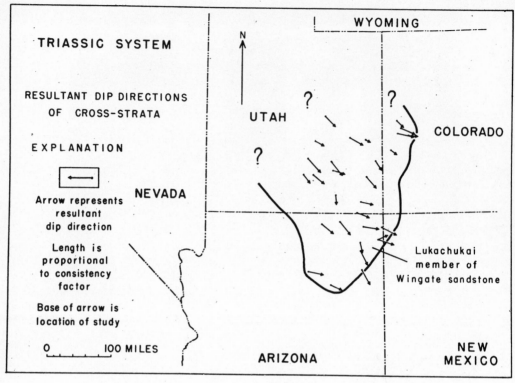

FIG. 8.—Map of resultant dip directions of cross-strata in Lukachukai member of
Wingate sandstone of Late Triassic age. From Stewart, Poole, and Wilson, 1957.

the Coconino of the Grand Canyon (Gilmore, 1926, 1927, 1928). From the fact that most of the Coconino tracks pertain to animals travelling only upward on dune surfaces it has been suggested that the creatures ascended the dunes chiefly after the sand had been moistened by rain or dew, and that they descended on dry sand in which tracks could not be preserved.

Occasional pitted and abraded pebbles are found in the eolian sandstones. In the Colorado Plateau these are most abundant in the upper few feet of the Navajo. These quartzitic stones do not show sharp faces or edges but are pitted and somewhat polished.

In addition to the larger structures mentioned above, eolian sands are generally characterized by simplicity of mineral suites, paucity of platy and micaceous minerals, low content of carbonate minerals, and uniformity of particle size. Occasionally a bimodal analysis occurs, indicating sorting into two chief grain sizes (McKnight, 1940, p. 92).

PALEOGEOGRAPHICAL INTERPRETATION AND
CORRELATION OF EOLIAN SANDSTONES

Several important distinctions must be made between the manner of deposition of eolian and water-laid sediments. Whereas streams invariably flow downhill and carry sediments from higher to lower areas, the winds do not necessarily do so. Wind currents and their sediments may travel uphill, cross topographic barriers, and may travel transverse to prevailing stream directions. It is difficult to relate eolian sands to specific source areas. No precise data exist as to the distance that wind-blown sands may travel, but it is certainly on the order of hundreds of miles.

The experience of stratigraphers in the Colorado Plateau has shown that the correlation of eolian deposits with each other and with other types of sediment is very difficult. The almost complete lack of fossils, especially those recoverable from wells, is an obvious obstacle. Perhaps more serious is the absence of key beds. Whereas most other types of sediment may contain ash beds, bentonite layers, thin conglomerates, zones of concretions, or organic layers, such things do not form or survive in dune areas.

Although the contacts of dune sandstones can generally be located quite precisely on the basis of the characteristic internal structures, the problem becomes very difficult where dune material has been reworked by running water. A typical sequence of events might include the delivery of mixed sediment into an area by intermittent stream action, the sorting and local accumulation of the sand fractions into dune patches, and a final local reworking of the dunes by streams. The movement of dune sand into or across the paths of streams and the simultaneous accumulation of fluvial and eolian deposits result in complex interfingering of sediments that are alike in all respects except the sedimentary structures imparted at the time of final burial. Such conditions are represented in many units of the sediments of the Colorado Plateau, and pose peculiar problems of nomenclature, mapping, and correlation. Thick and widespread formations such as the Entrada consist of interfingering bodies of wind- and water-laid silt and sand so intricate that discrimination is impractical or impossible (Fig. 10).

Because detection of exact boundaries between eolian and reworked eolian sand rests upon gross relationships or large scale internal structures, it may be impossible to draw very exact boundaries by subsurface methods.

THE FLUVIAL SANDSTONES

Rivers transport most of the sediment that is moved across land areas. However, only a small part of the sediment picked up by running water is caught and preserved in strictly fluvial environments. Fluvial deposits may be considered as material in transit toward more permanent depositional sites in bodies of water. Deposits are as varied as the rivers that produce them, and until more is known about the action of living

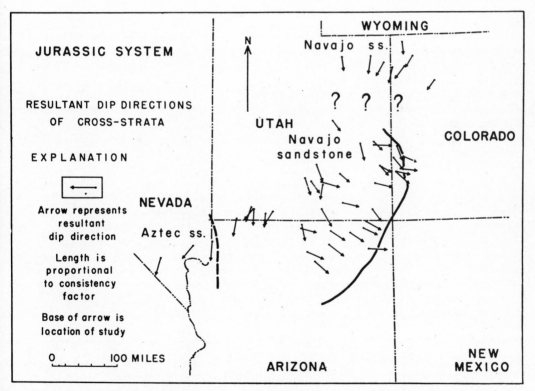

FIG. 9.—Map of resultant dip directions of cross-strata in Navajo sandstone of Jurassic? and Jurassic age, and the Aztec sandstone of Jurassic? age. From Stewart, Poole, and Wilson, 1957.

FIG. 10.—Contrasting outcrops of an eolian type of sandstone—the Bluff sandstone, below, and the fluvial
Salt Wash sandstone member of the Morrison formation, above. Northwest Carrizo Mountains area.

streams, fluvial deposits will be difficult to classify
and understand. In the absence of well established
principles or schemes of classification, the empirical approach is the safest and will be emphasized
in the following brief discussions of several types
of deposits in the Colorado Plateau. What can be
observed must be catalogued before it can be
explained.

One of the most obvious and fundamental
features of fluvial action and resulting deposits is
the sorting of coarse and fine fractions into channel and overbank deposits, respectively. Sediments of every grade size may be represented, but
the tendency is for the coarsest to become concentrated in the channels. The proportion of
channel sediments ranges from a very small
fraction to almost entire formations. Fluvial
accumulations may be designated as shale, sandstone, conglomerate, or, if the lithology is mixed,
merely as formations, depending on the nature
and abundance of the channel fraction.

So many factors influence the structure of a
flood plain, and even the geometry of individual
sedimentary units within it, that no simple clas-

sification is possible. It is proposed to proceed
directly to a description of several of the best
known fluvial deposits of the Colorado Plateau.

CHINLE FORMATION

The Chinle formation of the Colorado Plateau is predominantly of fluvial origin (Finch,
1959). Two members, the Shinarump and Moss,
Back, consist mainly of coarse sandstone and
conglomerate and occur in elongate bands that
are clearly ancient river systems. The term *channel* is used in reference to stream-deposited
features within these members (Fig. 11). As
defined by Finch, a *Shinarump channel* consists
of a prominent linear scour in the underlying
rocks and the filling of sedimentary rocks, almost
all of which are coarse grained and conglomeratic.
The chief characteristics of Shinarump channels
are well described by Finch (p. 135–136) as follows.

Channels increase the thickness of the Shinarump downward. Some channels have relatively steep sides and
rounded bottoms. Others are less clearly defined, and
must be measured accurately to the nearest foot in order
to define the sides, bottom, and general trend. Channels

form either as part of a continuous bed of normally uniform thickness or as long discontinuous lenses, like shoestring sands. The depth of scour of a channel is measured from the bottom of the uniformly thick bed to the lowest point of the scour. The depth of scour differs from place to place: in the Monument Valley it is as great as 125 feet, in White Canyon it is commonly less than 15 feet, in the Circle Cliffs it is rarely less than 25 feet or more than 50 feet. The Shinarump, which is generally only 30 to 50 feet thick in the areas between channels, attains a maximum thickness of about 225 feet in western Monument Valley. The width of the channels ranges from a few feet to more than a thousand feet in Monument Valley, and from a few feet to several hundred feet in the White Canyon and Circle Cliffs areas. Channels in the Shinarump have been traced for many thousands of feet. . . . The channels in the Monument Valley, White Canyon, and Circle Cliffs areas make up about 3 per cent of the area of the Shinarump in these areas.

The Moss Back member is younger than the Shinarump and has channels of similar nature. Both members contain significant deposits of uranium, vanadium, and copper that undoubtedly owe their existence to ground-water conditions of former geologic time.

The trend of the belts of Shinarump and Moss Back deposits in southern Utah and northern Arizona is generally northwesterly. The constituent pebbles of the Shinarump are mainly siliceous rocks—quartz, quartzite, chert, silicified limestone, and sandstone. Moss Back pebbles are mainly quartzite and chert. A highland of Precambrian and early Paleozoic rocks in central New Mexico or Arizona may have been the source.

The Chinle channels appear to rest in and upon two main unconformities; the Shinarump lies everywhere upon the Moenkopi, and the Moss Back either upon the lower mudstone member, or upon older rocks. Upon each unconformity the distribution of the coarse material is irregular but not entirely erratic. Channels in general follow the trends of the valley belts but may diverge considerably from each other within those belts. It is significant that there is considerable anastomosing so that the system appears as a coarse, irregular network.

PALEOGEOGRAPHY AND INTERPRETATION

The formation of a Shinarump-type channel system begins after the underlying formations have been deposited, have become more or less lithified, and have been eroded to considerable depth. In the case of the Shinarump the underlying formation is the Moenkopi, which is known to be of Early Triassic age. The Moenkopi is beveled by a prominent erosion surface so that it ranges in thickness from a featheredge in eastern Utah and western Colorado to 1,800 feet in southwestern Utah. The amount of material actually removed along the eastern zone is unknown, but it is doubtful that the formation there was more than a few hundred feet thick. The cutting of the unconformity is regarded by most geologists as having occupied all of Middle Triassic time, for no deposits of this age have been proven to exist in the area. It should be noted that the Moenkopi appears to have been thoroughly lithified by Shinarump time, since the chunks and fragments of the former embedded in the latter have every appearance of having been solid and coherent when torn loose and redeposited. According to the general view, the pre-Shinarump surface was shaped and prepared by previous erosion, and the Shinarump was spread into and along the pre-existing valley systems. Witkind (1956) has noted that the channels occupy the bottoms of low "swales" about 30 feet deep in the Monument Valley region. In other words, there was at the

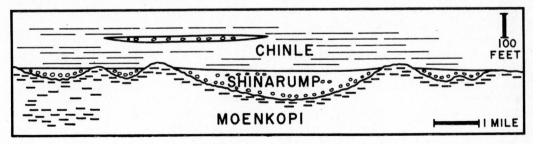

Fig. 11.—Generalized section, Shinarump-type channels.

beginning a bedrock terrain of homogeneous Moenkopi formation on which there was little if any soil or weathered debris, and no coarse material of external origin. The surface was irregular with broad, shallow valleys or waterways, and subdued divides.

This theoretical picture may perhaps be modified to fit what is known about the present-day behavior of gravel in arid regions. It seems logical to suppose that the gravel sheets were spread by a process of pedimentation. In other words, the cutting of the underlying unconformity and the spread of the gravel were not unrelated and separate events but progressed at the same time as an integrated process. According to this view, the gravel may have been introduced originally upon or across any kind of terrain. The original patches of gravel and patches of bedrock are subject to the same erosive forces but with very unequal results. The gravel is shifted downstream and its constituents reduced in size, but because it is constantly replenished it need not diminish in total area. The bedrock surface, on the other hand, is cut away to create additional low ground onto which the gravel may spread. The end result of pedimentation is thus a gravel-coated plain or bedrock surface. The surface is cut by slow degrees on the numerous occasions when streams cut through the gravel cover or against the edges of bedrock hills. It is irregular in detail but smooth in general profile.

The process of pediment formation involving gravel sheets on relatively soft bedrock surfaces is well exemplified at many places in the western United States and has been discussed by Rich (1935), and Hunt and others (1953). At any given time there will be parallel gravel-floored valleys and gravel-free valleys. The gravel-floored valleys either connect directly with a source of debris or have connected with such sources in the past. They may be occupied by permanent surface streams which are engaged in moving the debris outward, or the gravel cover may be in a state of stagnation. The gravel-free valleys receive only local sporadic precipitation and do not connect with sources of coarse debris. They are nevertheless in a state of erosion, and because of the relative rates of lowering of gravel-coated and gravel-free areas the usual result is that the

gravel-free strips are lowered below the level of the gravel-covered strips. When this occurs, a diversion or piracy of streams can and does take place across low divides or cols. This causes an immediate abandonment of stream segments, leaving their deposits as they were at the moment of diversion. The new course receives an immediate flow of water which will commence to bring in and spread coarse debris. If such an area is covered by subsequent fine-grained deposits, a cross section will reveal most of the conditions seen in a channel system of the Chinle type (Fig. 11). There will be broad tracts where channeled and eroded bedrock will be in direct contact with the newly deposited overlying sediment. Adjacent intervals will show coarse debris in the form of channels—some broad and shallow, others narrow and deep. In plan, the gravel will be seen to occupy subparallel courses with occasional interconnecting bodies between. The channels will show effects of strong cut-and-fill, and internal structures may be strongly developed, as would be expected to result from vigorous stream action.

MORRISON FORMATION
GENERAL STATEMENT

The Morrison formation has long been interpreted as an extensive fluvial accumulation (Mook, 1916; Baker, Dane, and Reeside, 1936; Stokes, 1944). The dinosaurs and uranium deposits it contains have been of such interest and importance that the Morrison has become the most intensively studied sedimentary formation in the western United States. The uranium-bearing Salt Wash and Westwater members have been very thoroughly investigated, especially in the vicinity of the major mineralized districts, and it is the sedimentary features of these members that are of most importance in connection with the present discussion.

GROSS STRUCTURE OF LOWER MORRISON MEMBERS

Through the concentrated work of many geologists, the broad depositional outlines of the uranium-bearing parts of the Morrison have become well known. The Salt Wash is the most extensive subdivision, covering an area of about 75,000 square miles. The area of deposition is roughly fan shaped with a projected apex very near what is now the western Grand Canyon. All evidence supports the conclusion that most of the Salt Wash sediments, with the possible exception of contributions of volcanic ash and tuff, were produced by one great river which debouched upon the pre-Morrison plain at the projected apex. From this point the water and sediments fanned outward to build up a thin but widespread alluvial formation. In terms of geomorphic form this deposit is an alluvial fan, but it has many features of a delta. It seems quite unlikely that any deposit now in process of building is similar to the Salt Wash member. In allusion to the peculiar origin, it has been referred to as an alluvial delta or delta fan.

A detailed study of the lithofacies of the Salt Wash has been presented by Mullens and Freeman (1957). Their method of treating the gross lithology is especially informative because it emphasizes the ratio of channel to flood-plain deposits rather than grain-size distribution or rock composition. They have prepared an isopach map (Fig. 12) which shows not only the fan-like shape but also the very regular gradation in thickness of the formation outward from a maximum of about 600 feet, near the apex, to a feather-edge at the margins. Several indentations break the regularity of the contours, and these can be related to known tectonic features. The most notable irregularity is a thinning of the formation over the site of the Monument upwarp in Utah, suggesting that this feature was in existence and was diverting the Salt Wash distributaries northward and southward during this time. There is also a tendency for the contours to outline the central part of the Paradox basin and even individual salt anticlines within it. This suggests that the streams may have been very sensitive to slow movements of the salt masses.

Channel Sandstones of Salt Wash Member

The term "channel" came into general use among geologists and miners during the early stages of the intensified search for uranium in the Salt Wash sandstone. It has been pointed out that the channel is regarded by miners as an underground porous body of sandstone representing an abandoned and buried water course in which valuable minerals may have been deposited (Stokes, 1953).

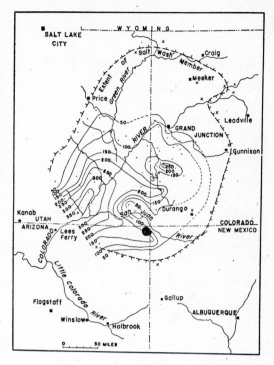

EXPLANATION

·Lithofacies Locality   ⟋—50⟍⟍⟍   Isopach Line, Dashed
where Inferred

×One Measured Section   ᴸᴸᴸ   Extent of Salt Wash Member

Isopach Interval 50 feet

Fig. 12.—Isopach map of stream deposits in Salt Wash member of the Morrison formation. Numbers indicate aggregate thicknesses of channel sandstone within the fan. From Mullens and Freeman, 1957.

When the term *channel* is used in the following discussion it has reference to a body of clastic material, generally sandstone, that originated by deposition from rapidly flowing water in an ancient stream course (Fig. 13). In spite of the great variations in size, shape, and arrangement of Salt Wash channels, a number of broad generalizations about their morphology may be made.

1. Channels range in length from 25 feet to several miles, with an average length of perhaps 1,500 feet. Information on this point is very meager, for the complete outlines of channels can rarely be determined either from drill records or from natural exposures. The width and thickness can generally be measured much more readily than the length.

2. Channels range in width from a few feet to per-

FIG. 13.—Segment of long, narrow, and gently curving channel sandstone in the Salt Wash member of the Morrison formation near Green River, Utah. All the ledges are segments of channels.

haps 2,000 feet, the average being about 200 feet. Although broader sheets of sandstone are known, these appear to be compact aggregations of many channels.

3. Channels range in thickness from about 2 feet to 100 feet, the average being about 15 feet. Mullens and Freeman (1957, p. 510) have arbitrarily classified all sandstones more than 2 feet thick as channel sandstones and those less than 2 feet thick as flood-plain sandstone. Again, if thicker sandstones exist, they consist of superimposed channels.

4. Practically all channels have a cross section that is plano-convex, the bottom convex, the top flat. The outline tends to be symmetrical but irregular in detail; the base of a typical channel is generally a definite erosional unconformity or scoured surface; the sides are generally gradational or show complex interfingering with flood-plain sediments, whereas the top may be an erosional unconformity or a gradational contact.

5. Practically all channels are curved so as to approach segments of true circles (Fig. 14). The curving sand bodies may occupy 5°–180° of arc, the average being perhaps 20° to 30°. Most patterns seen in plan view are definitely geometric and not erratic. Channels in any one area show a distinct preferred direction of curvature. In other words, looking "down stream" most channels will be seen to curve either to the right or to the left. It appears that the convex sides of the curves face the nearest topographically or tectonically high areas. The concave sides are therefore mainly toward the belts of stronger or more continuous water flow.

6. In general, the smaller the channel, the finer the

sediments it contains, and the weaker the internal primary structures. Conglomerate is found chiefly in the larger channels and is associated with strong cross-stratification of various kinds.

In addition to the obvious measurable characteristics listed above, a number of well-supported inferences regarding the sedimentary environments of Salt Wash time should be noted.

1. The sediments were laid down in a great distributary system, and the constituent streams generally decreased in size away from the apex by subdivision, undergound seepage, and evaporation. Precipitation on the plain itself must have been insignificant. The proportion of the plain under water at any one time must have been quite small, as the streams could occupy only a few channels in the same manner as those of modern deltas or alluvial fans.

2. Valley walls exercised little or no effect on Salt Wash rivers. Occasionally, at widely separated points a distributary might be deflected by a bedrock barrier or be confined between banks of older consolidated rock. In general, the stream systems were self-adjusting, ran on surfaces of their own construction, and were free to seek equilibrium conditions with maximum rapidity.

3. Vegetation was scarce and, as such, exercised little influence on stream processes. Most abundant growth was along active streams; the broad interstream belts may have been totally barren for long periods of time. Plant fossils are seldom found in

positions of growth and are commonly water worn and fragmentary.

4. Underflow and seepage along subsurface channels must have been especially active. Surface and subsurface water could possibly mix and exchange freely in one complex hydrologic system. It may be that the water transmitted underground greatly exceeded that on the surface during most seasons of the year. (For several views of a partly exhumed channel see Figures 15, 16, and 17.)

INTERNAL STRUCTURES

A variety of internal structures characterize Salt Wash sandstones. The most common and significant are cross-stratification, current lineation, rib and furrow, and ripple mark. These structures have value in determining direction of stream flow, energy relations of water and sediment load, and potential porosity and permeability.

Cross-stratification.—Many types of cross-stratification have been described (McKee and Weir, 1953). Festoon bedding is the most common in the Salt Wash. The cross-strata occupy elongate, symmetrical scoop-shaped troughs cut by strong current action in deeper, more energetic streams. Festoon bedding is especially valuable as a directional indicator, because the elongation of the trough axis, as well as the inclination of the cross-strata, gives current direction (Figs. 18 and 19).

Sediments making up festoon-bedded rock are coarser, less well sorted, and show less perfect circularity and roundness than the sediments in other primary structures (Stokes and Sadlick, 1953).

Current lineation.—Current lineation is a streamlining appearance of sand grains on smooth bedding planes (Fig. 20). The markings generally

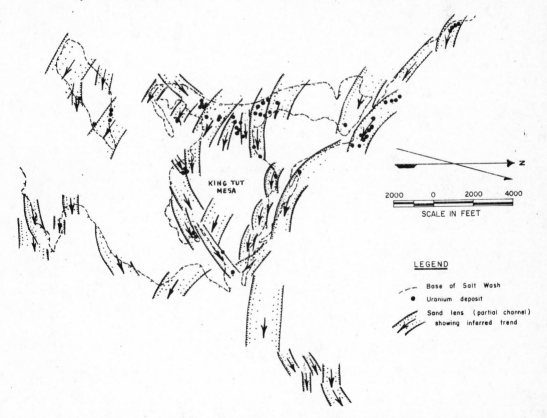

FIG. 14.—Sedimentary trends in the Salt Wash member of the Morrison formation in Carrizo Mountain District, Arizona. The curving channel segments shown diagrammatically and simplified were determined by a large number of observations of primary structures and surface exposures. From Stokes, 1953.

FIG. 15.—Aerial view of exhumed sandstone and conglomerate channel system in the Cedar Mountain formation near Green River, Utah. Length of the best-developed channel is about 6 miles. Ground views of this channel
are shown in Figs. 16 and 17. Width of photograph represents 4.5 miles.

occur on layers of rock 0.25–0.50 inch thick. The feature gives indications of opposing possible current directions and is thought to form in shallow but rapidly flowing water lateral to the central areas where festoon bedding occurs, but still under the influence of the main stream. It rarely diverges in direction from associated cross-stratification. Constituent grains are finer, better sorted, rounder, and more circular than those of festoon-bedded sediments.

Rib and furrow.—Rib and furrow is a poorly understood feature consisting of alternating crudely formed ridges and shallow, rounded depressions lying parallel with the direction of flow. The external appearance is similar to certain types of ripple mark. The internal structure is that of imbricating inclined laminae like very small-scale cross-bedding (Fig. 21). Rib and furrow is thought to form in water of shallow or moderate depth with low velocity, perhaps mainly in the floodplain environment. Constituent sediments are relatively finer, and show the most perfect sorting of the sands examined.

Ripple mark.—Ripple mark is relatively rare in the channel sandstones. Its formation is well understood; ripples are known to form transverse to the current direction in relatively slowly moving water through considerable depth range. Constituent sediments are similar to rib and furrow in being relatively fine, and are fairly well sorted.

Massive or structureless sandstone is also seen in

FIG. 16.—Surface and side of exhumed channel sandstone shown in Figs. 15 and 17. Low hills in right middle distance are parts of other channels in the same system.

FIG. 17.—Exhumed edge of the elongate channel shown in Figs. 15 and 16. Erosion has removed the softer flood-plain sediments and is undermining the margins of the former river bed.

FIG. 18.—Side view of festoon type cross-bedding, Burro Canyon formation, near Grand Junction, Colorado.

FIG. 19.—Festoon cross-bedding as seen on the eroded surface of a channel in the Salt Wash
member of the Morrison formation near Green River, Utah.

Fig. 20.—Lineated sandstone in the Salt Wash member of the Morrison formation, Carrizo Mountains, Arizona. Inferred current direction was parallel with hammer handle.

most outcrops. This tends to weather to lighter colors and is generally less well cemented than the other varieties. It is exposed either in smooth, rounded outcrops or under overhanging ledges (Fig. 22). The manner of formation is not understood, but it may represent material being shifted downstream along the main channels in low water stages. The constituents resemble those of festoon-bedded rock in being relatively coarse, poorly sorted, and with low circularity and roundness.

SEDIMENTARY PETROGRAPHY

The sedimentary petrography of the sandstones of the Salt Wash member has been intensively investigated by geologists of the U. S. Geological Survey, and is described by Craig and others (1955, p. 147–148) as follows.

Averages of the analytical results show that sandstones of the Salt Wash member may be classified as fine-grained, quartzitic sandstones. The average modal diameter of the sand is 0.176 mm. Of the detrital grains, 93 per cent are of sand size, and 7 per cent are of silt or clay size. The average composition of the sandstones is calcite (cement), 13 per cent; secondary silica (cement and overgrowths), 4 per cent; detrital grains, 83 per cent. Of the detrital grains, quartz (grains and overgrowths) comprises 86 per cent; feldspar (orthoclase to albite), 7 per cent; chert (silicified tuff and chert), 7 per cent. Only a small suite of light and heavy minerals is present.

In summary, the sandstone bodies of the Salt Wash consist of fine-grained, moderately rounded, quartz fragments with a moderate feldspar content and calcite cement. The fragments have been deposited by currents of water which created a variety of primary structures including curving and flat cross-beds, flat lineated surfaces, ripple-marked beds, and structureless masses.

The typical sandstone body is mostly surrounded by shale or mudstone but may make contact above, below, or laterally with several other lenses. It is longer than wide and wider than thick, with corresponding dimensions of about 1,500×200×15 feet. The cross section is plano-

FIG. 21.—Specimen of sandstone from the Salt Wash member of the Morrison formation, showing rib-and-furrow structure and inferred current direction.

convex, the lower contact representing a scoured surface and the other contacts either gradational or interfingering. In plan, the sandstone body curves rather smoothly through 20°–40° of arc, with all the internal structures conforming to the curving trend.

<h2>INTERPRETATIONS</h2>

The sandstone bodies of the Salt Wash are best interpreted in terms of fluvial action. The gross structure of the plain was determined by the composition and grade size of material supplied, the gradient of the depositional surface, the volume of water discharged onto and across any part of the area, and the variations in volume owing to seasonal effects of sporadic channel shifting.

Materials ranging from the finest clay fractions to cobbles up to 4 inches in diameter were supplied at the apex of the fan. There was a constant "running ahead of the fines" and an attrition of the coarser materials so that the outward gradation from coarse to fine was maintained. The original surface was probably essentially flat, for it was mostly the slightly modified bed of the Late Jurassic interior sea. The Salt Wash streams proceeded to build up a surface of sufficient inclination to move the available sediment outward and across this plain. Aggradational processes were dominant. More sediment was delivered to the area than was taken away. Erosion was local and mainly confined to very narrow channels. Sediment picked up was carried forward relatively short distances before being redeposited. Apparently, most of the coarse and much of the fine material was buried before it could complete the traverse across the fan surface. Near the end of the interval of deposition, fairly continuous unbroken sand sheets were built up in the central part of the area, owing, perhaps, to attainment of a graded condition.

The fluvial processes operating on the plain were regulated by energy relations and sediment load. The concept of the graded stream is applicable, for the action of single streams shifting laterally for a sufficiently long time will create a composite surface having a gradient and profile that is essentially the projection of one stream. Ignoring details, it may be said that a stream system exhibits all the features of a system seeking equilibrium. Its response to disturbances follows Le Chatelier's general law—*If a stress is brought to bear on a system in equilibrium, a reaction occurs, displacing the equilibrium in a direction which tends to absorb the effect of the stress* (Mackin, 1948). If the gradient is too low for transportation of available load, it will be built up; if initially too steep, it will be eroded. The common expression of the depositional process is the alluvial fan; of the degradational process it is the pediment. In both cases the gradient approaches equilibrium giving an identical surface configuration. Once a profile of equilibrium is reached, the surface is neither raised nor lowered but becomes a plane across which the available material is shifted forward slowly or rapidly, depending on available water.

By comparison with modern streams, the Salt Wash system was apparently subject to very few disturbing influences. The climate seems to have been uniform. The type of material supplied shows little change with time. The confining uplands were hundreds of miles apart so that space was practically unlimited. The base level represented by the toe or margin of the fan was apparently more stable than sea level, and tectonic disturbances within the depositional area were mild and

localized. Such conditions are almost ideal for the achievement and maintenance of equilibrium relationships. Geological features seen in the dissected remnants of the Salt Wash represent what can be expected by a river system operating without major disturbance over a long period of time.

The problem of what is the "normal" activity for rivers operating under the conditions just outlined is difficult in the absence of first-hand knowledge about the volume, velocity, and regimen of the streams. One process, however, is inevitable in aggrading river systems. This is the lateral shifting of streams so as to maintain a fairly uniform graded surface. The shifting may be accomplished entirely by meandering but generally involves the more spectacular process of avulsion during floods. This process must have been repeated many times on the Salt Wash plain and apparently explains many internal features of the formation. As pointed out by Melton (1936), the chief work of streams is accomplished during floods. Modification during low-water stages is of minor consequence.

The history of a typical distributary might be as follows. The original event is the flooding of a low, broad area by waters released from a former,

Fig. 22.—Typical view of the side of an eroded channel in the Salt Wash sandstone member of the Morrison formation, Carrizo Mountains, Arizona. The overhanging ledge is festoon bedded and relatively hard; the underlying stratum is almost structureless and is relatively soft. An erosional surface separates the two.

higher, and better defined course. At first the river would be wide and relatively shallow with low velocity or complete stagnation. At this stage the deposits would be in relatively thin, even beds with internal primary structures characteristic of slowly moving water. With the passage of time the main volume of water would become increasingly restricted to a narrower belt with the adjacent areas receiving only the finer sediments carried by marginal slack water. Through the building up of natural levees the central channel would become increasingly more confined and the general bed of the river would be elevated by addition of the heavier and coarser materials. Eventually, at a time of exceptionally high water, the river might break through its banks with the flood waters escaping to lower ground to commence the cycle over again.

It should be noted that the sudden abandonment of a stream bed by avulsion would leave the bottom sediments in the state they were in at the height of the flood. Presumably, therefore, the deposit left by a river at the last moment of its existence would be the bed-load, as it was in an active state of transportation with evidences of turbulent flow and erosive action on exposed bed material. The most commonly observed unconformities within the Salt Wash and most of the primary structures may have been created at times of flood.

ECONOMIC GEOLOGY OF FLUVIAL SANDSTONES

The fluvial sandstone bodies of the Colorado Plateau are of economic interest chiefly as channelways, host rocks, and reservoirs, for they contain practically no syngenetic materials of value. As channels they have served to convey mineral-bearing solutions, ordinary ground water, oil, and gas; as host rocks they are places of deposition and concentration of solid mineral deposits; and as reservoirs they may trap and preserve accumulations of liquid and gaseous materials, chiefly hydrocarbons. The erratic occurrence of economic materials within them indicates that not all channels are equally favorable for transmission or accumulation of introduced material, and much field and laboratory work has been done to determine controls or guides leading to the location of economic deposits or accumulations.

URANIUM

The most important economic product of the fluvial sandstone bodies of the Colorado Plateau is uranium, and the largest known accumulations are in the Morrison and Chinle formations. The uranium in a typical ore body is contained in an impregnation of fine-grained minerals, of which the most common are coffinite in the oxidized zone, and uraninite in the unoxidized zone. With few exceptions the minerals occupy pore spaces in sandstone, conglomerate, or fossil materials such as wood or bone.

The typical ore body of the Salt Wash is an elongate, tabular mass having a length from four to five times the width and a width two or three times the thickness (Fig. 23). The content of ore ranges from a few hundred pounds to several hundred thousand tons. The sides may be either sharp or gradational; the ends are, almost without exception, gradational. In general, the shape of the ore bodies mirrors on a smaller scale that of the containing sandstones, and the trend of the ore bodies in almost all instances is parallel to the margins and internal primary structures of the sandstone channels in which they lie.

The most obvious stratigraphic relationship of uranium-vanadium deposits in the fluvial sandstones is their abundance in the sandstone facies and their almost complete absence in the mudstone facies. In the sandstone facies ore bodies are found to favor the thicker channels, but not necessarily the wider or more continuous ones.

In most of the larger mineralized districts the ore bodies tend to be concentrated in certain zones of channel sandstones. Throughout practically all the Uravan mineral belt in Colorado this is in the uppermost Salt Wash; in the Carrizo Mountains, Arizona, it is near the base of the Salt Wash; in the Blanding district of Utah it is near the middle. At a few places the deposits may be scattered rather uniformly through the entire member.

There is also a preferential position for ore bodies within the channels—most bodies lie in the lower part of the containing lenses. Statistical studies of mineralization in the Club Mesa area show that ore deposits lie in the bottom half of the host sandstone in about 90 per cent of all holes penetrating ore and in the bottom quarter

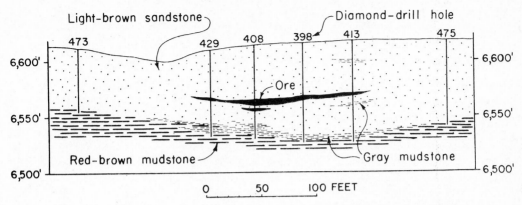

FIG. 23.—Geologic section showing typical relationship of ore and related features in the Calamity group of claims, Mesa County, Colorado. From Weir, 1952.

of the unit in more than 60 per cent of the ore holes. In some districts the ore may show a preference for the margins or edges of the channels rather than the bottoms. In general, the upper and central portions are least favorable and are rarely mineralized (Fig. 24).

Other geologic relationships that are guides to ore have been generally noted (Weir, 1952). Most deposits occur in sandstone that is dominantly pale to light yellow brown, speckled with limonite

FIG. 24.—Uranium mine in the Salt Wash member of the Morrison formation, Cottonwood Wash, west of Blanding, San Juan County, Utah. At this locality a number of superimposed lenses occur; the base of a large scoured surface can be seen above the mine opening on the right.

stain. Reddish tints are unfavorable. Mudstone in and adjacent to Salt Wash channels is normally (and presumably originally) red or reddish brown. Near ore bodies, however, the mudstone within and immediately below the ore-bearing sandstone has been altered to gray or greenish gray. The thickness or percentage of altered mudstone, in general, increases with the volume of ore bodies in the vicinity. Perhaps most important of all is the association with carbonaceous material. Fossil logs and fragmental plant remains of many types are widespread in the Salt Wash, but the distribution is erratic and nonuniform. Experience has shown that ore is generally associated with this fossil plant material.

The geologic relationships of mineralization in the Chinle sandstone bodies are similar. The ore bodies occur most commonly in the thicker lenses, have their long axes parallel with that of the enclosing channel, favor a location at the base or margins of the containing body, and generally occur with carbonaceous material. Rocks in the vicinity of ore are also commonly altered from red to gray and green.

THEORIES OF ORIGIN

From the fact that practically all types of igneous, metamorphic, and sedimentary rocks contain uranium in the western United States, it may be assumed that there is a deep seated common source, and that there have been several periods of uranium production. Differences of opinion arise chiefly over the history of uranium during the various stages of migration, dissemination, and reconstitution that have occurred since its release from within the crust.

To account for the origin of uranium deposits such as those in the Morrison and Chinle, the following theories have been proposed.

1. A hydrothermal theory that requires the precipitation of ore minerals from heated solutions of igneous origin. The theory allows for lateral migration of rising solutions through favorable channels, and even a certain amount of dilution with ordinary ground water, but requires direct derivation of the uranium through deep-seated fractures.
2. A circulating ground-water theory resting on the assumption that the uranium has been derived from normal ground-water solutions which picked it up at the surface during erosion of areas of Precambrian basement rock. No high-temperature effects are required but there must be large scale lateral migration.
3. The ash-leach theory, which derives the uranium from volcanic ash such as is known to exist in large quantities in many formations of Paleozoic, Mesozoic, and Cenozoic age. According to this theory, movement of the mineral constituents would be chiefly downward and laterally.
4. The syngenetic theory, which would have the uranium deposits formed contemporaneously with the enclosing sediments. Weak solutions of the essential metals built up the ore bodies within the sediments during and chiefly after deposition.

The above theories agree that the ore deposits have been concentrated from circulating solutions, probably slightly mineralized ground water. It is also admitted that organic material in some form is favorable or essential to ore formation. Disregarding the ultimate source of the metallic ions and the solutions, any theory of ore formation requires the passage of large volumes of ground water through the channel systems of the host rocks. The known facts support the general conclusion that the thicker and more continuous channels or systems of channels have provided avenues for passage of metal-bearing solutions and that the organic material created the necessary chemical environment for precipitation. The carbon may have provided local areas of reducing environment (Gruner, 1956), or it may have localized the activity of anaerobic bacteria which released H_2S with the same reducing effects (Jensen, 1958).

The fact that ore is most common at the base or edges of certain channels leads to one or more assumptions—(1) Organic material grew or was buried more abundantly in these areas. Certainly, stranded tree trunks would be expected to come to rest on the margins of streams. (2) Many channels were only partly full of water, which flowed along the lowest possible route under the influence of gravity. (3) Some channels were full of water, perhaps under pressure, but the water in the central parts of the lenses moved more rapidly than that at the margins, so that local stagnated pockets and an interface between active and stagnant areas of flow came into existence. The peculiar ore structures called "rolls," which curve vertically across the bedding, may represent deposition on such an interface (Shawe, 1956).

It has been suggested by Phoenix (1958) on the basis of much good evidence which cannot be given here, that a significantly high proportion of ore deposits in the Salt Wash lies immediately under a system of fossil stream channels in the basal part of the overlying Brushy Basin member of the Morrison. Phoenix believes that underflow conditions related to these stream systems had much to do with localizing the groups of ore bodies.

PRESENT-DAY GROUND-WATER CONDITIONS

Because of the extreme dissection of the Colorado Plateau there are few extensive reservoirs of ground water in the Mesozoic rocks. However, much of the water that is obtained from wells or emerges from springs is geologically related to sedimentary conditions in the fluvial and eolian sandstone bodies of the area. In the Colorado Plateau there are probably hundreds of springs and seeps localized at the outcroppings of channel sandstones. In general, surface water gains ready access into the channels because of their greater permeability and porosity. Downward movement is generally stopped by underlying impervious beds, so that the water moves into and along the lowest parts of the channels until the surface is reached and a spring or seep results.

The location of springs or successful wells can generally be explained, but seldom predicted. The complexities of the channel systems undergound and the consequent devious routes of subsurface flow are made evident by present-day conditions just as they are in the distribution of ancient ground-water effects.

OIL AND GAS

Fluvial sandstones are minor sources of oil and gas in the Colorado Plateau. The only field where significant production is derived from the Morrison and related formations lies along the projection of the Uncomphagre uplift in Grand County, Utah, and Mesa County, Colorado. The area is only partly developed, but it is evident that stratigraphic control is more important than structural control. The belts of production show a northeasterly trend in conformity with depositional belts and channel systems in the Dakota, Buckhorn, and Salt Wash stratigraphic units. Production may be expected in synclines as well as anticlines, if the right trends are followed. From lack of correlation and the spotty nature of production it is evident that the reservoir rocks

consist of a maze of channels in which oil, water, and gas are irregularly distributed in different proportions. Some channels are evidently entirely devoid of fluids. More work will be needed before a meaningful picture can be presented.

It should be mentioned that the eolian sandstone bodies have yielded practically no oil or gas (except carbon dioxide). They are obviously not good source rocks and may be too perfect as reservoir rocks. Like gigantic blotters, they can absorb practically unlimited quantities of oil under conditions that prohibit its subsequent release.

CONCLUSION

The Colorado Plateau presents unparalleled opportunity for the study of eolian and fluvial sandstone bodies. The recent search for uranium has included an intensive and thorough investigation of these important host rocks. The amount of geologic information collected is very extensive, but much is not generally available and may never be published. The complexity of ancient ground water solutions and of their routes of migration has been made abundantly clear. The difficulty of explaining why uranium ore bodies occur in one place, in one channel, or in one area, in preference to other localities apparently just as favorable, emphasizes the difficulty of reconstructing ancient geologic conditions, especially those involving transitory effects of undergound solutions. Even with abundant surface exposures, thousands of drill holes, and the application of the best talents and techniques available, there are many unsolved and perhaps unsolvable problems.

REFERENCES

Baker, A. A., Dane, C. H., and Reeside, J. B., Jr., 1936, Correlation of the Jurassic formations of parts of Utah, Arizona, New Mexico, and Colorado: U. S. Geol. Survey Prof. Paper 183, 66 p.

Craig, L. C., Holmes, C. N., and others, 1955, Stratigraphy of the Morrison and related formations, Colorado Plateau region, a preliminary report: U. S. Geol. Survey Bull. 1009-E, p. 125–168.

Eardley, A. J., 1952, Colorado Plateau, in Utah Geol. Soc. Guidebook 7, Cedar City, Utah, to Las Vegas, Nevada: p. 22–26.

Finch, W. I., 1959, Geology of uranium deposits in Triassic rocks of the Colorado Plateau region: U. S. Geol. Survey Bull. 1074-D, 164 p.

Gilmore, C. W., 1926, 1927, 1928, Fossil footprints from the Grand Canyon: Smithsonian Misc. Coll., v. 77, no. 9, 41 p.; v. 80, no. 3, 78 p.; v. 80, no. 8, p. 1–16.

Grundy, W. D., and Oertell, E. W., 1958, Uranium deposits in the White Canyon and Monument Valley mining districts, San Juan County, Utah, and Navajo and Apache Counties, Arizona, *in* Intermountain Assoc. Petroleum Geologists Guidebook 9th Ann. Field Conf.: p. 197–207.

Gruner, J. W., 1956, Concentration of uranium in sediments by multiple migration-accretion: Econ. Geology, v. 51, no. 6, p. 495–520.

Harshbarger, C. A., Repenning, C. A., and Irwin, J. H., 1957, Stratigraphy of the uppermost Triassic and the Jurassic rocks of the Navajo country: U. S. Geol. Survey Prof. Paper 291, 74 p.

Heylmun, E. B., 1958, Paleozoic stratigraphy and oil possibilities of Kaiparowits region, Utah: Am. Assoc. Petroleum Geologists Bull., v. 42, no. 8, p. 1781–1812.

Hilpert, L. S., and Corey, A. F., 1957, Northwest New Mexico, *in* Geologic investigations of radioactive deposits; semiannual report for Dec. 1, 1956 to May 31, 1957: U. S. Atomic Energy Comm., Oak Ridge, Tenn., TEI-690, book 2, p. 366–381.

Hunt, C. B., Averitt, P., and Miller, R. L., 1953, Geology and geography of the Henry Mountains region, Utah: U. S. Geol. Survey Prof. Paper 228, p. 1–234.

Jensen, M. L., 1958, Sulfur isotopes and the origin of sandstone-type uranium deposits: Econ. Geology, v. 53, p. 598–616.

Kiersch, G. A., 1950, Small scale structures and other features of Navajo sandstone, northern part of San Rafael swell, Utah: Am. Assoc. Petroleum Geologists Bull., v. 34, no. 5, p. 933–942.

Kunkel, R. P., 1958, Permian stratigraphy of the Paradox basin, *in* Intermountain Assoc. Petroleum Geologists Guidebook 9th Ann. Field Conf., p. 163–168.

McKee, E. D., and Weir, G. W., 1953, Terminology for stratification and cross-stratification in sedimentary rocks: Geol. Soc. America Bull., v. 64, no. 4, p. 381–389.

Mackin, J. H., 1948, Concept of the graded river: Geol. Soc. America Bull., v. 59, no. 5, p. 463–512.

McKnight, E. T., 1940, Geology of area between Green and Colorado Rivers, Grand and San Juan Counties, Utah: U. S. Geol. Survey Bull. 908, p. 10–146.

Melton, F. A., 1936, An empirical classification of flood-plain streams: Geog. Review, v. 26, no. 4, p. 593–609.

Mook, C. C., 1916, A study of the Morrison formation, Colorado Plateau: New York Acad. Science Ann., v. 27, p. 39–191.

Mullens, T. E., and Freeman, V. L., 1957, Lithofacies of the Salt Wash member of the Morrison formation, Colorado Plateau: Geol. Soc. America Bull., v. 68, no. 4, p. 505–526.

Newberry, J. S., 1876, Geological report, *in* Macomb,

J. N., Report of the exploring expedition from Santa Fe, New Mexico to the junction of the Grand and Green Rivers of the great Colorado of the West in 1859: Washington, D. C.

Phoenix, D. A., 1958, Uranium deposits under conglomeratic sandstone of the Morrison formation, Colorado and Utah: Geol. Soc. America Bull., v. 69, no. 4, p. 403–418.

Reiche, Parry, 1938, An analysis of cross-lamination; the Coconino sandstone: Jour. Geology, v. 46, no. 7, p. 905–932.

Rich, J. L., 1935, Origin and evolution of rock fans and pediments: Geol. Soc. America Bull., v. 46, no. 6, p. 999–1024.

Shawe, D. R., 1956, Significance of roll ore bodies in genesis of uranium-vanadium deposits on the Colorado Plateau, *in* Page, L. R., and others, Contributions to the geology of uranium and thorium by the U. S. Geol. Survey and Atomic Energy Comm. for the United Nations Internat. Conf. on peaceful uses of atomic energy, Geneva, Switzerland, 1955: U. S. Geol. Survey Prof. Paper 300, p. 239–241.

Stewart, J. W., Poole, F. G., and Wilson, R. F., 1957, Triassic studies, *in* Geologic investigations of radioactive deposits; semiannual report for Dec. 1, 1956 to May 31, 1957: U. S. Atomic Energy Comm., Oak Ridge, Tenn., TEI-690, book 2, p. 346–351.

Stokes, W. L., 1944, Morrison formation and related deposits in and adjacent to the Colorado Plateau: Geol. Soc. America Bull., v. 55, no. 8, p. 951–992.

———— 1950, Pediment concept applied to Shinarump and similar conglomerates: Geol. Soc. America Bull., v. 61, no. 2, p. 91–98.

———— 1953, Primary sedimentary trend indicators as applied to ore findings in the Carrizo Mountains, Arizona and New Mexico: U. S. Atomic Energy Comm., Tech. Inf. Service, Oak Ridge, Tenn., RME-3043, pt. 1.

———— 1954, Relation of sedimentary trends, tectonic features and ore deposits in the Blanding district, San Juan County, Utah: U. S. Atomic Energy Comm., Tech. Inf. Service, Oak Ridge, Tenn., RME-3093, pt. 1.

———— 1958, Continental sediments of the Colorado Plateau, *in* Intermountain Assoc. Petroleum Geologists Guidebook 9th Ann. Field Conf.: p. 26–30.

———— and Sadlick, W., 1953, Sedimentary properties of Salt Wash sandstones as related to primary structures: U. S. Atomic Energy Comm., Tech. Inf. Service, Oak Ridge, Tenn., RME-6067, pt. 2.

Weir, D. B., 1952, Geologic guides to prospecting for carnotite deposits on Colorado Plateau: U. S. Geol. Survey Bull. 988-B, p. 15–27.

Witkind, I. J., 1956, Uranium deposits at base of Shinarump conglomerate, Monument Valley, Arizona: U. S. Geol. Survey Bull. 1030-C, p. 99–130.

PERMIAN BLANKET SANDSTONES OF COLORADO PLATEAU[1]

D. L. BAARS[2]

Farmington, New Mexico

ABSTRACT

Three widely distributed sandstone bodies—the Cedar Mesa, De Chelly, and Coconino-Glorieta sandstones—are conspicuous components of the Permian System of the Colorado Plateau. All are light colored, highly cross-stratified, quartzose sandstones, but they differ radically in geometric configuration, geographic distribution, source area, primary bedding features, and depositional environment.

The Cedar Mesa sandstone is present in the western part of the plateau as a thick sequence of light colored, nearshore-marine to littoral deposits that occur in a linear north-south trend. The unit grades eastward through abrupt facies changes into lagoonal red beds of the Cutler group that were derived from a different source.

The De Chelly sandstone is considerably more widespread, and is present over most of the province, except southwestern Colorado. The red sands were derived from Cutler sediments and distributed by northeasterly winds, forming an eolian desert in the greater Four Corners area, that graded southward into horizontally bedded marine deposits along the southern margin of the plateau. The sea encroached upon the vast dune area from the south and reworked the eolian deposits in its path, but did not reach the northern desert.

The Coconino-Glorieta sandstone was deposited as a fan-shaped wedge in northern Arizona, by eolian processes. The central Arizona source also supplied sands to a relatively stable marine area in central New Mexico, where they were deposited in shallow-marine to littoral environments. The marine deposits were widely and uniformly distributed—in marked contrast to their eolian counterparts in Arizona that were physically separated by the slightly positive Defiance uplift near the Arizona-New Mexico State line. The geometric configuration of the dual-environment formation is very distinctive.

INTRODUCTION

Widespread sandstone bodies are present as prominent constituents of the Permian System over much of the Colorado Plateau. Three separate formations—the Cedar Mesa sandstone, De Chelly sandstone, and Coconino-Glorieta sandstone—merit special attention because of their broad regional extent and stratigraphic significance. Each of these units has been considered eolian in origin since the earliest geologic studies on the plateau. Recent studies indicate, however, that these sand bodies are probably marine in character over large areas. Despite their similarities in origin, each has distinctive characteristics which include (1) separate source area, (2) geographic distribution, (3) geometric configuration, (4) primary bedding features, and (5) sedimentary petrography.

The oldest of the principal sand bodies—the Cedar Mesa sandstone (Fig. 2)—is largely a littoral to near shore-marine unit that was deposited

[1] Manuscript received, November 1, 1960. Published by permission of the Shell Oil Company.

[2] The Shell Oil Company. The writer is grateful to J. A. Peterson, who encouraged the initiation of this paper, and offered many helpful suggestions.

along the western third of the Colorado Plateau. The formation is exposed at numerous outcrop, on the Kaibab uplift, the Kaiparowits Plateau, the Monument upwarp, and the San Rafael swell (Fig. 1). Although primarily of marine origin, the Cedar Mesa locally contains eolian deposits.

The widespread De Chelly sandstone is the youngest Permian deposit of the Four Corners area. The unit is a prominent orange colored eolian sandstone over much of southeastern Utah, but grades into extensive marine sandstones in northern Arizona and New Mexico. The De Chelly is best known for its exposures on the Monument upwarp, where it forms a major part of the scenic beauty of Monument Valley, and in the Canyon de Chelly National Monument.

The youngest of the three sandstones is the Coconino-Glorieta of the southern Colorado Plateau. The Coconino is well known in northern Arizona as a typically eolian deposit (McKee, 1933). This highly cross-stratified sandstone is the lateral equivalent of the Glorieta of central New Mexico, which is mainly a marine sandstone of similar lithology. The Glorieta, unlike the Coconino, is a very widespread and uniform accu-

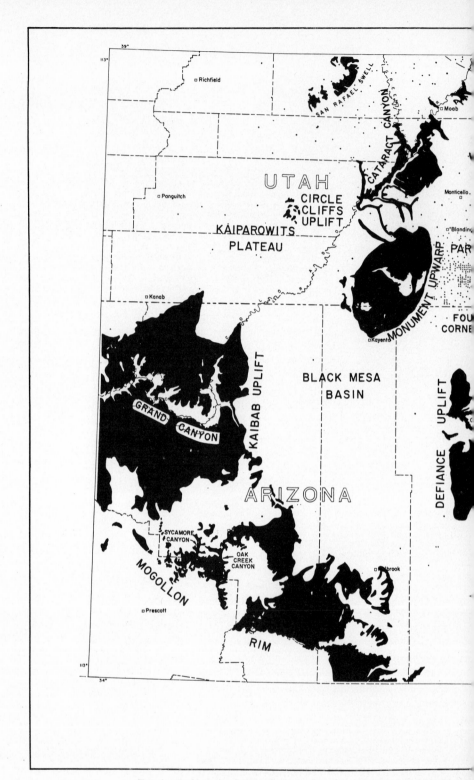

FIG. 1.—Index map of Four Corners area, showing outcrops of Permian r

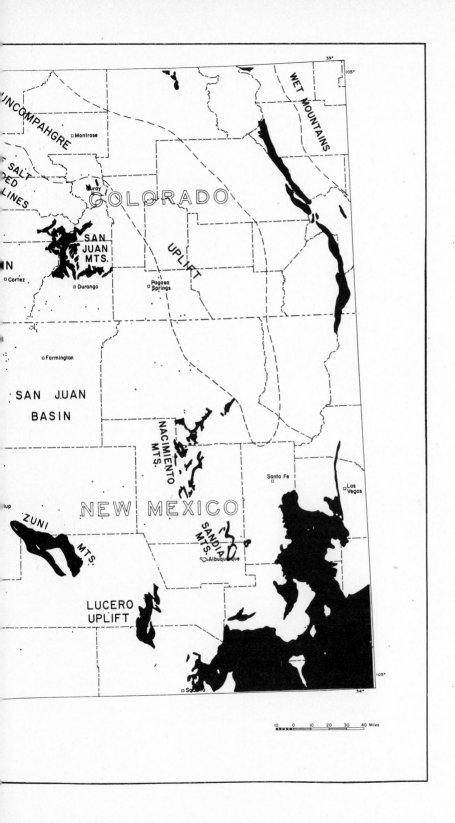

mulation that is present as a relatively thin unit over most of central and southern New Mexico and adjacent areas. In this paper the Coconino sandstone will be considered in its entirety, but only that portion of the Glorieta that lies within the Colorado Plateau will be discussed.

REGIONAL CORRELATIONS

The regional stratigraphic relationships of the Permian System on the Colorado Plateau have recently been discussed in some detail by Baars (1961), and will be only briefly summarized in this paper. The arkosic red beds that make up a large part of the Permian System were derived primarily from the ancestral Uncompahgre uplift that was a prominent topographic feature from middle Pennsylvanian time through the Wolf-campian Epoch (lower Permian). Sediments near the source area are coarse arkosic and conglomer-

atic sandstones, with interbeds of finer red clastics that make up the undifferentiated Cutler forma-tion of southwestern Colorado and southeastern Utah. South and west of the positive element, the red beds become finer in grain size, and are segregated into distinguishable units that have been given formation status in the Cutler group. These extensive red beds grade generally to marine deposits along the southern and western margins of the plateau.

Sedimentary rocks equivalent to the lower por-tion of the Cutler (undifferentiated) have been designated the "Lower Cutler" in the Four Cor-ners area, the Abo formation of New Mexico, and the true Supai of northern Arizona (Fig. 2). The "Lower Cutler" is a sequence of red shales, silt-stones, and fine-grained sandstones that contains thin beds, nodules, and irregular-shaped masses of primary anhydrite. Equivalent red beds extend

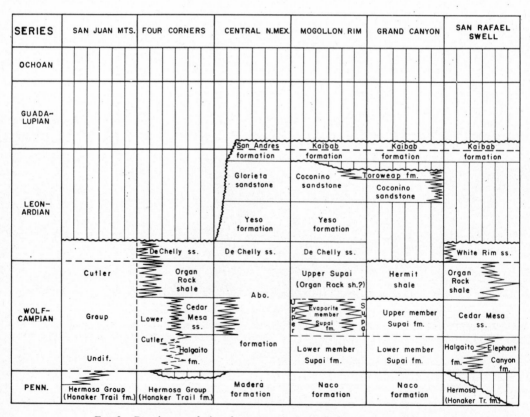

FIG. 2.—Permian correlation chart—proposed terminology and correlations.

onto the Monument upwarp as the basal Permian Halgaito shale. The upper half of the "Lower Cutler" interfingers with light colored marine sandstones of the Cedar Mesa sandstone along the eastern margin of the Monument upwarp. The Halgaito interfingers toward the northwest with marine carbonates of the Elephant Canyon formation, which gradationally underlies the Cedar Mesa sandstone west and north of the Colorado River (Fig. 3). South of the Four Corners the "Lower Cutler" grades into red beds of the New Mexico Abo formation and the Supai (restricted) of northern Arizona. Both the Halgaito and Cedar Mesa lithologies are recognizable in the Supai of the Grand Canyon, but are not apparent in the Supai of east-central Arizona, which contained rocks younger than the type Supai, until restricted by Baars (1961).

"Upper Cutler" equivalents are the Organ Rock-Hermit shale of the Four Corners to Grand Canyon area, and the overlying De Chelly sandstone. The Organ Rock-Hermit is very similar to the Halgaito and "Lower Cutler" in lithology, being fine-grained red beds of Cutler derivation. This unit is largely restricted to the southern Utah and northern Arizona region. The De Chelly sandstone extends southward from the same general area into central New Mexico, where it was previously included in the "Meseta Blanca member" of the Yeso formation; and into east-central Arizona, where past workers placed it in the upper Supai formation. Baars (1961) excluded the De Chelly and the overlying Yeso formation from the eastern Supai, making the formation approximately equivalent to the type Supai of the Grand Canyon.

Post-De Chelly sedimentation was restricted to the southern and western margins of the Colorado Plateau (Fig. 3). The oldest of these deposits are the restricted marine red beds, carbonates, and evaporites of the Yeso formation of lower to middle Leonardian age in New Mexico. The Yeso thickens rapidly southward, with a marked increase in evaporites, from a featheredge that trends approximately east-west across the southern Colorado Plateau. Yeso sediments are gradational with both the underlying De Chelly sandstone and the overlying Glorieta sandstone. The Coconino sandstone is the Arizona equivalent of the Glorieta, and gradationally overlies Yeso equivalents except in the Grand Canyon, where the Yeso is not present. The Coconino is an eolian deposit derived from a central Arizona positive area, thinning rapidly away from the source in all directions. Winds from the Coconino source area supplied sands to the New Mexico seas, where they were deposited in a nearshore complex of beaches, local dune areas, and offshore bars. The Glorieta sandstone grades upward into the shallow-marine San Andres carbonates, and locally interfingers with it. The Arizona dune deposits grade upward into marine sediments of the Toroweap formation on the Kaibab uplift, but elsewhere underlie the younger Kaibab carbonates disconformably. The youngest Permian sediments on the Colorado Plateau are the upper Leonardian Kaibab formation of Arizona, and the equivalent San Andres formation of New Mexico. The marine deposits accumulated in shallow seas along the southern margin of the plateau and northward into Utah along the western part of the province. Although limestones are a prominent component of the Kaibab-San Andres, terrigenous clastics are generally present, and local deposits of evaporites are known.

No Guadalupian or Ochoan sediments are recognized on the Colorado Plateau, so that Lower Triassic deposits disconformably overlie the lower to middle Permian rocks. Physical features of the disconformity are mild channeling and weathered surfaces over most of the area, with only locally extreme erosion and angular discordance. Uplift of the area during late Permian or early Triassic time was apparently epeirogenic in nature and rather mild.

CEDAR MESA SANDSTONE

The Cedar Mesa sandstone is a light colored, highly cross-stratified unit that is present as a distinctive formation only in the Monument upwarp, Kaiparowits Plateau, and San Rafael swell areas of southeastern Utah. In this region the Cedar Mesa is a very resistant unit, forming spectacular and impassable cliffs, and capping broad plateaus. Equivalent sandstones are present in the Grand Canyon as the upper Supai formation, or "Esplanade sandstone" of the early workers. The Cedar Mesa sandstone gradationally overlies red

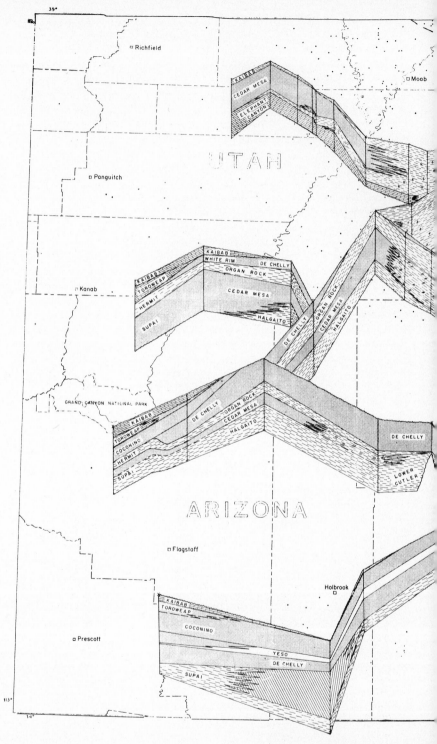

FIG. 3.—Fence diagram of Permian Sy

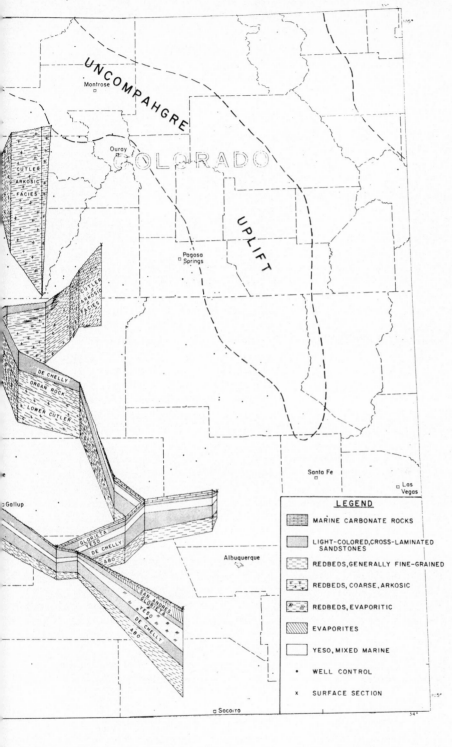

UNCOMPAHGRE

Montrose

COLORADO

Ouray

UPLIFT

Pagosa
Springs

CUTLER
ARKOSIC
FACIES

CUTLER
ARKOSIC
FACIES

DE CHELLY
ORGAN ROCK
LOWER CUTLER

Santa Fe

Las
Vegas

Gallup

GLORIETA
YESO
DE CHELLY
ABO

Albuquerque

SAN ANDRES
GLORIETA
YESO
DE CHELLY
ABO

Socorro

LEGEND

MARINE CARBONATE ROCKS

LIGHT-COLORED, CROSS-LAMINATED SANDSTONES

REDBEDS, GENERALLY FINE-GRAINED

REDBEDS, COARSE, ARKOSIC

REDBEDS, EVAPORITIC

EVAPORITES

YESO, MIXED MARINE

•   WELL CONTROL

x   SURFACE SECTION

0   10   20   30   40 Miles
0
250
500
FEET 1000

D.L. BAARS

beds of the Halgaito shale on the southern Monument upwarp and interfingers with the Halgaito west of the uplift (Fig. 3). Toward the northwest the sandstone conformably overlies marine carbonates of the Halgaito-equivalent Elephant Canyon formation and locally interfingers with the carbonates (Baars, 1961). The contact with the overlying Organ Rock-Hermit shale is abrupt but apparently conformable. The Cedar Mesa grades eastward into the upper portion of the "Lower Cutler" along outcrops on the southern Monument upwarp and interfingers with Cutler arkoses in exposures near the junction of the Green and Colorado Rivers at the north plunge of the upwarp.

The Cedar Mesa sandstone was named for exposures at the south end of Cedar Mesa, a few miles northwest of Mexican Hat, Utah, by Baker and Reeside (1929). The formation is composed of white to light-gray sandstone that is locally tan, light brown, or even pale reddish brown. It is a typically fine to medium grained, well rounded to subangular sandstone with varying amounts of calcareous cement. Bedding characteristics vary from thin to medium, horizontally bedded units, to massive and highly cross-stratified beds, but dips of the cross-strata rarely exceed 25°, and dips ranging from 12° to 20° are more common. Well defined bedding planes are numerous, and thin, light red or green shales and sandy limestones are commonly present. Marine invertebrates have been reported from a few localities by Darton (1925), Gregory and Moore (1931), and Baars (1961), suggesting that deposition was in a marine environment.

The distribution and thickness of the Cedar Mesa sandstone are shown on Figure 4. The geometric configuration is somewhat unusual in that the sandstone does not thin to a pinchout, but instead changes facies abruptly into the Cutler red beds at thicknesses of 400–800 feet, in outcrops on the east flank of the Monument upwarp. The sandstone thickens gradually toward the west and northwest to a maximum known thickness of about 1,400 feet along the western margin of the Colorado Plateau. Lack of outcrops and subsurface control prevents an adequate analysis of the Cedar Mesa's lateral relationships toward the west.

Lateral relationships.—Sandstones of the type Cedar Mesa grade eastward into Cutler red beds along the eastern flank of the Monument upwarp in southern Utah and northern Arizona. Sears (1956) and Kunkel (1958) described the exposed facies change near the San Juan River where it crosses the Comb monocline. There the massive Cedar Mesa sandstones change rapidly eastward to gray gypsiferous sandstone, greenish and purplish gray crystalline limestone, bedded sandy gypsum, and light red gypsiferous shales of the "Lower Cutler" sequence. This spectacular facies change takes place in a distance of 1 to 2 miles, and is observable in surface exposures southward as far as the Arizona portion of Monument Valley. The narrow belt of change also parallels the monoclinal flank in the subsurface toward the north, emerging again at exposures along the northeast flank of the upwarp, in the vicinity of the junction of the Green and Colorado Rivers. In this area the Cedar Mesa interfingers eastward with arkosic red sandstones of the Cutler, with no intervening evaporitic beds. The interfingering occurs within a northwest-trending belt that approximately parallels the northeast flank of the upwarp. Thin tongues of the red arkosic Cutler extend 4–6 miles westward into the white Cedar Mesa. The lithologic characteristics of the Cutler clastics contrast sharply with the Cedar Mesa tongues. The Cutler sandstones are dark brownish red, of very fine- to medium-grain size, poorly sorted, very argillaceous, arkosic, and calcareous. The cross-laminations are extremely variable, but are generally of medium-scale bedding characterized by long, sweeping curves of the fore-set beds, whose dip averages 12.5° with an average direction of S. 26° E. (Fig. 5-*A*). The contrasting Cedar Mesa sandstones are white to light tan, of very fine- to fine-grain size, well sorted, very calcareous, with large scale uniformly inclined cross-strata with an average dip of 20.5° and an average direction of S. 35° E. (Fig. 5-*B*).

Bedding characteristics.—Cross-stratification is a prominent feature of the Cedar Mesa sandstone, although the bedding characteristics within the formation are rather variable. Thin to medium horizontal bedding is everywhere a prominent feature, and long, sweeping cross-strata with less than 5° dips are common. Thin beds of sandy

limestone and pale red and green shale are generally present, and locally numerous. Bedding is
characteristically medium to massive at most
outcrops. The beds are generally cross-stratified
at angles rarely exceeding 25°, with dips of 12°–
20° most common. The inclined strata almost
everywhere dip toward the southeast in simple
planar sets that are truncated at the upper surface. The surfaces of truncation provide prominent horizontal bedding planes. In local areas
such as near the top of the Cedar Mesa at Natural

Bridges National Monument, bedding types similar to those of the eolian Coconino sandstone
and the Jurassic Navajo sandstone are prominent
features (Fig. 6). Dips of the cross-bedding in
these areas are somewhat steeper, averaging 25°–
30°, and cross-stratification surfaces are generally
concave upward in randomly oriented wedge-
shaped sets.

Depositional environments.—The environment
of deposition of the Cedar Mesa sandstone has
long been considered to be an eolian desert, but

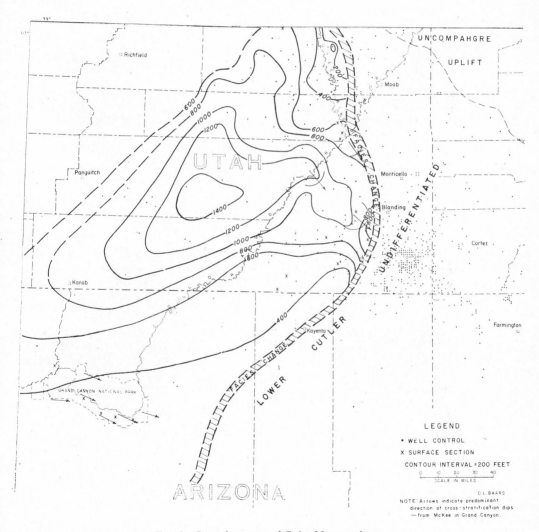

Fig. 4.—Isopachous map of Cedar Mesa sandstone.

Baker and Reeside (1929), Gregory (1938), and others, have recognized that water deposition played at least a minor role. A comparison of the primary structures with Recent deposits of known origin (McKee, 1957), as well as recognition of the lateral relationships, suggests that the Cedar Mesa sandstone was deposited in shallow-marine to littoral environments with local occurrences of possible back-beach dunes. Low angle to horizontal bedding and related thin- to medium-bedded strata are suggestive of beach deposition. Simple sets of low- to moderate-angle cross-strata in uniform units are typical of water-deposited sands resulting from unidirectional and persistent

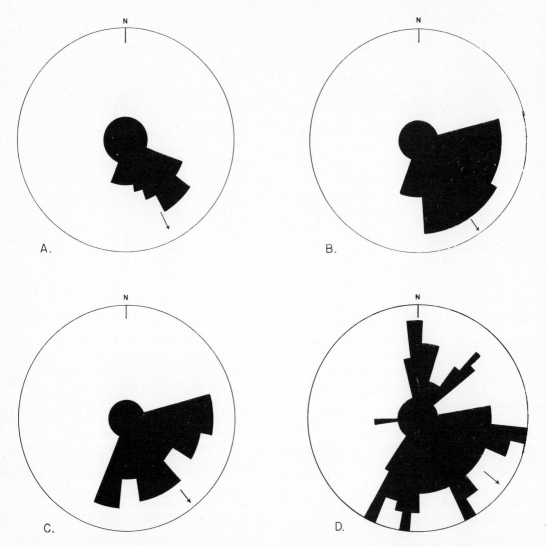

Fig. 5.—Cross-stratification characteristics of the Cedar Mesa sandstone. A—Tongue of Cutler arkose in Cedar Mesa sandstone at Squaw Valley near confluence of Green and Colorado Rivers, Sec. 26, T. 30 S., R. 19 E., Utah. B—Cedar Mesa sandstone at same locality. C—Cedar Mesa sandstone near Mille Crag Bend opposite mouth of Dark Canyon on the Colorado River. D—Cedar Mesa sandstone at the Fish Creek area 15 miles northeast of Mexican Hat, Utah. After Reiche, 1938. The inner black circle represents 5° of dip; the outer circle is 30° of dip. The small arrow indicates the average direction of dipping cross-strata.

FIG. 6.—The Cedar Mesa sandstone at Natural Bridges National Monument, Utah. Horizontal bedding of the light-colored sandstone is prominent in the foreground at the base of the natural bridge and in the capping strata. Steeply dipping, large-scale cross-stratification seen in the background below the skyline may represent eolian deposition in an otherwise marine unit.

currents. Thin beds of pastel-colored shales and limestones are unquestionably the result of water deposition. Horizontal bedding planes and smooth truncation of cross-stratified beds are generally considered to be indicative of water modifications of sediments. These features are very common in the Cedar Mesa (Figs. 7 and 8). Local occurrences of high angle, complexly cross-stratified deposits imply that a limited amount of eolian sedimentation was prevalent in restricted lateral and vertical positions.

Regional stratigraphic relationships suggest a close proximity of the Cedar Mesa to marine environments. Near the junction of the Green and Colorado Rivers and on the San Rafael swell, the sands of the Cedar Mesa interfinger with carbonates of the underlying marine Elephant Canyon formation. The sandstones of the type Cedar Mesa grade eastward into the water deposited evaporitic "Lower Cutler" red beds, that are probably related to a partially restricted lagoonal environ-

ment. Beds of equivalent age in the Cordilleran geosyncline, to the west, are apparently marine carbonates. The long linear configuration of the sandstone body is in itself suggestive of shoreline sedimentation.

The only fossils known from the Cedar Mesa sandstone are probably of marine origin. Darton (1925) reported finding "Kaibab" invertebrates in limestone lenses near the top of the Cedar Mesa in the Monument Valley area, and Gregory and Moore (1931) reported an occurrence of "marine shells" in outcrops of the Circle Cliffs area. Baars (1961) described invertebrate fragments from limey sandstones of the basal Cedar Mesa in Cataract Canyon.

The above facts strongly suggest a marginal marine to beach environment for the Cedar Mesa sandstone. The presence of marine current-deposited beds indicates an offshore environment, but beach-like deposits are equally common. Back-beach eolian accumulations are present, but are of

Fig. 7.—The Cedar Mesa sandstone near the type section northwest of Mexican Hat, Utah. The conspicuous horizontal bedding is the result of nearshore-marine deposition. Eolian aspects are noticeably lacking in this upper portion of the formation, which is about 200 feet in thickness, as shown in the photograph.

Fig. 8.—The upper cliff-forming unit is the Cedar Mesa sandstone at its type section on the southeastern margin of Cedar Mesa, a few miles northwest of Mexican Hat, Utah. The horizontal-bedding characteristics of the nearshore marine deposits are conspicuous in the 400-foot exposure. The Cedar Mesa sandstone is underlain by steep slopes of the lower Permian Halgaito shale and the upper Pennsylvanian Honaker Trail formation, which lies at the base of the photograph.

very limited occurrence. These deposits may be associated with beach ridges, or with offshore bars that were built above sea level. The entire sandstone body apparently accumulated along the gentle eastern shoreline of the Cordilleran seas and seaward from a broad tidal flat and lagoonal area that received clastics from the Uncompahgre uplift toward the east. The bedding features of the sands and their lithologic contrast to Cutler sediments preclude an Uncompahgre source for the Cedar Mesa. The trend of the shoreline and the current directions as revealed by regional cross-stratification studies make a northwesterly source seem probable. Perhaps the source of the Cedar Mesa clastics was the same as that of the Weber sandstone of the Wasatch and Uinta Mountains, or possibly reworking of the Weber provided the clastic material. The fact that the zone of Cedar Mesa-Cutler facies change so closely parallels the eastern flank of the Monument upwarp suggests that a slightly positive tectonic trend in that area may have helped to localize the Cedar Mesa shoreline and the adjacent "Lower Cutler" lagoonal area to the east.

DE CHELLY SANDSTONE

The De Chelly (pronounced Dĕ-Shāy') sandstone is typically a massive, reddish unit that is highly cross-stratified in its northern occurrences. It is probably best known for exposures in Monument Valley along the Utah-Arizona border, where it forms the massive cliffs, spires, and buttes for which the area is renowned (Fig. 9). The formation was named by Gregory (1917) for the spectacular exposures in Canyon de Chelly National Monument in eastern Arizona (Fig. 10). The formation is primarily water-laid toward the south, but is a prominent cliff-forming unit in most outcrops, such as the massive red cliffs of Oak Creek Canyon at Sedona, Arizona, a few miles south of Flagstaff (Fig. 11). The De Chelly sandstone is widespread on the Colorado Plateau, covering all but small portions of southeastern Utah, northeastern Arizona, and western and

FIG. 9.—Mitten Buttes in Monument Valley along Utah-Arizona border. Buttes are capped by thin beds of Triassic rocks underlain by massive cliffs of the Permian De Chelly sandstone and ledgy slopes of the Organ Rock shale. Monument Valley is the site of a new Navajo tribal park.

FIG. 10.—Well-developed cross-stratification of eolian origin in Canyon de Chelly near eastern Arizona border. Photograph was taken near White House Ruin Trail in Canyon de Chelly National Monument at type section of De Chelly sandstone.

central New Mexico. It is absent over most of southwestern Colorado (Fig. 12). It conformably overlies the Organ Rock-Hermit red beds in the Four Corners area, the Supai (restricted) in northeastern Arizona (excepting the Grand Canyon where the De Chelly is missing), and the Abo formation in New Mexico. The equivalent White Rim sandstone toward the northwest rests directly upon the Cedar Mesa sandstone on the San Rafael swell, owing to a northwesterly pinchout of the Organ Rock. The De Chelly is disconformably overlain by Triassic and Triassic? red beds in the north, but conformably underlies marine sediments of Permian age along most of the southern plateau.

The De Chelly is typically an orange red, fine grained, highly cross-stratified sandstone. The sandstone is generally well sorted except for numerous large, well rounded, and frosted quartz grains that are abundant in the Four Corners area. The De Chelly becomes slightly coarser and more arkosic northeastward toward the Uncompahgre source area. Grain size ranges from fine to medium at Canyon de Chelly and Monument Valley, and is largely medium where it grades into the undifferentiated Cutler. The quartz grains are mostly very fine to silt size along the southern Colorado Plateau where the De Chelly is probably marine. The sand grains are commonly well rounded and sporadically frosted, but subangular to subrounded grains are generally present. Ferric iron oxide is the most common cementing agent, but the unit becomes calcareous toward the southern marine phase. It is generally poorly cemented and friable. The sandstone is composed largely of white and red quartz grains, but contains minor amounts of feldspar, which becomes more prominent toward the source.

Regional distribution.—The De Chelly sandstone thins gradually northward from the type section in Canyon de Chelly to a featheredge a short distance north of the San Juan River, in southern Utah. Another sandstone is present northwest of the Colorado River which was named the White Rim sandstone by Baker and Reeside (1929). The White Rim is similar to the De Chelly in type of lithology, cross-stratification, and stratigraphic position in its southern occurrence, but is whiter, and more closely resembles the Cedar Mesa in bedding characteristics toward the northwest. The White Rim-De Chelly relationships are discussed in detail by Baars (1961). Neither the White Rim nor the De Chelly is present east of the Colorado River and north of about the latitude of Blanding, Utah. The De Chelly grades rapidly eastward into arkosic

Cutler deposits along the southern Utah-Colorado border.

The De Chelly thickens westward from the Defiance uplift into the Black Mesa basin, where it attains its maximum thickness of more than 1,000 feet. It thins abruptly onto the east flank of the Kaibab uplift and is missing in Grand Canyon. This north-south trend of thinning is the result of positive tendencies along the Kaibab uplift during De Chelly deposition, accompanied by a gradual sedimentary thinning toward the north. The formation is thick along the Mogollon Rim of central and eastern Arizona, where it is massively bedded with little cross-stratification,

FIG. 11.—Outcrops of De Chelly sandstone ("upper Supai") near Sedona, Arizona, south of Flagstaff. The massively bedded unit is here water-deposited, and may be of marine origin.

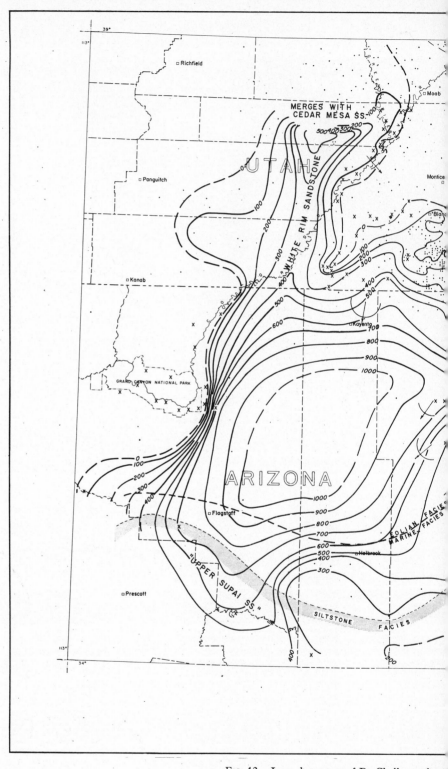

FIG. 12.—Isopachous map of De Chelly sandstor

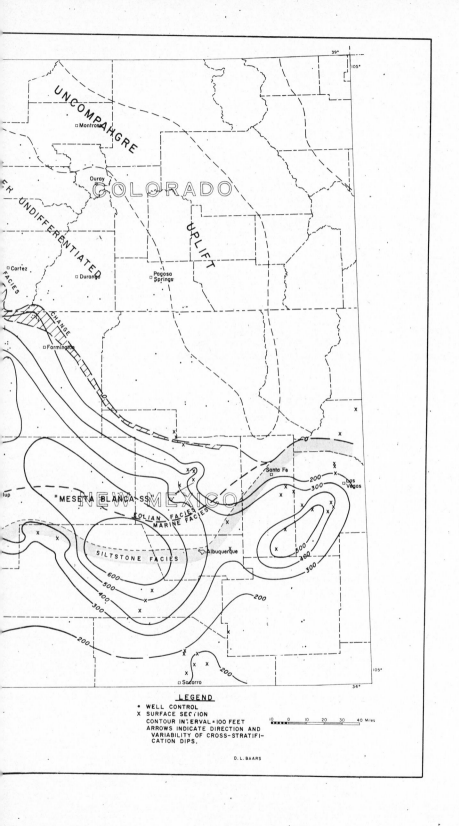

Fig. 13.—Eolian De Chelly sandstone ("Meseta Blanca member") at right, and overlying ledgy Yeso formation and upper cliffs of Glorieta sandstone at left background, near Cañones, north of Albuquerque, New Mexico.

and apparently is subaqueous in origin. Until recently the sequence was included in the upper Supai formation (Baars, 1961). The upper De Chelly interfingers eastward with restricted marine deposits of the Yeso formation (restricted).

The De Chelly sandstone thins abruptly southeastward from Canyon de Chelly onto the Defiance uplift, which was apparently positive during much of Permian time (Fig. 12). The De Chelly is 825 feet thick at the type section but is reduced to about 450 feet only 20 miles to the south, and 185 feet south of Fort Defiance, near the central part of the uplift. South of the approximate latitude of Fort Defiance, late Permian truncation did not remove the younger beds of the Yeso, Glorieta, and occasional remnants of San Andres from above the De Chelly sandstone. The Permian section of the southern Defiance uplift is nearly identical with the typical New Mexico sequence toward the south and east.

The De Chelly thickens slightly into the San Juan basin, east of the Defiance uplift, and grades laterally into Cutler red beds along the northeast flank of the basin. In the Nacimiento Mountains, on the southeast flank of the basin, an identical unit was named the "Meseta Blanca member of

the Yeso formation" by Wood and Northrop (1946). This unit, which is present over central New Mexico as a red sandstone and siltstone, is considered to be equivalent to the De Chelly (Baars, 1961), and the term "Meseta Blanca" is considered to be unnecessary. The De Chelly is eolian in the Nacimiento Mountains outcrops (Fig. 13), but is a thin to massively bedded non-cross-stratified unit throughout its occurrences in the Zuni Mountains and southward into central New Mexico. There the strata grade upward into marine red beds, carbonates, and evaporites of the Yeso formation (restricted), and are probably also marine in origin. The post-De Chelly sequence was truncated northward along the Nacimiento uplift as on the Defiance uplift until the De Chelly is overlain by Triassic deposits in the northern exposures. There the De Chelly grades north and east into Cutler arkosic red beds as in the eastern San Juan basin.

The geometric configuration of the De Chelly sandstone is strikingly different from that of the Cedar Mesa sandstone (Fig. 20). The De Chelly thickens gradually southwestward from the belt of facies change with the undifferentiated Cutler, attains a maximum thickness in the Black Mesa basin, and gradually thins toward the south. This relatively uniform pattern is disturbed only by the position of paleo-structures such as the Defiance and Zuni uplifts. The Cedar Mesa sandstone, on the other hand, is a localized, elongate sand body with abrupt and complicated facies relationships.

Bedding characteristics.—Highly cross-stratified massive beds are typical of the De Chelly sandstone northward from the southern Defiance uplift and Nacimiento Mountains. The massive bedded units are commonly as thick as 100 feet, with steeply dipping cross-strata inclined at 15°–35°. Cross-strata are generally in simple planar sets that are considerably more erratic in lateral extent than are those in the Cedar Mesa. However, the sets are not as erratic and wedge shaped as those in such classic eolian formations as the Navajo sandstone or the Coconino sandstone. Although dips of the cross-beds are extremely variable, they commonly are 25°–35° in inclination, and the average direction of dip is generally in the southwest quadrant (Fig. 14). These massive sets of cross-strata are generally truncated at the upper surface in a smooth, horizontal manner, suggesting occasional marine invasions of the coastal dune desert (Fig. 10).

Exposures of the De Chelly sandstone along the southern Colorado Plateau exhibit a very different array of bedding features. The outcrops along the Mogollon Rim in central Arizona are generally in massive beds, but cross-stratification is conspicuously rare or not developed. The sand deposits are obviously water-laid, but strong depositional currents appear to have been an insignificant depositional factor. Bedding features in outcrops toward the east, in central New Mexico, are similar in that the sands were apparently water-deposited, but massive bedding is not a prominent feature. Thin to medium bedding is the most conspicuous primary feature of the De Chelly in the Zuni Mountains in west-central New Mexico and cross-stratification is almost nonexistent. Exposures toward the south and southeast are very similar to the Zuni Mountains occurrences, but the formation becomes less distinct.

Depositional environments.—The depositional environment of the De Chelly sandstone has long

been considered an eolian desert. Bedding characteristics described above substantiate an eolian origin for deposits in the general Canyon de Chelly-Monument Valley country, where the formation was originally defined. However, the nature of primary bedding features and stratigraphic relationships along the southern Colorado Plateau strongly indicates a subaqueous and probably marine depositional environment for that area. The De Chelly sandstone was apparently derived from the undifferentiated Cutler red beds from an Uncompahgre uplift source area. The sand grains were probably blown from the red clastics during their sedimentation in fluvial and marginal-marine environments. The winds were fairly persistent in direction, blowing the sand southwestward away from the source deposits—as indicated by the direction and nature of cross-stratification within the formation. In the Four Corners area a plentiful supply of sand was available and much was blown into the ancestral Black Mesa basin. There the persistent winds supported large lateral and longitudinal dunes, whose deposits were less erratic than the barchan-type dune deposits of other, similar, formations of the Colorado Plateau. A slower rate of sedimentation along the front of the southern Uncompahgre source accounted for the thinner De Chelly deposits of central New Mexico. The long linear nature of the source area provided a basis for widely distributing the De Chelly clastics.

The eolian sands migrated toward the south and west until they encountered the seas encroaching from the south. The transgressive sea reworked the eolian sands and provided a marine depositional site for wind-blown sands. Strong longshore currents were not available for the redistribution of the sands, so current cross-stratification was not a common feature. The relatively quiet sea was the depositional medium for the restricted marine Yeso sediments that gradationally overlie the marine De Chelly sandstone. Distribution of the sands in the marine environment was accomplished largely by the northward advance of the water. An occasional landward fluctuation of the sea gently smoothed the surface of the coastal dune area and provided the few truncated surfaces present in the otherwise eolian deposits.

Although the White Rim sandstone of the northwestern Colorado Plateau is directly related to the De Chelly, its source and mode of distribution were somewhat different. The White Rim sandstone was probably derived by reworking of the underlying Cedar Mesa sandstone of the San Rafael swell area. As previously stated, the White Rim merges with the Cedar Mesa in that area, as a result of the northwestward pinchout of the intervening Organ Rock shale. The White Rim is very similar in lithology and bedding characteristics to the Cedar Mesa sandstone in that

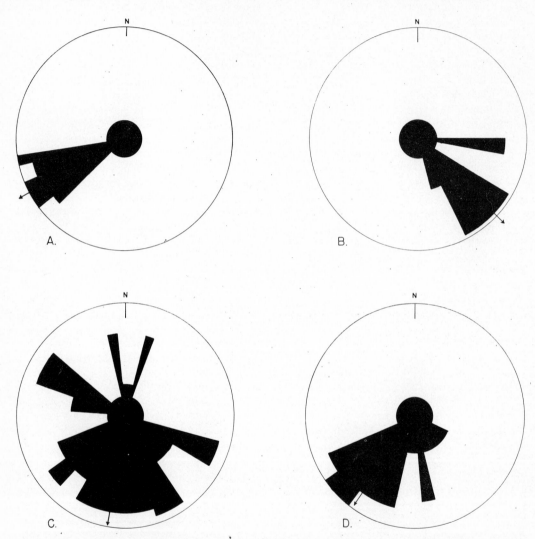

Fig. 14.—Cross-stratification characteristics of the De Chelly sandstone. A—Outcrops of the De Chelly ("Meseta Blanca member") near Cañones, New Mexico, Sec. 3, T. 16 N., R. 2 E. B—Cross-stratification of the White Rim sandstone at Pete's Mesa, west of the Colorado River, south of the junction of the Green and Colorado Rivers, Utah. C—Cross-stratification in the De Chelly sandstone in Monument Valley, Arizona. After Reiche, 1938. D—Cross-strata along White House Ruin Trail in Canyon de Chelly National Monument. From Reiche, 1938. The inner black circle represents 5° of dip; the outer circle is 30° of dip. The small arrow indicates the average direction of dipping cross-strata.

area (Baars, 1961), and cannot be distinguished where the Organ Rock red beds are missing. Distribution of the White Rim sands was by longshore currents, beach, and eolian mechanisms (Heylmun, 1958) that apparently moved toward the southeast, as determined by cross-stratification studies. Sands from the White Rim environment apparently merged with the De Chelly sands along the west central Monument upwarp (Fig. 13).

COCONINO-GLORIETA SANDSTONE

The Coconino sandstone of northern Arizona and the Glorieta sandstone of central New Mexico represent a continuous body of sand that extends across the southern margin of the Colorado Plateau. Both formations are similar in every respect except mode of deposition. The Coconino terminology is here used for eolian deposits in Arizona, whereas the term Glorieta is used for equivalent marine deposits in New Mexico. Practically the entire areal extent of the Coconino sandstone is within the Arizona portion of the province, but the Glorieta is very widespread in central and southern New Mexico and adjacent states.

The Coconino sandstone, as described by McKee (1933), is a white, uniformly fine-grained orthoquartzite with large-scale cross-stratification of a distinctly eolian type. The unit is coarser grained and thicker toward a source area south of the present Mogollon Rim in central Arizona. Sand grains of the Coconino are typically rounded and commonly pitted or frosted, and are cemented with silica. The nature of both the sand grains and the cross-stratification strongly suggests eolian sedimentation, as does the presence of vertebrate tracks, raindrop impressions, and ripple marks of eolian type. The Coconino sandstone overlies the Hermit shale (Organ Rock) in apparent conformity, although the missing De Chelly sandstone may be suggestive of a hiatus. It conformably underlies and may grade laterally into the marine Toroweap formation.

The eolian Coconino grades eastward into marine deposits of the Glorieta sandstone along the Arizona-New Mexico State line. Like the Coconino, the Glorieta is a white siliceous sandstone of generally fine- to medium-grain size that dis-

plays a considerable amount of cross-stratification. The nature of the bedding is considerably different, however, and thin to massive, uniform cross-stratification in simple planar sets is the most common form. Eolian-type cross-bedding is locally present, but is not a prominent feature of the Glorieta. The nature of the primary structures in the Glorieta implies a depositional environment of littoral to somewhat offshore-marine aspects with local eolian conditions. The Glorieta sandstone gradationally overlies the restricted marine Yeso formation and grades upward or interfingers with the overlying marine San Andres formation.

Distribution.—The Coconino sandstone covers much of northeastern Arizona in a fan-shaped accumulation that thins rapidly away from the source area in the central part of the state. The isopachous configuration is variable, but distinctly thins northward, westward, and eastward from the central Mogollon Rim (Fig. 15). The Coconino pinches out south of the Utah border and is not present in that state. Many geologists have mapped the "Coconino" in exposures on the San Rafael swell of east central Utah, but those sandstones are of the older and marine Cedar Mesa sandstone, previously discussed. It is noteworthy that the geometric configuration and the coarser grain size toward the south indicate a southern source for the Coconino, yet the average direction of cross-stratification dips is generally toward that same area. It is obvious that if the location of the source area is correct, the winds did not originally distribute the sands. It is probable that the sands were originally distributed by streams coming from the southern highland (Mazatzal land), and penecontemporaneously redistributed by the winds from the northwest. Cross-stratification dips change from a southeasterly direction to a more easterly direction along the eastern Mogollon Rim, as shown by the large arrows on Figure 15. This westerly wind component supplied Coconino sands to west-central New Mexico, where the clastics were deposited in a shallow-marine environment.

The New Mexico deposits of the equivalent sandstone are termed the Glorieta sandstone. The configuration of this unit is different from that of

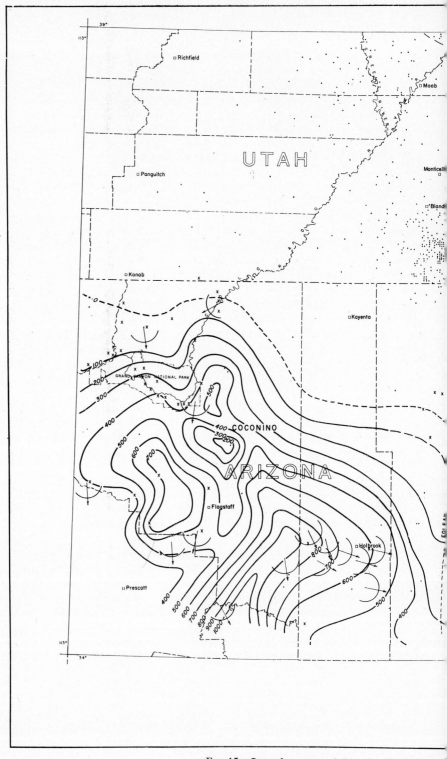

FIG. 15.—Isopachous map of Coconino-Glorieta sand

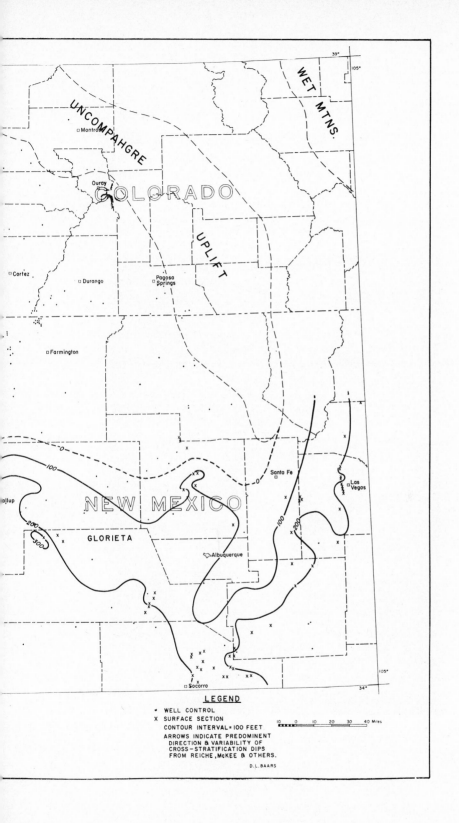

LEGEND

•   WELL CONTROL

X   SURFACE SECTION

CONTOUR INTERVAL=100 FEET

ARROWS INDICATE PREDOMINENT
DIRECTION & VARIABILITY OF
CROSS−STRATIFICATION DIPS
FROM REICHE,McKEE & OTHERS.

D.L.BAARS

its Arizona equivalent, and is a widespread, relatively uniform, accumulation that extends over most of central and southern New Mexico, and into the Texas Panhandle, and southeastern Arizona. The marine nature of the Glorieta is evident from the types of cross-stratification and the presence of local limestone and gypsum deposits within the sandstone. The relatively smooth and gentle geometric configuration of the sand body may also be suggestive of a marine depositional environment, especially when compared with the rapidly thinning wedge-shaped

configuration and highly variable thickness pattern of the eolian Coconino deposits. The isopachous map (Fig. 15) demonstrates this relationship of dual depositional environments. The two distinct isopachous patterns are separated by the north-south trend of thinning along the ancestral Defiance uplift, which was probably the governing factor in separating the two environments.

Bedding characteristics.—Bedding in the Coconino is invariably characterized by massive cross-stratified units that locally attain great thickness. Cross-stratification planes are steeply dipping,

FIG. 16.—Eolian cross-stratification in sandstones of the eastern phase of Toroweap formation in Walnut Canyon National Monument near Flagstaff, Arizona. Bedding characteristics of the unit closely resemble the Coconino of the same area and, in fact, should be considered as upper Coconino, as the two units become indistinguishable east of this outcrop area. Horizontal beds overlying the eolian sandstone are in the marine Kaibab formation of middle Permian age. Overhanging beds of limestone of the Kaibab protect ancient Indian ruins in the upper portion of the photograph.

averaging 25°–30°. The cross-strata are generally concave upward and in randomly oriented wedge-shaped sets that give the bedding an extremely erratic appearance (Fig. 16). The formation commonly contains raindrop impressions, and vertebrate tracks are well preserved in the lower part of the Coconino in Grand Canyon exposures. These features, along with the common occurrence of wind-type ripple marks, are almost conclusive evidence for an eolian origin for the Coconino sandstone (McKee, 1933).

Although other lithologic characteristics are almost identical, the bedding in the Glorieta sandstone is decidedly different from that described for the Coconino. Glorieta bedding more closely resembles the Cedar Mesa sandstone, in that thin to massive cross-stratified beds are generally composed of simple planar sets that are smoothly truncated at the upper surface. The horizontal bedding planes are so numerous as to imply horizontal bedding when viewed casually (Fig. 17). The primary dips of the cross-strata are of considerably lower magnitude than in the Coconino, with 10° to 20° dips the most common.

FIG. 17.—Permian outcrops in Zuni Canyon, Zuni Mountains, near Grants, New Mexico. Upper half of the view shows San Andres formation with thin tongues of quartzose sandstone in a calcarenite unit; lower half is thin, horizontally bedded Glorieta sandstone, which is probably a nearshore- to littoral-marine accumulation at this locality. Lowest exposures are the uppermost red beds of the Yeso formation.

FIG. 18.—Exposure of Glorieta sandstone in Cottonwood Canyon, Zuni Mountains, near Grants, New Mexico. Upper beds of photograph display horizontal bedding and thinly truncated cross-stratified beds that are strongly suggestive of shallow-marine sedimentation; lower beds contain large-scale cross-stratification with steeply inclined bedding that may be eolian deposits of very local lateral and vertical distribution. These eolian? deposits may be remnants of barrier bars or back-beach ridges.

The large scale eolian-type bedding of the Coconino is commonly lacking in the Glorieta, but local occurrences are known in the Zuni Mountains exposures (Fig. 18). The eolian deposits are very local in nature, being of limited lateral and vertical extent. These areas may have been temporarily exposed to subaerial conditions in an otherwise shallow marine environment, owing to minor marine regressions, or may have been offshore bars that were built above normal sea level. Short lived local beach conditions are suggested by fairly common low angle, broadly developed cross-strata. Other primary features suggestive of marine deposition include the local occurrence of thin limestone and gypsum deposits within the sandstone, and the interfingering nature of the upper contact with marine carbonates of the San Andres formation in the eastern Zuni Mountains.

Depositional environments.—Primary bedding characteristics leave no doubt that the Coconino sandstone was deposited on a coastal dune desert. The source of the sand was in central Arizona and the original distribution of the sand was probably by stream action. The clastics were rapidly redistributed by northwesterly winds that shifted to a westerly direction along the north flank of the source highlands (Fig. 19). This westerly wind component along the eastern Mogollon Rim supplied sands to the central New Mexico seas. Coconino sedimentation was halted by the eastward advance of the Toroweap seas, which reworked the upper surface of the dune sands into a smooth plane. The marine Toroweap deposits grade to Coconino-like sandstones in the eastern extremes of the formation and may grade into the upper Coconino along the central Mogollon Rim.

The contemporaneous Glorieta seas of central New Mexico received large quantities of Coconino sands across the slightly positive Defiance uplift and deposited them in littoral to slightly offshore environments. Well developed marine currents distributed the sands extensively and produced abundant current cross-stratification features in the sediments. These deposits are intermixed locally with both beach and dune accumulations, suggesting that the sea was shallow and that minor fluctuations produced rather widespread shoreline conditions. Associated offshore and barrier bars appear to have been prominent features of the marine environment. Gradational and interfingering contacts with the underlying restricted marine Yeso formation and the overly-

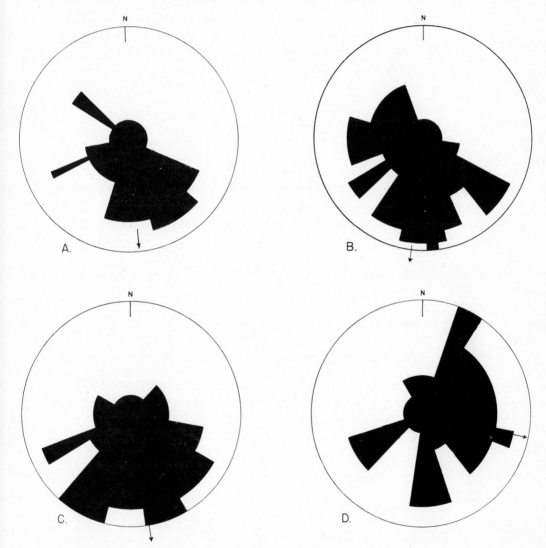

FIG. 19.—Cross-stratification characteristics of the Coconino sandstone. From Reiche, 1938. *A*—Cross-stratification in the Coconino sandstone near Seligman, Arizona. *B*—Cross-stratification in outcrops along Bunker Trail in Grand Canyon National Park, Arizona. *C*—Cross-stratification characteristics at lower Clear Creek east of Winslow, Arizona. *D*—Coconino bedding characteristics two miles east of Holbrook, Arizona. The inner black circle represents 5° of dip; the outer circle is 30° of dip. The small arrow indicates the average direction of dipping cross-strata.

ing shallow-shelf carbonates of the San Andres formation add credence to the marine nature of the Glorieta environment, as do the local occurrences of thin limestone and gypsum deposits within the sandstone.

COMPARISONS AND CONCLUSIONS

The three major sandstone bodies of the Colorado Plateau—Cedar Mesa, De Chelly, and Coconino-Glorieta—are somewhat similar in character, as all are light colored, prominently cross-strati-

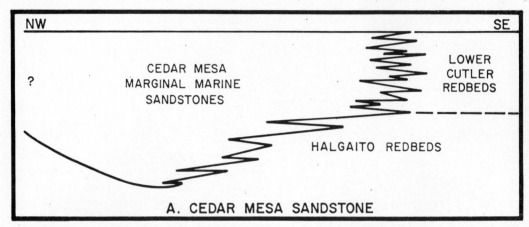

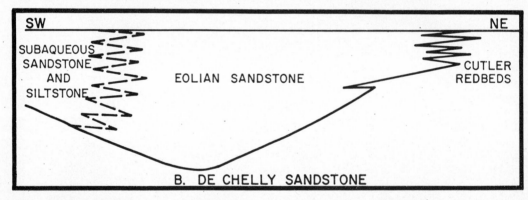

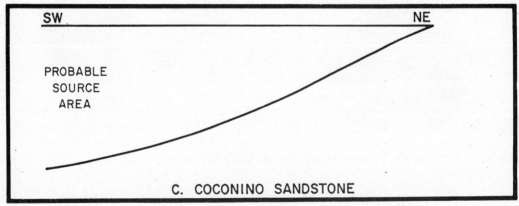

FIG. 20.—Generalized cross sections comparing the geometric configuration of the three Permian sandstone bodies of the Colorado Plateau, normal to sedimentary strike.

fied sandstones composed of clean, well sorted, and rounded quartzose sands. They are basically distinctly different, however, in such important aspects as geometric configuration, geographic distribution, source area, primary bedding features, and depositional environment.

The Cedar Mesa sandstone is present along the western Colorado Plateau in a linear north-south-trending accumulation. The unit is a uniformly thick deposit that grades eastward through abrupt facies changes into lagoonal red beds of the Cutler that were derived from the Uncompahgre ancestral mountain range. The sands of the Cedar Mesa were derived from an unknown source area toward the northwest and transported into the region by longshore currents. Deposition took place in a nearshore to littoral environment along the eastern margin of a major seaway.

The De Chelly sandstone is extensively distributed on the Colorado Plateau, as a relatively uniform blanket deposit. The quartz and feldspar sand grains of the De Chelly were derived from the Cutler red beds along the front of the Uncompahgre uplift and were blown away from the source deposits by northeasterly winds. Sedimentation near the linear source area in southern Utah and northwestern New Mexico was eolian, grading generally southward into marine environments in central Arizona and New Mexico. The coastal eolian desert was onlapped and partially reworked by the northward encroachment of the sea. Marine deposition was in a relatively quiet sea, for current cross-stratification is rarely present in the sandstones and siltstones.

The Coconino-Glorieta sandstone is restricted in distribution to the southern portion of the Colorado Plateau, but the Glorieta is extensive in central and southern New Mexico and adjacent areas. The deposit is in the form of a fan-shaped wedge in northern Arizona, thinning in all directions from the central Arizona source area. The Arizona deposits are distinctly eolian in character, and are termed the Coconino sandstone. Westerly winds supplied the New Mexico sea with abundant sand from the Coconino source that accumulated in nearshore-marine to littoral environments to form the Glorieta sandstone. The Glorieta sea was restricted to New Mexico by the slightly positive Defiance uplift. Well developed currents distributed the sands widely, forming a thin, uniform blanket deposit over much of the state. The two-fold nature of the geometric configuration of the partly eolian and partly marine accumulation is distinctive. The geometry of the Coconino-Glorieta sandstone differs from that of the De Chelly because the geographic position of the Glorieta sea was relatively stable (Fig. 20), whereas the De Chelly sea encroached upon the coastal eolian deposits and reworked the sands in its path. The result was that the Coconino-Glorieta isopachous configuration reflects the two relatively stable environments, but the geometry of the De Chelly is rather uniform, reflecting the gradual merging of the divergent depositional modes.

REFERENCES

Baars, D. L., 1961, Permian System of the Colorado Plateau: Am. Association Petroleum Geologists Bull. [scheduled for publication in 1962].

Baker, A. A., and Reeside, J. B., Jr., 1929, Correlation of the Permian of southern Utah, northern Arizona, northwestern New Mexico, and southwestern Colorado: Am. Assoc. Petroleum Geologists Bull., v. 13, no. 11, p. 1413–1448.

Darton, N. H., 1925, A résumé of Arizona geology: Arizona Bur. Mines Bull. 119, geol. ser. 3, p. 298.

Gregory, H. E., 1917, Geology of the Navajo country, a reconnaissance of parts of Arizona, New Mexico, and Utah: U. S. Geol. Survey Prof. Paper 93, 161 p.

——— 1938, The San Juan country, a geographic and geologic reconnaissance of southeastern Utah: U. S. Geol. Survey Prof. Paper 188, 123 p.

——— and Moore, R. C., 1931, The Kaiparowits region, a geographic and geological reconnaissance of parts of Utah and Arizona: U. S. Geol. Survey Prof. Paper 164, 161 p.

Heylmun, Edgar B., 1958, Paleozoic stratigraphy and oil possibilities of Kaiparowits region, Utah: Am. Assoc. Petroleum Geologists Bull., v. 42, no. 8, p. 1781–1811.

Kunkel, R. P., 1958, Permian stratigraphy of the Paradox basin: Intermountain Assoc. Petroleum Geol. Guidebook 9th Ann. Field Conf., p. 163–168.

McKee, E. D., 1933, The Coconino sandstone—its history and origin: Carnegie Inst. Washington Pub. 440, Contr. Paleontology, p. 77–115.

——— 1957, Primary structures in some Recent sediments: Am. Assoc. Petroleum Geologists Bull., v. 41, p. 1704–1747.

Reiche, Parry, 1938, An analysis of cross lamination; the Coconino sandstone: Jour. Geology, v. 46, no. 7, p. 905–932.

Sears, Julian D., 1956, Geology of Comb Ridge and vicinity north of San Juan River, San Juan County, Utah: U. S. Geol. Survey Bull. 1021-E.

Wood, G. H., and Northrop, S. A., 1946, Geology of Nacimiento Mountain, San Pedro Mountain, and adjacent plateaus in parts of Sandoval and Rio Arriba Counties, New Mexico: U. S. Geol. Survey Oil and Gas Inv. Prelim. Map 57.

CHARACTERISTICS OF SANDSTONE RESERVOIRS IN UNITED STATES[1]

BRUCE F. CURTIS[2] AND SANDSTONE RESERVOIR COMMITTEE[3]

ABSTRACT

A statistical study of 7,241 reservoir sandstones in various oil-producing regions of the United States was completed by a committee of petroleum geologists. The study shows that 68 per cent of the sandstones are of Tertiary age, although each geologic age from Cambrian to Pleistocene, inclusive, is represented. Most of the sandstones are restricted in physical dimensions; they commonly cover less than 100 square miles of areal extent, and have an average thickness of about 39 feet.

The factors which control petroleum accumulation in the sandstones more commonly result from the structural configuration (56 per cent of reservoirs) than from stratigraphic conditions (10 per cent) or from combinations of structural and stratigraphic features (34 per cent), and it is found that the thicker sandstones tend to be broader and better reservoirs than their relative thickness, alone, would suggest. A closer analysis of the sandstones involved in stratigraphic type accumulations shows that 61 per cent of them were deposited under shoreline or nearshore conditions. It is found that 54 per cent of all the reservoir sandstones studied contain mainly oil, 27 per cent contain gas, and the remainder carry substantial amounts of both oil and gas.

INTRODUCTION

Over the years geologists have collected information about thousands of petroleum reservoirs and have used it to make scientific analyses

[1] Read before the Association at Atlantic City, New Jersey, April 25, 1960. Manuscript received, January 1, 1960.

[2] Department of Geology, University of Colorado, Boulder, Colorado.

[3] Committee consists of the following members and area representatives.

Chairman: Bruce F. Curtis

Statistical work: Ruth B. Curtis, Consultant, Boulder, Colo.

California, Central: C. A. Bengtson, Standard Oil Co. of California, Oildale, Calif.

Louisiana, South: Jules Braunstein, Shell Oil Co., New Orleans, La.

San Juan Basin: Harrell Budd, Consultant, Farmington, N. Mex.

Kansas: Virgil B. Cole, Consultant, Wichita, Kans.

Texas, East; Louisiana, North; Arkansas: Bruce W. Fox, The Atlantic Refining Co., Tyler, Tex.

Oklahoma: Harry Glover, Texaco, Inc., Tulsa, Okla.

Colorado, North; Nebraska; Utah: Penn L. Gooldy, The British-American Oil Prod. Co., Denver, Colo.

Appalachian Basin: T. P. McCann, Shell Oil Co., Pittsburgh, Pa.

Illinois Basin: D. P. Meagher, Humble Oil and Refining Co., Carter Division, Mattoon, Ill.

Permian Basin: R. F. Meyer, Humble Oil and Refining Co., Roswell, N. Mex.

Texas, North: North Texas Geological Society, Wichita Falls, Tex.

Texas, Southeast: J. H. Pound, Houston Geological Society, Houston, Tex.

California, South and North: Keith L. Rathbun, Continental Oil Co., Los Angeles, Calif.

Mississippi, Alabama: Ted R. Russell, The Atlantic Refining Co., Jackson, Miss.

Wyoming, South: F. D. Spindle, The Ohio Oil Co., Casper, Wyo.

of conditions of oil accumulation. The resulting numerous studies of individual reservoirs and oil fields form the ultimate basis of much of the science of petroleum geology. This report attempts to make further use of some of the accumulated geological data to depict the com-

Texas, Panhandle: S. Keith Tuthill, Panhandle Geological Society, Amarillo, Tex.

Texas, Southwest: R. D. White, Southern Minerals Corp., Corpus Christi, Tex.

Wyoming, North: John H. Wiese, Richfield Oil Corp., Casper, Wyo.

Montana: D. L. Zieglar, The California Co., Billings, Mont.

The committee gratefully acknowledges the work of many other geologists and organizations who assisted the area representatives. The following contributed particularly large parts of the study—*California, Central:* J. W. Bedford, J. S. Bigelow, R. D. Hoffman, T. A. Roy, T. S. Wyman. *Louisiana, South:* Eugene Miller. *Texas, Southeast:* R. T. Carville. *Kansas:* Roy P. Lehman, L. B. Fugitt. *Ark-La-Tex Area:* Gerald W. Thomas, William Champion, Gerald C. Merket. *Oklahoma:* J. B. Petta. *Colorado-Nebraska-Utah:* Arthur W. Johnson, David C. Gagliardo. *Appalachian Basin:* New York Museum Science Service (John C. Broughton, State Geologist) Arthur Van Tyne, William L. Kreidler; Pennsylvania Geological Survey (Carlyle Gray, State Geologist) Addison Cate, William S. Lytle; West Virginia Geological Survey (Paul H. Price, Director) Oscar L. Haught; Ohio Geological Survey (Ralph L. Bernhagen, Chief) Theodore A. DeBrosse; Ashland Oil and Refining Co., Frank Fisher and staff. *Illinois Basin:* J. C. Tolle, Dale C. Finley, Jr., S. H. Stith, A. S. Braumiller, James H. Griffith. *Permian Basin:* E. E. Kinney, R. F. Montgomery, John Runyon, N. A. Sax, B. A. Belknap, M. L. Feldman, Monty Gist, Eugene Greenwood, Raymond Nicholas. *California, South and North:* F. E. Minshall, R. B. Kelly. *Wyoming, South:* W. L. Skipp, Robert Steed. *Texas, Southwest:* Gene Dressler. *Wyoming, North:* Leonard M. Taucher.

posite character of the reservoir sandstones of the United States. The necessarily statistical approach is used in order to collect a quantity of information concerning reservoir sandstones, and to classify and summarize it either in characteristic groups or as numerical values. The resulting statistics are then analyzed for patterns of geological significance.

The committee chairman has placed a number of geological interpretations, none of them revolutionary, on the statistical results; but the data plainly will permit some conclusions different from those presented. When the results of the study are considered, it should be kept in mind that the interpretations are not unique and, furthermore, that the statistics are limited by a selection of original data, as discussed below.

STUDY METHOD AND LIMITATIONS

Twenty-one geologists, working in the various oil-producing areas of the United States, form the committee responsible for this study, which considers sandstone reservoirs discovered before January 1, 1959. Many other geologists have worked with committee members to provide statistical information and geological opinions (Footnote 3). In order to complete the project within a year, very small oil fields have not been analyzed; rather, only fields have been studied whose one or more sandstone reservoirs are estimated to contain at least 5 million barrels of oil or 10 billion cubic feet of gas.

The effect of this initial screening on the resulting figures is not known precisely, but it is estimated that elimination of carbonate reservoirs and the less important sandstones resulted in a study representing the sandstone reservoirs in about 15 per cent of the total oil fields of the United States. The proportion of fields considered is highly variable geographically. For instance, in California, an area of notably large accumulations, nearly 46 per cent of all fields are included, whereas, by contrast, in the Michigan basin with its numerous small fields and predominance of carbonate reservoirs, only about 2 per cent of the fields qualified for study. Had the smaller sized fields of the United States been included, somewhat reduced average values undoubtedly would have resulted for sandstone thicknesses, areal

extent of sandstones, and quantities of petroleum present. Furthermore, it may be guessed that inclusion of small fields would have increased the indicated proportion of stratigraphic traps; because total reserves of the size eligible for study are more likely to appear in fields of structural type, with their common aspect of several sandstone pays stacked vertically, than in stratigraphic fields which commonly involve only a single-reservoir sandstone. The figures for geologic ages and kinds of fluids produced probably are not affected by the preliminary selection of data.

Further limitations on the study are imposed by the committee's working definition of a sandstone. Although practically all the rocks studied have mean particle sizes within the accepted Wentworth sand grades, conglomerates also were considered, but they constitute less than one per cent of the reservoirs studied. Only clastic rocks consisting primarily of silica or silicate minerals, or both, were investigated; thus limy sandstones were studied, but sandy limestones were not.

Generally the committee members and their associates analyzed each separate sandstone reservoir within each field which qualified for study; however, in a few areas there are so many such reservoirs that a study of each one would have been a gratuitous waste of time and effort. In these few areas the work was done by examining a representative sample of fields and adjusting the resulting figures to the known total of eligible fields. The areas studied by such sampling procedures are—Texas, Southwest; Louisiana, South; Texas, Southeast (T.R.C. Dist. 3); and Illinois basin. The chairman assembled the data on a few areas such as Alaska and Michigan where production from sandstones is not large.

The categories under which the sandstone bodies have been classified by the committee members and their associates are shown in the next paragraph. It is readily apparent that deciding on the allocation of a given sandstone to almost any of these groups involves some geological inference, interpretation, or estimation. Consequently no attempt was made to set forth strict criteria for determining the grouping of the sandstones on the tabulation forms; instead, the forms employed the widely used, general, descrip-

tive terms as shown below, and provided additional space for grouping of those sandstones
which cannot be fitted readily into any of the
named classifications. As always happens in
petroleum geology, some of the groupings had to
be made from scanty and incomplete information.
The committee members noted diversity of geological opinion concerning some of the allocations,
and expressed personal uncertainty about classification of many of the sandstones. Nevertheless
it is felt that the committee succeeded fairly well
in assembling the opinions of geologists closely
familiar with the reservoir sandstones represented
in the study.

The basic information assembled for each sandstone reservoir is—

1. Average net thickness of the sandstone body.
2. Geologic age[4]
3. Nature of trapping of petroleum in sandstone—
   classified as
   a. *Structural* if pool edges are essentially controlled
      by shape of fold or fault features
   b. *Stratigraphic* if pool edges are entirely controlled
      by lithologic or permeability discontinuities
   c. *Combination* if both types of pool edges are in-
      volved
4. Approximate areal extent of sandstones associated
   with structural or combination trapping—classified
   as
   a. *Regional*—covering more than 100 square miles
   b. *Limited*—extent less than 100 square miles, but
      greater than the area of the structural feature in-
      volved
   c. *Local*—sandstone body approximately limited to
      area of the field
5. Genetic grouping of sandstones associated with
   stratigraphic traps—classified as
   a. *Broad types*—regional facies change, unconfor-
      mity, others
   b. *Local types*—channel, bar, beach or strand line,
      nearshore marine, others
6. Group classification of gross ultimate petroleum in
   the reservoir, arranged according to the plan
   shown in Table I
7. Statement of the fluids produced—principally oil,
   principally gas, both fluids.

Many more facts covering lithologic details,
fluids, porosity, permeability, etc., were gathered
for some of the reservoirs. Unfortunately they
could not be used in the summary because a
statistical study of this sort can be no more
ambitious than permitted by the poorest data

---

[4] A few reservoir sandstones span major geologic time
boundaries. If three ages are concerned, the sandstone
has been assigned to the central age. If two ages appear,
assignment is made to the more recent age.

available. The information needed for closer
analysis simply does not exist for some of the
areas, particularly those developed early in the
history of the petroleum industry, but the num-
bered facts could, with difficulty, be found or
estimated for all of the reservoirs.

A total of 1,658 fields were found to be eligible
for study under the qualifications set up, and these
fields contain 7,241 sandstone reservoirs.

RESULTS OF STUDY

AVERAGE NATURE OF FIELDS CONTAINING
SANDSTONE RESERVOIRS

The fields considered have an average of 4.4
reservoirs per field—the vast number of single-
reservoir fields being offset statistically by the
Gulf Coast and California fields with their multiple pays. In 84 per cent of the fields a single
type of trapping accounts for the accumulations
in all of the sandstone pools present (Fig. 1)—a
fact which reflects the preponderance of structural
fields in which similar trapping conditions are
repeated in several reservoirs. Of all fields, 12 per
cent involve both structural and combination
trap types and 2 per cent incorporate both stratigraphic and combination traps. The pairing of
structural and stratigraphic trapping in a single
field is predictably rare (1 per cent of fields
studied), and it is perhaps surprising that as
many as 1 per cent of the fields contain all three
types of traps in their various reservoirs.

GEOGRAPHY OF SANDSTONE RESERVOIRS

Those parts of the United States which contain
sandstone reservoirs of sufficient consequence to
qualify for this study are shown in Figure 2.
Within each area outline is printed the percentage
of reservoirs it contributed to the study. Some
important oil regions of the United States are not
prominent on this map because they produce
mainly from carbonate rocks. Especially influen-
tial in the study are the numerous Tertiary
reservoirs of the Louisiana and Texas Gulf Coast,
the many late Paleozoic sandstones of the Mid-
Continent, the accumulations in the thick Tertiary sediments of California, and the multitude of
relatively thin Paleozoic sandstone reservoirs of
the Illinois and Appalachian basins.

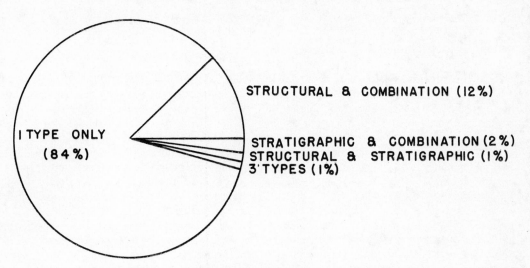

FIG. 1.—Percentages of fields with sandstone reservoirs which display various combinations of trapping conditions.

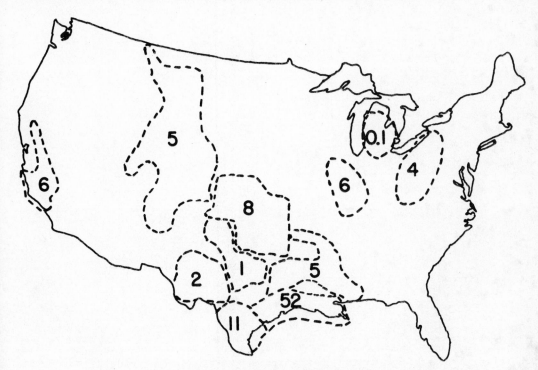

FIG. 2.—United States areas of important sandstone reservoirs. Numbers show percentages of all fields studied which lie within the areas.

AGES AND THICKNESSES OF
SANDSTONE RESERVOIRS

In Figure 3-*A* the number of sandstone reservoirs assigned to each geologic age is charted on a vertical logarithmic scale against an approximate arithmetic time scale. Tertiary rocks, productive on the Gulf Coast and in California, contain 68 per cent of the reservoir sandstones of the United States, but petroleum is produced from sandstones of all ages from Cambrian to Pleistocene, inclusive. Large numbers of sandstone reservoirs also are present in rocks of the Pennsylvanian, Mississippian, and Cretaceous Periods.

The United States reservoir sandstones studied average 39 feet in thickness, but they range from as thin as 2 feet to as thick as 1,500 feet. The graph in Figure 3-*B* shows the average sandstone thicknesses by geologic ages, and it is notable that most of the values closely approach the 39 foot average line (A–B). The vertical lines which are dashed represent geologic ages for which the number of sandstones is so small that the plotted values are of very questionable significance. Only the Pliocene reservoir sandstones display an important departure from the statistical average of thickness, and a further analysis of this anomaly reveals that 63 per cent of the Pliocene

reservoirs are in California fields notable for their thick sandstone zones.

RESERVOIR SANDSTONE THICKNESS COMPARED
WITH QUANTITY OF FLUID

A table of average sandstone thicknesses for the various sizes of petroleum accumulations (Table I) shows the expected result that thick reservoir sandstones, though fewer in number, contain more large accumulations of oil. For this table, the gas, in those reservoirs containing substantial quantities of both oil and gas, was converted to an oil equivalent, using the energy-based conversion factor developed by Lahee (1958, p. 2041).

Two peculiar features may be noted in the table. The first is that there are fewer gas pools in the lowest size group than in the next larger group. This is attributed to the fact that the smallest gas accumulations are commonly left behind pipe or otherwise neglected during field development because of economic considerations. Many small gas pools doubtless went unrecognized in the study because the available data either did not show their existence or failed to reveal them as being large enough to qualify for the study.

The second feature of interest is observed in

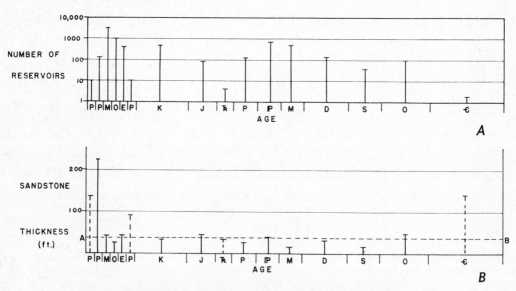

Fig. 3.—*A*—Number of sandstone reservoirs studied shown by geologic ages.
B—Average thicknesses of reservoir sandstones by geologic ages.

TABLE I. AVERAGE SANDSTONE THICKNESSES FOR VARIOUS SIZES OF
PETROLEUM AND GAS ACCUMULATIONS

Accumulation Size Group	Number of Reservoir Sandstones	Average Thickness of Reservoir Sandstones (feet)
Oil and Oil-Gas Pools (Size in millions of barrels)		
Small Less than 5	3,121	25
Moderate 5–25	1,701	47
Large 25–125	390	114
Very large More than 125	101	209
Gas Pools (Size in billion cubic feet)		
Small Less than 10	685	28
Moderate 10–100	1,141	32
Large 100–1,000	91	50
Very large More than 1,000	11	93

the marked, though different, rates at which the sizes of oil and gas accumulations increase with respect to reservoir sandstone thickness. If constant reservoir area and saturation of the entire thickness of the sandstone were assumed, the volume of liquid might be expected to increase approximately in proportion ot the average sandstone thickness. A survey of the data, however, shows that accumulation size increases at a considerably greater rate than sandstone thickness. Approximate curves fitted to the table values indicate that the pool sizes are exponential functions of sandstone thickness, modified by some numerical constants. The relations involve the square of sandstone thickness in the case of oil, and thickness to a power between the square and the cube for gas. If there is geologic meaning in these trends derived from the rough classifications, it is elusive; but a few general suggestions may be made. For one thing, reservoir areas undoubtedly are not constant. The thicker sandstones which correlate with the larger accumulations are less erratic than thin sandstones. They are more likely to spread good pay sections over large areas. Furthermore, their porosities and permeabilities would seem likely to be much higher than those of thinner sandstones. Thus it is observed that a thick sandstone tends to be a much broader and much better reservoir than its relative thickness alone would suggest. This statement applies with greater force to gas-bearing sandstones than to oil reservoirs—mainly, no

doubt, because of the broad areal extent of most big gas accumulations.

TRAPPING CONDITIONS

Structural traps control petroleum accumulation in 56 per cent of the reservoirs studied (Fig 4-A), and combination traps in 34 per cent; whereas stratigraphic traps are responsible for only 10 per cent of the pools. Regardless of trapping conditions, there are many more small pools than large ones (Table I); however, if the few large and very large accumulations are considered as a group (Fig. 4-B), it is found that structural trapping accounts for 70 per cent of the pools, and combination traps for 16 per cent. Stratigraphic traps are slightly more important among large accumulations (14 per cent) than when all pools are considered. Experimentally, the trap types were compared with geologic ages—no statistical trends appeared except for an indication that stratigraphic trapping is especially common in the sandstone reservoirs of the Silurian and Devonian rocks in the Appalachian basin.

AREAL EXTENTS OF RESERVOIR SANDSTONES

Petroleum geologists long have recognized that upward structural growths must cause persistent topographic highs that are linked to sorting effects in the superposed sediments, and that such conditions should, in turn, lead to preferential development of sands in places where structural and combination traps develop.

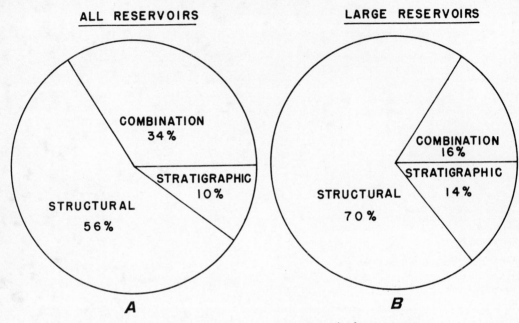

Fig. 4.—Trapping conditions in sandstone reservoirs, by trap types.

To gather data on this subject the investigators classified, as to areal extent, those reservoir sandstones involved in structural and combination trapping. This grouping has been discussed under the heading of *Study Method and Limitations,* but a few added comments are desirable. The estimates of extent suffer, of course, from incomplete stratigraphic knowledge, and in many instances depend on geological inference as to sandstone continuity. This statement applies especially to areas which were drilled heavily before good well records became common. According to the best estimates the committee could make, sandstones involved both in structural and combination traps are more commonly of limited and local areal extent (less than 100 square miles) than of regional coverage (Fig. 5-*A* and *B*); however, the percentage distributions do not seem to show conspicuous trends. Rather, they are susceptible of various interpretations either favoring or discounting structural control of sand distribution. It is not surprising to find the regional sandstones of small importance among the instances of combination trapping (Fig. 5-*B*) because, by defini-

tion, some of the edges of combination accumulations are determined by stratigraphic discontinuities superposed on structural features, and such stratigraphic interruptions are predictably less common in broad-area sandstones. The combination traps, roughly only 60 per cent as numerous as structural traps, do display the expected tendency of localizing of sandstones in the area of the oil field, itself.

It was, perhaps, more unforeseen that a substantial percentage of the sandstones associated with purely structural traps are of local extent. Nevertheless, the structural traps, which are 1.7 times as numerous as combination traps, involve more sandstones of regional extent than of the more restricted areal groups.

A factor not analyzed statistically emerged in the remarks made by the geologists who studied the sandstones—in many instances, better sorting of the sandstones or increase of porosity and permeability over the field areas was noted, suggesting the possiblity of slight topographic elevation of the ancient depositional surfaces in the areas of some oil fields.

ORIGINS OF RESERVOIR SANDSTONES ASSOCIATED WITH STRATIGRAPHIC TRAPS

A genetic classification was employed in the further analysis of those sandstones linked with stratigraphic accumulations (Fig. 6). Stratigraphic conditions of broad areal extent are represented by the groups labeled as regional facies change, unconformity, and others (broad). Features placed in the last category by the committee include patchy permeability in sandstones of regional extent, lenticular but essentially continuous basal conglomerates of regional extent, and fluviatile flood-plain and delta deposits with broad extent but with erratic permeability distribution.

Stratigraphic conditions of more local nature account for the bulk of the stratigraphic traps, and include channels, bars, beach deposits, lenticular sandstones believed to have been deposited under nearshore-marine conditions, and a group called other (local). The sandstones in the last category are few in number but very diverse in character, including sandstones identified as alluvial fan deposits, locally permeable phases of very calcareous sandstones (origin not identified), lagoonal back-reef sandstones, unidentified permeability barriers probably dependent on matrix or cement material, tar seal sandstones, and isolated lenses in continental sediments probably fluviatile in origin. In short, this group encompasses the few unusual conditions which are difficult to classify.

It is notable that lithified sand bars form the greatest number of stratigraphic traps, followed closely by nearshore marine lenticular sandstones, and then by beach deposits. Regional facies changes come next in importance, and the other stratigraphic types are represented in markedly fewer numbers. From the data it appears that the shoreward edges rather than the seaward edges of complex sandstone bodies are to be preferred for petroleum exploration. The concept is a familar one to petroleum geologists.

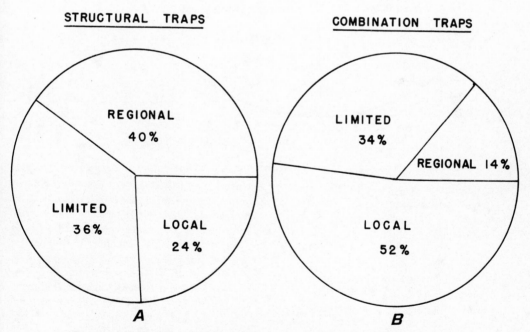

Fig. 5.—Areal extents of reservoir sandstones shown as percentages of all reservoirs contained by structural traps and combination traps.

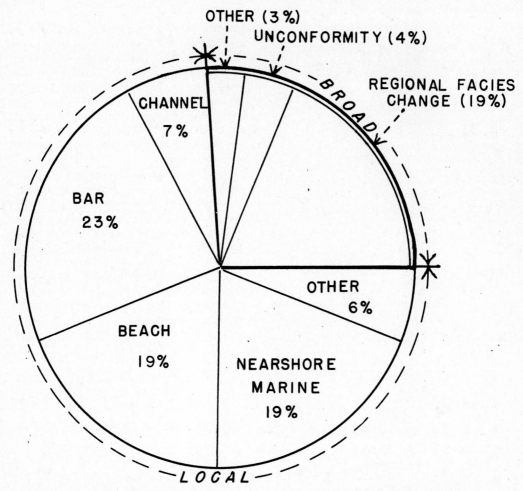

Fig. 6.—Kinds of stratigraphic traps as percentages of all stratigraphic traps studied.

STRATIGRAPHIC-TRAP TYPES COMPARED WITH
ACCUMULATION SIZE

The percentages of large stratigraphic accumulations (more than 25 million barrels of oil or 100 billion cubic feet of gas) discovered in sandstones of the various genetic types are shown in Figure 7. Although sand bars form the most common kind of stratigraphic trap among pools of all sizes (Fig. 6), the greatest percentage of large stratigraphic pools occurs in sandstones identified as of beach origin. Nearshore-marine deposits are of next importance among the large stratigraphic pools, and bars fall into third place. The restricted areal

extent of sand bars doubtless accounts for their lesser importance among the large accumulations.

A seeming anomaly appears in the stratigraphic-pool data in that accumulations depending on regional facies changes, unconformity traps, and other stratigraphic conditions of a broad nature, are strongly concentrated in the small-pool sizes (Figs. 6 and 7); whereas the more local types of sandstone bodies account for fully 88 per cent of the large pools (Fig. 7). It is suggested that the phenomenon is a reflection of a tendency for very local pools to form within the confines of complex, broad scale stratigraphic changes. Perhaps more important, it indicates the likelihood of some structural features developing which locally so modify the configuration of the sandstones involved in such broad stratigraphic changes, that the accumulations fall into the structural or combination classes.

STRATIGRAPHIC TRAPS COMPARED WITH GEOLOGIC AGE

The statistical information was analyzed to see if rocks of particular geologic ages display preferential tendency to include stratigraphic traps of any given kinds in their sandstones. The ages in order of their importance as to number of stratigraphic traps are—Pennsylvanian (172), Oligocene (124), Mississippian (94), Devonian (94), Cretaceous (84), Miocene (48), Silurian (35), Permian (30), Eocene (20), Pliocene (8), Pleistocene (4), Ordovician (3), and Jurassic (1).

With a single exception, the same ages which contain the greatest numbers of stratigraphic traps also display the greatest diversity of kinds

of stratigraphic traps. The exception to this generalization is the Oligocene, whose stratigraphic traps are 86 per cent of the regional facies-change variety. These, of course, are mainly in the sandstones of the Gulf Coast.

Otherwise, there is no clear pattern of stratigraphic-trap types as compared with age. Bars and beach deposits achieve greatest frequencies in the Pennsylvanian—a direct result of the occurrence of many such traps in the Mid-Continent. Channels are more common in the Mississippian rocks than those of any other age, and they occur principally in the sediments of the Appalachian basin, as do the nearshore-marine sands of local nature which attain their greatest frequency in the Devonian beds.

CONTAINED FLUIDS AND TRAPPING CONDITIONS COMPARED WITH SIZE OF ACCUMULATION

If trapping conditions are compared with the fluids contained in the individual reservoirs, a rather consistent pattern appears (Fig. 8-A). For

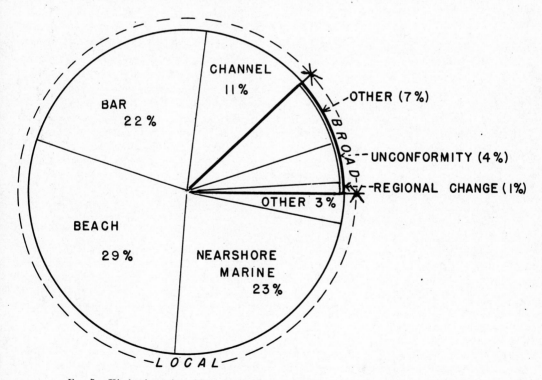

FIG. 7.—Kinds of stratigraphic traps as percentages of large stratigraphic accumulations.

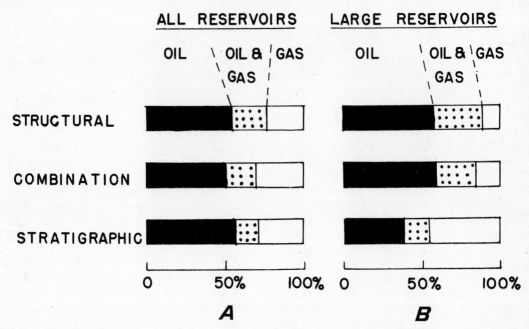

F<small>IG</small>. 8.—Fluids in reservoirs contained by traps of the three classes, shown as percentages of traps of the given types.

each of the three groups, 50–60 per cent of the reservoir sandstones contain oil, 10–20 per cent contain both oil and gas, and 20–30 per cent contain gas.

If attention is directed to the large accumulations alone (more than 25 million barrels of oil or more than 100 billion cubic feet of gas) a slightly different picture emerges (Fig. 8-*B*). Among structural and combination traps, the percentages of reservoir sandstones containing gas are decreased to about one-half those observed for such traps of all sizes. The difference is largely offset by the increased percentages of combination and structural traps which contain both oil and gas. They are about 1½ times as frequent among large pools as among all pools.

The truly striking departure in the figures for large versus small accumulations is found in the data for stratigraphic pools. The percentages clearly show that large stratigraphic traps are more likely to contain gas than oil or mixed fluids. This trend represents a reversal of the slight, possibly non-diagnostic, tendency of large structural or combination traps to contain oil or mixed fluids rather than gas. A suggested interpretation of this seeming anomaly is that stratigraphic traps of large size are likely to be found in relatively thin but widespread sandstones whose permeabilities are low. Gas, because of its lower viscosity and greater mobility and buoyancy, may very commonly enter and be trapped in such rocks; whereas oil, if present, may be excluded because of its unfavorably different physical properties. This speculation is in part confirmed by the tracing of the bulk of the large stratigraphic gas fields to the San Juan basin, the Appalachian basin, and the Mid-Continent areas where geological conditions such as those described exist.

SUMMARY OF RESULTS AND COMMENTS

The Sandstone Reservoir Committee hopes that the facts brought together here constitute a useful outline of the average geologic and geometric characteristics of reservoir sandstones in the United States. It appears from the study that most sandstone fields display only a single kind of trapping. Most commonly, structural trapping controls petroleum accumulation in sandstone reservoirs, and it is even more prevalent when large pools are considered alone.

Sandstones of Tertiary age are predominant in importance as reservoirs, but each geologic age from Cambrian to Pleistocene, inclusive, contains some producing sandstones. The sandstones average 39 feet in thickness, and thickness averages for given geologic ages do not depart markedly from this figure, except the average for the Pliocene, which is a rather startling 222 feet. The amounts of fluids in the reservoirs improve with respect to increasing sandstone thicknesses much more rapidly than might be anticipated.

Regardless of the kind of trapping involved, it appears that reservoir sandstones of limited and local areal extent considerably exceed in number those of regional dimensions. Relatively high percentages of the traps in Silurian and Devonian rocks are of stratigraphic type, and, as of the study date, sandstone reservoirs of these ages have been found only in the Appalachian basin.

Among the sandstones containing stratigraphic accumulations, those originating as sand bars are most common and are followed in frequency by nearshore-marine sandstones, and then by beach-deposited sandstones. However, if large stratigraphic accumulations only are considered, beach deposits occupy the position of first importance, followed by nearshore-marine deposits, and then by bars. It is somewhat surprising to note that broad scale stratigraphic changes are responsible for only 12 per cent of large stratigraphic pools, whereas the more local types of sandstone bodies contain 88 per cent of such pools, and it is found that large stratigraphic accumulations are more likely to contain gas than oil or mixed fluids.

The geologic ages whose rocks contain the greatest numbers of stratigraphic traps are—Pennsylvanian, Oligocene, Mississippian, Devonian, and Cretaceous. The degree of diversity in kinds of stratigraphic traps closely follows the relative numbers of such traps in the given ages, except that 86 per cent of the numerous Oligocene stratigraphic traps are of the regional facies-change variety. In the course of the sandstone reservoir study it was noted that the bulk of the prolific sandstone fields of the United States produce from Tertiary and Cretaceous rocks which contain a multitude of thin sandstones not easily separable as individual sandstone bodies.

The broad nature of this study should be kept in mind when the results are considered, and it should be remembered that a very large number of less important sandstone reservoirs in the United States have been excluded purposely from the study. Furthermore, although geological interpretations of the data have been suggested, other explanations of the statistical trends are entirely possible. It should be recognized that a study covering the entire United States necessarily merges and mixes data from highly diverse geological provinces.

The nationwide patterns do not diverge markedly from widely held geological theories. They say, in essence, that the recipe for finding oil in sandstones has been—Pick some rocks of an age of crustal instability within the area of search, showing partiality to Tertiary rocks. Try to find places where the thickest sandstones may occur; look for structural traps and depend to some degree on sandstones of regional extent for reservoirs; but give preference to known or suspected areas where sandstones of limited extent may appear. Concentrate on trying to find shoreline trends and play these along their landward sides. Pursue local, rather than regional, facies changes. This is the general pattern of past success. It should still be a practical general guide.

REFERENCE

Lahee, F. H., 1958, Statistics on natural gas discoveries: Am. Assoc. Petroleum Geologists Bull., v. 42, n. 9, p. 2037–2047.

PROSPECTING FOR STRATIGRAPHIC TRAPS[1]

DANIEL A. BUSCH[2]

Tulsa, Oklahoma

ABSTRACT

Many stratigraphic traps are related directly to their respective environments of deposition. An understanding of the depositional environment is essential to successful prospecting for oil or gas in this type of reservoir. Isopach studies of shale sequences directly above, or both above and below, a lenticular reservoir sandstone, are of considerable value in reconstructing depositional environments. Variations in thickness of such shale intervals, either directly above a reservoir sandstone, or embracing it, are completely independent of present-day structural configuration. Isopach maps of such genetic sequences serve as realistic indicators for locating certain lenticular sands. Depositional trends of beach sands, strike-valley sands, and offshore bars are determined readily from such studies. Structure maps, constructed on a reliable time marker within the arbitrarily selected genetic interval, serve as a means of locating oil or gas accumulation within any of these reservoir types. In all such studies electric-log data are essential because such genetic sequences rarely are named formational units. The thinner the genetic sequence, the greater the necessity for accurate selection of correlation points on electric logs.

Deltaic reservoirs are poorly understood and only rarely recognized by the geologist. This type of reservoir is, nevertheless, abundantly preserved in the sedimentary section. Regional isopach studies of depositional environment are a prerequisite for the construction of meaningful exploration maps of this type of reservoir. An understanding of the trends of distributary fingers and of the influence of differential compaction in producing drape structures, likewise, is essential.

INTRODUCTION

Most exploration geologists loosely refer to elongate bodies of sand as sand bars. Such pronouncements generally are made without any knowledge or consideration of the environment of deposition. Such loose references frequently are made without any knowledge of where the shoreline was or any recognition of where the seaward versus the lagoon side of the bar might be. The source of such sediments, the cross-sectional shape of the sand body, and the relation these sand bodies bear to the enclosing shales are all diagnostic factors which are seldom if ever taken into account before loosely referring to an elongate body of sand as a sand bar.

The purpose of this paper is to consider four types of stratigraphic traps, all of which consist of elongate bodies of sand which are lenticular in cross section. Factors controlling their respective environments of deposition are quite different and the sands themselves are, indeed, different. All illustrations are selected from the Pennsyl-

vanian of the Mid-Continent region, but the principles involved are known to be applicable to all parts of the stratigraphic section in sedimentary basins throughout the world.

The first type of deposit to be considered is the beach sand which is laid down at, and parallel with, the shoreline. The second type of sand is a new one only insofar as the literature is concerned, and is referred to as a "strike-valley" sand. The third type is the familiar offshore bar, and the fourth is the channel type of sandstone. It should be borne in mind that all four types are alike in that they are elongate and lenticular in cross section, but distinctly different in other respects. It is these differences, together with ways and means of recognizing them, that constitute the main subject of this report.

BEACH SANDS

Figure 1 represents the structural configuration of the Mississippian limestone in the northwestern part of the Anadarko basin in northwestern Oklahoma. This structure map illustrates the rate of dip of the non-conformable surface at the top of the Mississippian. The top of the Mississippian is truncated progressively deeper toward the north. It was over the eroded surface of the Mississippian that the early Pennsylvanian sea transgressed

[1] Presented before the Association at Dallas, March 18, 1959. Manuscript received, June 15, 1959. Reprinted from Am. Assoc. Petroleum Geologists Bull.. Vol. 43, No. 12, p. 2829–2843, 1959.

[2] Consulting geologist.

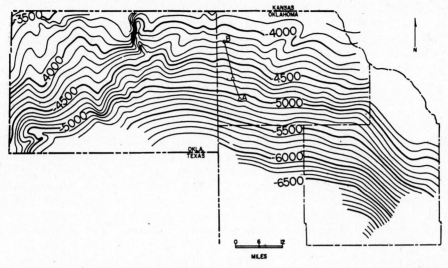

FIG. 1.—Structure of Mississippian limestone in northwestern Oklahoma. Contour interval, 100 feet.

step by step from south to north. Figure 2 is a south-to-north cross section (*A–B*) of the basalmost part of the Pennsylvanian—the Morrow formation. The location of this section is indicated on Figures 1 and 3. The Morrow formation is defined by the eroded Mississippian at the base, and the upper limit is coincident with the base of the "Thirteen Finger" limestone, as illustrated in Figure 2. This stratigraphic interval at the base of the Pennsylvanian in northwestern Oklahoma is a genetic sequence devoid of any significant unconformities. As it represents a south-to-north transgressive unit, the progressive increase in thickness toward the south is accomplished by the introduction of progressively older beds at the base in that direction. Time lines are essentially parallel with the base of the Thirteen Finger limestone. Thus, progressively lower (older) time lines impinge against the truncated surface of the Mississippian.

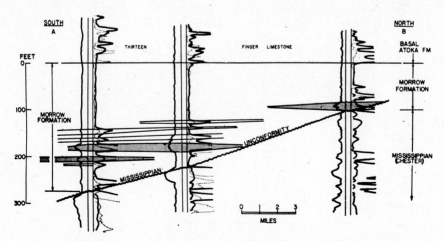

FIG. 2.—South-north cross section A-B (Fig. 1), showing onlap relation of several Morrow sands on the southward-dipping, truncated Mississippian.

Three principal sands can be picked out readily from this cross section that were deposited in early Morrow time. They are not one sand body, but bear an *en échelon* relation to each other, each wedging out in a basinward direction toward the south. Each of these sands represents a shoreline stage in a series of cyclic transgressions of the early Pennsylvanian sea; each shoreline stage is characterized by a separate beach type of sand. Although only three of these sands are illustrated in this cross section, at least a dozen of them are known in the northwestern part of the Anadarko basin. Each is a separate reservoir, and each is abundantly productive of gas.

From the exploration standpoint we are concerned with the method of tracing each of these *en échelon* beach sands. In order to get at this problem, reference is made to the over-all thickness of the genetic sequence (Morrow formation) of which these sands are significant and distinct facies components. The Morrow formation represents more or less continuous sedimentation in spite of the fact that the shoreline, or the sea level, was shifting in a cyclic manner. An isopach map of this genetic sequence (the Morrow forma-

tion, Fig. 3) shows that the trends of the thickness contours are not the same as those of the structure map of the Mississippian surface (Fig. 1). In other words, this isopach map is independent of present-day structure and emphasizes the nature of the topographic configuration of the erosion surface of the Mississippian at the time the early Pennsylvanian sea transgressed this area. By superimposing on this map the individual sand trends (shaded areas) it may be noted that beach sands are as much as 30–40 miles long. Individual sand members can be traced in a direction subparallel with the thickness contours of the genetic sequence in which the sands were laid down. Another way to interpret Figure 3 properly is to visualize the base of the Thirteen Finger limestone (Fig. 2) as sea level. Then, the rate of divergence of the thickness of the Morrow formation, in one sense of the word, simulates the rate of slope of the Mississippian surface over which the early Pennsylvanian sea transgressed. It is for this reason that these individual "stairstep" sands tend to parallel thickness contours of the genetic sequence in which the sands were laid down.

Figure 3 is incomplete. There are many more

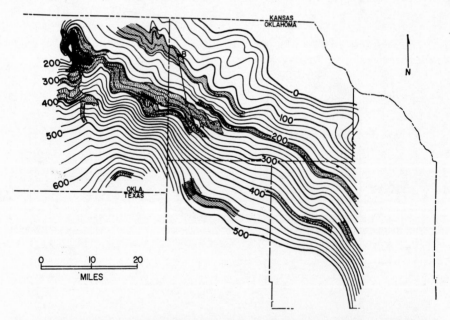

Fig. 3.—Isopach of Morrow formation in northwestern Oklahoma, showing subparallelism of individual sandstone members (stippled). Contour interval, 20 feet.

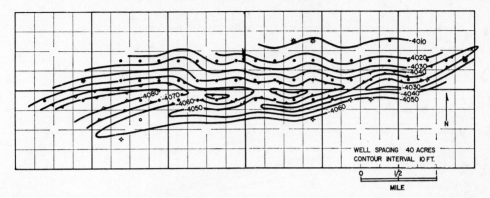

Fig. 4.—Structural configuration of Mississippian, showing synclinal position
of overlying Cherokee sand production.

sands that have been discovered in this area since this illustration was prepared, and several of the illustrated trends have been extended for considerable distances by new discoveries. It is all the more remarkable that one can correlate these individual bands of sand in view of the fact that the well spacing in the Morrow is one well per section.

STRIKE-VALLEY SANDS

Strike-valley sands derive their name from the fact that they are deposited in the low areas between cuestas at the time the land surface is inundated by a transgressive sea. Such cuestas may be either erosional escarpments or fault scarps. Erosional escarpments are the result of progressive truncation of a series of alternating resistant and non-resistant strata, all of which have been regionally tilted.

Figure 4 shows the structural configuration of the Mississippian in a pool area where there is an abundance of subsurface control; well spacing is one well per 40 acres. The contour interval is 10 feet; all the control consists of electric-log data. A very narrow, apparently anticlinal ridge plunges westward along the southern border of the mapped area. There is a conspicuous, narrow, westward-plunging, asymmetric trough adjacent on the north. This is not a true structure map but a combination of post-Mississippian topography and structure imposed by post-Pennsylvanian southward tilting. With this picture of the Mississippian surface in mind, an attempt is made to explain the direct relation of this surface to the

distribution of the basal Cherokee sand, the lowermost Pennsylvanian sand in this area. The maximum thickness of this sand is 50–55 feet.

Figure 5 is a north-south cross section of the same body of lower Cherokee sand as that which produces from the pool shown in Figure 4. This section, however, occurs several miles east of the pool shown in Figure 4. The cross section in the upper half of the figure is drawn with a limestone datum of reference, a thin limestone that is persistent and easily recognized; the Mississippian unconformity is indicated by a wavy line which is not parallel with the limestone datum. This unconformity exhibits progressive truncation interrupted by a thin resistant limestone escarpment which occurs just basinward from the southernmost of the producing wells in the lower Cherokee sand. The sand body is shaded black and is very asymmetric in cross section, being tear-drop in profile. The relation of a strike valley sand body to this combination of topographic and structural surface is more than coincidence. The lower half of Figure 5 illustrates the same condition as that shown in the upper half except that it has been drawn with a sea-level datum. The lower Cherokee sand plunges at a rate similar to the rate of dip of the Mississippian surface, but it wedges out abruptly close to the escarpment that terminates it on the south.

Figure 6 is a block diagram to illustrate the principle of the strike-valley sand. By referring to sea-level position No. 1, it may be noted that the shoreline was in the middle of the block dia-

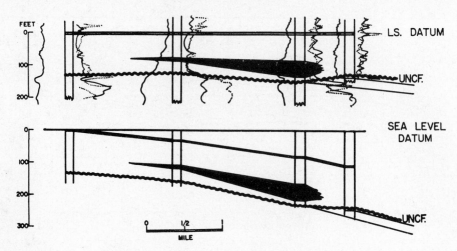

FIG. 5.—North-south profiles, showing relation of Cherokee sand reservoir
to pre-Pennsylvanian erosion surface.

gram and the lower body of sand (shaded black) was accumulating on the escarpment side of the more seaward ridge. With continued transgression of the surface of deposition, the shoreline shifted from right to left (south to north) and a second body of sand was deposited behind the next higher topographic escarpment. From a diagram of this type it is apparent that the top of the Mississippian is not a true structural surface, but is a combination of structure and topography, and that this type of surface, when inundated, controls the sites, trends, and linearity of the sands being deposited.

The characteristics of a sandstone of this type may be summarized as follows. The lengths of the individual bodies of sand may be many miles. The lower Cherokee sand (Fig. 6) has been traced more than 40 miles. The widths may vary from

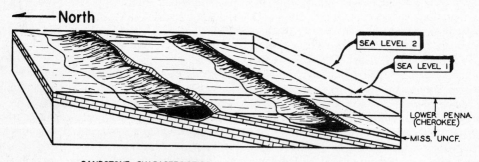

FIG. 6.—Block diagram, illustrating relation of strike valley sands to erosional
escarpments developed on tilted and truncated Mississippian surface.

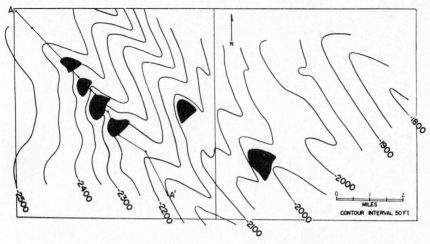

FIG. 7.—Structure map, showing relation of oil pools (black) to axes of several northwest-plunging structural noses.

half a mile to one mile and the cross-sectional shape is biconvex. It was an abrupt seaward shaleout and a transitional landward pinchout. Two or more sand bodies are generally sub-parallel. The trends are controlled by post-Mississippian structure and not by the present structural grain of the Mississippian.

OFFSHORE BARS

Offshore bars are poorly understood insofar as their recognition and delineation in the sub-surface are concerned. They might be either single, isolated bodies of elongate, lenticular sand, or consist of a series of subparallel sand ridges built up on a base of sheet sand. In the latter case the situation is more complex and the over-all composite sheet-sand aspect is the result of marine transgression.

Figure 7 is a structure map of a two-township area drawn with a contour interval of 50 feet. It is drawn on a limestone time marker which can be identified readily on all electric logs of that area. The most conspicuous aspect of this map consists of several prominent, northwest-plunging struc-tural noses with a series of oil pools (shaded in black) occurring on the plunging axes of three of the noses. These oil pools are producing from a sand which occurs in stratigraphic proximity to the limestone time marker on which the structure map is drawn. The structure is not mapped on the

top of the reservoir sand because (1) the sand is very irregular on the upper surface, and (2) the sand transgresses the time lines by as much as 150 feet in the selected area of study. The transgres-sive aspect of this sand is illustrated in Figures 8 and 9. These stratigraphic profiles trend north-west-southeast along the axis of the southernmost of the several plunging structural noses shown in Figure 7 (section A-A').

The datum of reference is not sea level, but is an arbitrarily selected electric-log marker which can be correlated readily. It is immediately ap-parent that the datum of reference is as much as 50 feet below the top of the reservoir sand on the left-hand side of Figure 8 and as much as 100 feet above it at the right-hand side of Figure 9. This progression of the top of the sand, relative to the reference datum, is clear-cut proof of a transgres-sive sand, transgression being from southeast to northwest. Also, there is a divergence in the over-all thickness of the shales that overlie the sand. This local observation, together with regional studies, presents clear-cut evidence that these profiles represent a component of basinward di-vergence. The depositional basin was situated on the southeast. From such cross sections (Figs. 8 and 9) as these it is obvious that a structure map drawn on this sand would be somewhat meaning-less; the top is not a time marker. The reference datum line is that horizon which was used in

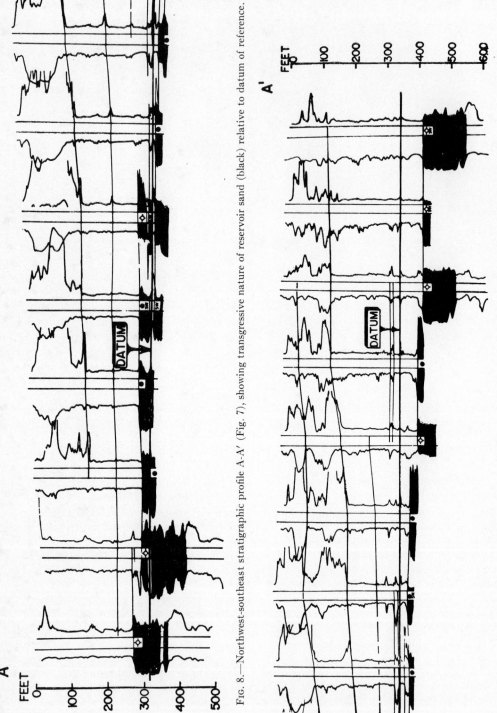

FIG. 8.—Northwest-southeast stratigraphic profile A-A′ (Fig. 7), showing transgressive nature of reservoir sand (black) relative to datum of reference.

FIG. 9.—Southeastward extension of Figure 8.

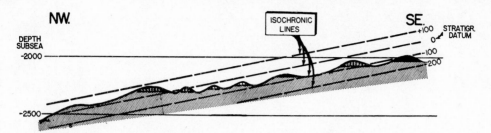

FIG. 10.—Idealized northwest-southeast structural profile, showing location of two oil pools (black) and five postulated oil pools (vertically shaded), all occurring on crests of sandstone bars built up on transgressive sheet sand. Depths in feet.

plotting the structural contour map shown in Figure 7.

Figure 10 is a composite, diagrammatic illustration of what is shown in Figures 8 and 9. This scaled profile is drawn with a sea-level datum of reference, thus showing the present structural attitude of the individual beds. The top of the sand is shown as a hummocky surface tilted northwest. By rotating Figure 10 in a clockwise direction so that the zero stratigraphic line of reference is horizontal, it is apparent that the sandstone transgresses the isochronic lines and that there is divergence of the overlying shale section to the southeast. In other words, the depositional basin itself was tilted southeast in this area, and later tilted northwest.

The structure map (Fig. 7) is drawn on this zero stratigraphic reference datum. The stratigraphically highest part of the sand is about 50 feet above this reference datum (to the northwest), and the stratigraphically lowest part of the sand is almost 100 feet below it (to the southeast). Thus, there is about 150 feet of topographic relief, over-all, along this profile. Several oil pools (shaded black) are shown where this profile intersects known pools. Several other pools that have not yet been discovered are postulated and indicated by cross shading. All of this is more clearly illustrated in Figure 11, which includes the same profile as that shown in Figure 10. Figure 11 also includes an isopach map drawn from the stratigraphic datum of reference to the top of the sand. This stratigraphic reference datum has been assigned arbitrarily a numerical value of zero. Thus, there is a variable number of feet of shale beneath this reference line and the top of the sand in the southeastern two-thirds of the area. Conversely, there is a variable number of feet of sand above this reference datum to the top of the sand in the northwestern third of the mapped area. By assigning minus-footage values where the top of the sand is *beneath* the stratigraphic datum of reference and plus-footage values where the top of the sand is *above*, there is, thus, established a series of numerical values which permit the construction of a meaningful isopach map. The minus contours represent the thickness of the shale below the zero stratigraphic datum of reference down to the top of the reservoir sand. The plus contours show sand thickness above this datum of reference. The isopach map of the interval below the datum of reference (minus contours) shows clearly a series of subparallel "ridges" and "valleys" of shale, or, inversely interpreted, a series of topographic ridges of sand beneath the shale. These ridges of sand are steeper on the southeast (seaward) side and merge into a single body of sand at the base. In other words this is a transgressive sheet sand, the upper surface of which has been reworked by the opposing forces of wave action and undertow. The result of this modification is a series of subparallel sand bars built up on a transgressive sheet sand.

Ordinarily, an isopach map of the reservoir sand would point up the ridges of bar sand on the upper surface. It is not possible, however, to construct such a map in this area, because most of the wells fail to penetrate the entire thickness of the sand. In spite of this limitation it is possible to understand the origin, nature, and distribution of the sand by the means discussed. It has been pointed out previously that the structure map (Fig. 7) was drawn on the zero stratigraphic datum of reference. The down-dip edges of the

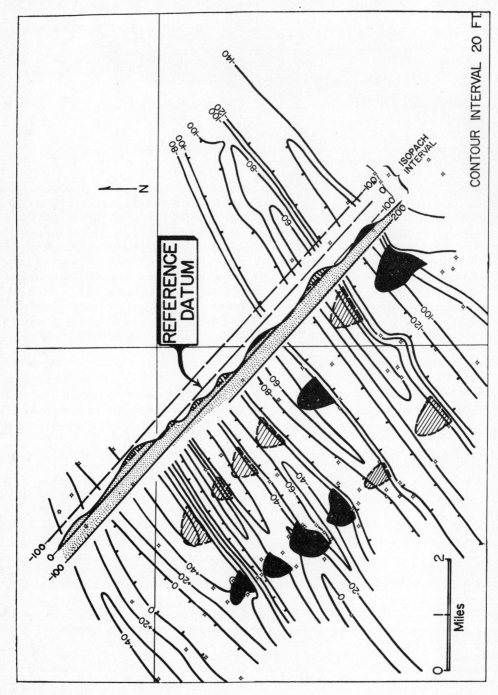

FIG. 11.—Isopach map of stratigraphic interval above (plus contours) or below (minus contours) reference datum to top of reservoir sand. Oil pools (black) and postulated oil pools (diagonal shading) occur in localized areas of intersection of sand ridges and northwest-plunging structural noses.

several pools in this area are controlled by an oil-water contact subparallel with the structure contours. The southeast margins of these pools, on the other hand, are controlled by an abrupt facies change from sand to shale. Thus, we have the two basic criteria for the explanation of these individual pools, namely, several structural noses, the plunging axes of which intersect a series of offshore bars which trend approximately at right angles to the structural axes. Dry holes clearly separate individual pools along the axes of these plunging structures. These dry holes occur between successive offshore bars where the upper part of the sand grades abruptly into what purports to be lagoonal shale.

By such an analysis of the six oil pools shown in Figure 11 (shaded black), it becomes obvious that similar favorable structural and stratigraphic conditions are present elsewhere in this area of study. Seven such areas, as yet untested, are outlined and shaded with diagonal lines in Figure 11. A detailed stratigraphic and structural analysis of a series of pools in the same sand thus serves as a basis for outlining additional drillable prospects.

CHANNEL SANDS

Channel sands can be distinguished readily from offshore bars in that the former increase in thickness downward. Conversely, the offshore bar increases in thickness by mounding of sand in the upper part of the sand body. Channel sands generally trend in a direction essentially perpendicular to a trace of the shoreline, whereas offshore bars are generally built up in a direction subparallel with the shoreline. There are numerous petrographic (many controversial) characteristics of these types of sand bodies, but they are not a part of this discussion.

Most channel sands are elongate, lenticular, and commonly erratic. They may be completely isolated lenses of sand, enclosed in shale, or they may spread out sheetwise in the uppermost part, and in this manner merge laterally with other neighboring channel sands. The latter situation is exemplified by the sands of the Booch delta which were deposited in the northwestern shelf zone of the McAlester basin of Oklahoma in early Pennsylvanian time. This delta covers an area of more than 2,000 square miles (Fig. 12). It consists of a generalized deltaic distributary system of channel sands which diverge in a basinward direction south-southeast into the McAlester basin. These are elongate bodies of sand which in many places are connected in the interdistributary areas by a fine grained, argillaceous sheet sand. In some areas the channel facies are parallel or subparallel, and in other areas they clearly converge and merge into a single body of sand. This is typical of a deltaic-type sand body. It was possible to construct this map only after a series of stratigraphic profiles had been made as a basis for constructing an isopach map of the genetic unit (McAlester formation) of which the Booch is a part. The isopach of this genetic sequence clearly identifies the shelf and the less stable basin, which are separated by a hinge line. Thus, we have the depositional framework over which to superimpose the large delta shown in Figure 12.

Figure 13 is a detail map of a selected one-township area shown in generalized fashion in Figure 12. It is a structure map of the Booch sandstone drawn with a contour interval of 20 feet, on which are superimposed the oil pools (black) and postulated (shaded) oil-pool areas. The oil pools bear very little relation to structure except in a limited area of the southeastern part of the map. In the south-central part of the map the elongate body of sand is clearly on the northeast flank of a prominent structure. In this area good sand development is synonymous with oil and gas accumulation. Since this figure was prepared, several of the stippled areas have been proved productive. The key to the problem of exploring for this type of distributary channel sand is to find the sand and follow it. Structure is of little importance. There is some predictability to the width of these channel sands. Lateral shaleout is abrupt, so abrupt in fact that a 10-acre offset to a 60-barrel-per-hour well in 13–15 feet of sand can be devoid of any sand at all. Those wells with the highest permeability, and consequently the highest initial productivity, generally occur in the middle of the "fairways."

SUMMARY

In summary, four principal types of elongate, lenticular bodies of sand have been considered.

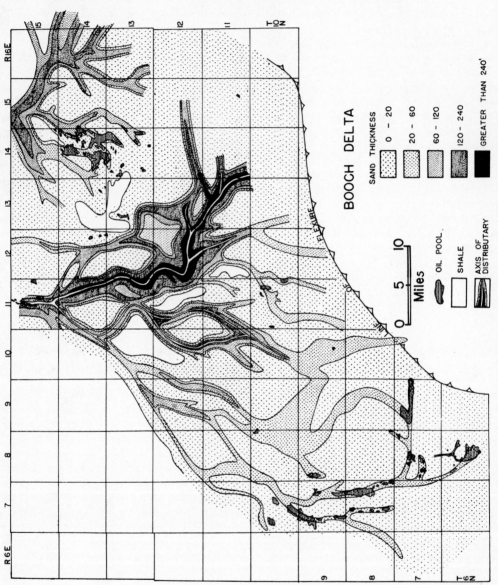

FIG. 12.—Isopach map of Booch sandstone in Greater Seminole district of eastern Oklahoma. Thickness in feet.

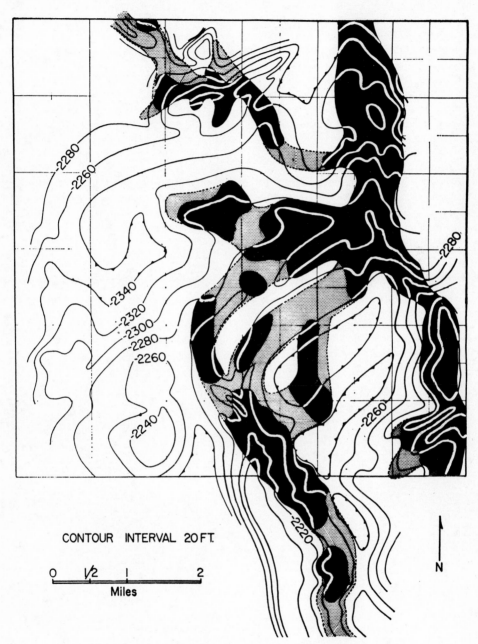

FIG. 13.—Structure map of Booch sandstone in T.8 N., R. 7 E., showing oil pools
(black) and postulated extensions of oil pools (stippled).

DANIEL A. BUSCH

These are by no means the only types of stratigraphic traps, but they are the ones most frequently confused. Each one requires a different technique for exploring and developing. Each requires a considerable amount of available subsurface data, and each should be approached in a different manner. It is extremely significant to take into account the genetic sequence in which each sand occurs. In other words, we are dealing with a preponderance of shale deposition interrupted by sand deposition, and where a stratigraphic interval can be defined which is devoid of any significant unconformities, that interval then becomes a genetic sequence. This stratigraphic sequence, when isopached, may give a very definite clue about the topographic surface on which the sand was laid down and the relation that any included sand body bears to that surface. In a *beach sand*, the sand is parallel with traces of the shoreline; therefore, it is essential to know where the shoreline was. In the *strike-valley sand*, one must know where the topographic and structural ridges were that controlled sand deposition—depositional trends. In the *offshore bar*, one must know not only the shoreline trend, but also what the structure is; and the structure can not be mapped intelligently on the top of the sand, but must be mapped on a time horizon which occurs in proximity to the reservoir sand. The relation of the long dimension of the *channel-type sand* to the topographic configuration of the basin is of paramount importance. In almost all channel sands the trend is not parallel or even subparallel with the trace of the shoreline.

These techniques can be applied to many areas —areas of clastic sand deposition—and they can be applied throughout the entire stratigraphic section. They are presented with the idea that the reader might wish to modify and develop them further. They do not answer all questions, but they are significant exploratory tools which can be explained in simple terms to operators who do want this type of information. The stratigraphic approach to oil and gas exploration goes beyond the usual structural contouring of closures to justify a drill site.

INDEX[1]

A

Abo formation, 192
abyssal plains of ocean, 65
accumulations, oil and gas, 213, 218
  average sandstone thickness, 213
  conditions of, 208
  fluids in reservoirs, 218
  size, compared with fluids and trapping conditions, 217
  stratigraphic trap types, 216, 217
age, geologic, of stratigraphic traps, 217
alluvial cones, references in literature to, 11
  fans, 11, 71, 143, 215
  plain, 146, 150
Almond formation, 84
  intertonguing relations, 85, 87
Anadarko basin, 220
Ancestral Rockies, 152, 154
ancient bar-finger sands, 38, 50, 51
  deposits, interpreted from Recent deposits, 10, 28
  eolian ss., 155–61
  fluvial channel-sand bodies, 145, 146, 161–77, 229–32
  turbidites, 67
Andros Island, 55
  platform, oölite shoals on, 55
animal tracks in eolian ss., 158
Appalachian basin, 120, 121
  Mountains, 123
Arguello deep-sea fan, 71
arid regions, sedimentary processes of, 154
ash-leach theory, uranium deposit origin, 176
A-10 sand, turbidite, 78
  isopach map of, 79
Aux Vases ss., 123, 124
Aztec ss., cross-strata in, 161

B

Baars, D. L., 179
Bahama Banks and environs, 54
BAHAMIAN OÖLITE SHOALS, 53
balls and lows, 14
barchans, oölite, 59
BAR-FINGER SANDS OF MISSISSIPPI DELTA, 29
  absence of faunas in, 38
  ancient, 38, 50, 51
    identification of, 38
  and delta platform, Mississippi River, 30
  bird-foot delta, outline of, 34
  clean-sand zone, 42
  cores of deposits, 44
  criteria for recognition, 48
  cross-bedding in, 45
  deformation of, by mud lumps, 48
  dimensions and age of, 50
  distribution and form of, 50
  Eocene Cockfield and Sparta, 52
    Wilcox, 50
  facies relationships, 50
  geometric and sedimentary characteristics, 36, 38, 49, 50
  grain size and sorting, 38
  in Southwest Pass, historic development of, 32

[1]Titles of papers are shown in capital and small capital letters.

Miocene and Oligocene, Gulf Coast, 52
Pennsylvanian Booch sand, 50, 51, 145, 146, 229–31
sedimentary characteristics, 38
stratigraphic traps, exploration for, 52
structures of, 50
  sedimentary, 45
  see also Mississippi Delta
Barker Dome tongue, 112, 113, 114
barrier beaches, spits, and islands, 14
  definition, as used by Price, Shepard, and others, 14
bars, 12, 13, 14, 215, 220, 225, 232
  barrier, 9
    offset of, 5
    references in literature to, 11
  LONGSHORE, AND BEACHES, LABORATORY EXPERI-
    MENTS ON FORM AND STRUCTURE OF, 13
    cross sections of, 18, 19, 22–25
    cross-strata, angle of dip in, 20, 25–27
    height-to-width ratios, 20
    modern, structures in, 25–27
    profiles of, 27
    shape and structure of, 17–20
    stages in growth of, 14–16
  Mississippi River, at Southwest, Southeast, South,
    and North Pass, and at Pass a Loutre, 30–33
  offshore, 14, 220, 225, 229, 232
  subaqueous, references in literature to, 12
Basin and Range province, 152
basin-floor turbidites, 71
Baxter (Mancos) shale, 83
beach and shoreface terrace deposits, height-to-width
    ratios, 21
  barrier, 14
  cross sections of, 22–25
  deposits, 215, 220, 222, 232
  en échelon sands, 222
  references in literature to, 11
  shape and structure of, 21–24
  top-set beds on, 21
BEACHES AND LONGSHORE BARS, LABORATORY EX-
    PERIMENTS ON FORM AND STRUCTURE OF, 13
Bearpaw shale, 92
bench sand, definition, 99
  in Cliff House formation, 107, 108, 110, 111, 113, 114,
    116
  in Point Lookout formation, 112
Berea sandstone, 143, 145
Big Horn Mountains, 96
Big Snowy anticlinorium, 94
  Mountains, 96
Bimini Island, North, longshore bars off, cross sections,
    26–27
Bimini Islands, 55
bird-foot delta platform, Mississippi River, 31
Black Mesa basin, 152, 193
Blanding district, uranium ore of, 174
blanket sand, 9
  sandstones, Permian, Colorado Plateau, 179–207
Blue Ridge, crystalline and metamorphic terrain, 121,
    123
Bluff ss. member, Morrison formation, 135, 155, 157,
    162
  sandstone pipes in, 148
Bolivar Peninsula-Galveston Island, 5

233